Stewardship
Second Edition

Instruction Manual

By Steven P. Demme

BUILDINGFAITH
FAMILIES

1-888-854-MATH (6284) — mathusee.com
sales@mathusee.com

Acknowledgments

Special thanks to the Stewardship team of graphic designers, videographers, content editors, and proofers who included: Jeff, Joseph, Isaac, Timothy, Heather, Dan, Miriam, Drew, Becca, Amy, Sherry, John, Beth, Renita, Bethany, and Catherine.

The students in the class, whose names you will see in some of the exercises, were: Maggie, Collin, Clayton, Abigail, Christianna, Darby, Adam, Faith, Rachel, Ernest, Isabella, Chloe, Madeline, Isaac, James, Teagan, Sarah, Anna, Savanah, Maddie , Cyrus, and Mercy. I am very grateful for these students for being my class as we filmed these sessions. They were a delight to teach, asking good questions, being attentive, finding mistakes, and for selecting my ties.

Ultimately all glory be to God for the great things He has accomplished through us.

Stewardship Instruction Manual
Second Edition
©2019 by Steven P. Demme
Published and distributed by Demme Learning

For support or other information: mathusee.com
1-888-854-6284 or +1 717-283-1448 | demmelearning.com
Lancaster, Pennsylvania USA

ISBN 978-1-60826-362-2
Revision Code Version 1219

For information regarding CPSIA on this printed material call: 1-888-854-6284
and provide reference #1219-121119

To show reverence and be consistent, I have chosen to capitalize all pronouns which represent the Triune God in scripture references as well in my writing.

Contents

HOW TO TEACH STEWARDSHIP

Access the video instruction at stewardshipmath.com. Read through the Instruction Manual and the Biblical Studies book. Work through the Student Worksheets which have five worksheets per lesson. If you would like to have a test for each lesson consider setting aside one page for that purpose. When the problems have each been checked and compared with the Solutions in the back of the Instruction Manual, move on to the next lesson. There is a some continuity in this course, but each lesson can also studied as an independent unit.

SUPPORT AND RESOURCES

With this new edition of Stewardship we expect that there will be some typos and other errors. When we find mistakes, we will be posting errata at mathusee.com/errata. We have made an effort to proofread the material but we probably have not found all the mistakes. Please accept our apologies for any consternation this may cause, and if you find any additional errors, please help us by sharing them with customer support.

To reach customer support you can visit mathusee.com or call 888-854-6284.

I will be adding resources to the lessons periodically. You will see in the books that there are links to podcasts and interviews with other knowledgeable people and recommended reading for more study. These and more can also be found at stewardshipmath.com.

A WORD ABOUT GRADING

We recognize that the instructor is the best judge of how well a student is progressing. Some instructors may choose not to issue grades at all, while others may be required to do so.

The Solutions give an answer for all student work and show how the student might arrive at a given solution. You will need to compare your student's answer to the sample to make sure the student understands the concept covered by the question. In cases where there is more than one way to solve a problem or more than one valid answer, the Solutions will only give one way of solving the problem and only one solution. Other solutions may be equally valid.

Stewardship contains many questions where students are expected to interview their parents or grandparents, apply their knowledge to their own unique situation, make lists of pros and cons, and answer open-ended questions about the Biblical Studies material. In all these cases, parents should discuss the student's answers with the student, but not assume that the solution given in the Solutions is the only correct answer. For example you may find a question which asks the student to compare three different items offered for sale and choose what they think is the best value. The Solutions will give my opinion on which is the best value, but if students think that one of the other options provides a better value it would be an excellent opportunity for parents to discuss the answer.

INVOLVEMENT OF THE FAMILY

Throughout the book, I will be asking the student to interview his or her parents for input on the lesson being studied. I do this for several reasons.

1. Parents have valuable experience and wisdom that their children need to hear. I am hoping that the questions in the lessons will facilitate discussion that will benefit parent and student alike. This curriculum is filled with stories and illustrations from Steve's life and understanding, but each parent and grandparent has their own wisdom and experience and I am hoping the student can learn from them.

2. Most of the lessons where these interview questions are found deal with topics that don't have a right or wrong answer. In discussing the topics you will see facets of the problem that you probably wouldn't have seen by yourself.

3. Parents have a God-given responsibility to teach and instruct their children. God tells us that His wisdom is to be passed on in everyday occurrences. "Repeat [God's commandments] again and again to your children. Talk about them when you are at home and when you are on the road, when you are going to bed and when you are getting up" (Deuteronomy 6:7, NLT). These starter questions could be the topic of conversation around the dinner table or in the car.

GRANDPARENTS

There are also some questions for grandparents. While God's principles are eternal and applicable to all generations, they can be fleshed out differently in different time periods. When you discuss these topics with more seasoned people, notice trends from one generation to another. If you do not have ready access to your grandparents, perhaps a respected church member or elderly neighbor could help you complete your assignment.

As a father and a grandparent I have a lot of experiences and memories. It is my privilege to share many of them with you in the pages of this curriculum. But I hope you will also learn to patently listen to the experiences and wisdom of your grandparents as well as your parents. They have so much to offer. If you will humbly ask them to share what they have learned and draw them out by asking questions and being sincerely interested, you and these blessed seasoned citizens will have a wonderful experience.

Someday you will understand what it feels like to be a son, a father, and a grandfather at the same time. I will always be a son to my parents, and still feel like a young man at heart. I am also an older man with much to share with those who are teachable and willing to listen. Joel 2:28 makes an interesting observation of how the outpouring of the Spirit impacts sons, young men, and old men. "It shall come to pass afterward, that I will pour out my Spirit on all flesh; your sons and your daughters shall prophesy, your old men shall dream dreams, and your young men shall see visions."

As young adults you will have dreams, visions, and hopes for the future. That is right and is the way God has made you. The older people in your life also have drams, but they are mostly about the past. This is the way they are wired. Learn to appreciate each other's strengths and inclinations. Humble interaction between all ages in your family is what God designed when he made the wonderful institution of the family.

FOR THE STUDENT

I hope you have a healthy relationship with your parents and grandparents. God chose your family. He then gave instructions to parents and children. The one command that applies specifically to all of us is to honor our father and mother. Paul notes in Ephesians 6 that this is the only command accompanied with a promise. The promise is that you will live long and that it will go well with you. If our attitude toward our dad and mom is not what it should be, let's ask God to turn our heart toward our folks and their hearts toward us. Based on Malachi 4:6 and 1 John 5:14–15, I am confident He will do just what you ask. "He will turn the hearts of fathers to their children and the hearts of children to their fathers." (Malachi 4:6)

"This is the confidence that we have toward Him, that if we ask anything according to His will He hears us. And if we know that He hears us in whatever we ask, we know that we have the requests that we have asked of Him." (1 John 5:14–15)

Jesus Himself submitted to His parents. "And he went down with them and came to Nazareth and was submissive to them." (Luke 2:51)

I am pretty sure He was tempted to not honor them. When we are young we think we know a lot, but He really did! He was fully God and fully man. As a man, He was also successful in fighting the temptation to rebel and as such is uniquely qualified to help you and me do the same. "This High Priest of ours understands our weaknesses, for He faced all of the same testings we do, yet he did not sin." (Hebrews 4:15, NLT)

When you ask your parents for their input on the questions in the lessons, do so with a humble attitude and listen with a teachable spirit. God has placed you in your parents' home to learn from and to be discipled by them. Your attitude of honoring them will go a long way in determining whether this will be a positive experience for your family. You don't have to agree with all of their conclusions, but hear them out. They have your best interests at heart. The following verse in Hebrews was not specifically written for parents and children, but I think it does have application since your parents are your primary disciplers. Note the last phrase in particular. "Obey your leaders and submit to them, for they are keeping watch over your souls, as those who will have to give an account. Let them do this with joy and not with groaning, for that would be of no advantage to you." (Hebrews 13:17)

It is my prayer that as you work through this curriculum, "the God of our Lord Jesus Christ, the Father of glory, may give you the Spirit of wisdom and of revelation in the knowledge of Him." (Ephesians 1:17)

May God bless each of you as you work through these studies,

Steve Demme

EARNING MONEY

Money is what we use to conduct commerce. Money which we call currency, or dollars and cents is what we use to function in the matter of working, buying, and selling. Generally, the more valuable our work, the more money we receive for our work. My first paying job was shoveling snow off of driveways for a few dollars. The longer the driveway, the more I charged. I then moved on to grass cutting and received $3.00 at one yard and $4.00 at another. I even had a paper route, but that was a lot of walking and had to be done every day. Plus, I didn't like dogs, or rather they didn't like me. So that job only lasted a few weeks. None of those jobs required any special training, and as a result I received low compensation.

When I turned 16, I worked as a busboy, then a stock boy, and finally a carpenter's helper, all of which paid minimum wage. The minimum wage, set by the government, is the lowest amount workers over 16 can be paid per hour. That year, I got between $1.40 and $1.60 per hour for each of those jobs.

At the end of the summer of working as a carpenter's helper, I was asked to paint the back gutter of a two-story house. It required being on a ladder three stories up. First I stripped the gutter, then primed it and finally painted it. I worked for five hours and went inside to be paid. The man asked me what I thought it was worth, and after some quick thought I took a deep breath and mentioned $15.00, which was double what I had been getting paid. He quickly wrote out a check for $20.00. When I told my dad about it, he said it was hard to find painters willing to be on a ladder, and that what I had done was specialized work. But that wasn't the end of the story. The next-door neighbors who had seen me painting the gutter asked me to do the high trim on their home. I worked eight hours and charged $32.00. Receiving $4.00 per hour, I felt rich! But more importantly, I was learning a lesson in economics about the relationship between money and the value of labor.

Example 1

If my wages were $1.50 per hour, how much would my paycheck be for working 28 hours as a busboy?

Solution 1

$28 \times \$1.50 = \$42.00$

Example 2

When I was painting the high places on a house I was being paid $4.00 per hour. How much did I make during a three day job when I worked 22.5 hours?

Solution 2

$22.5 \times \$4.00 = \$90.00$

Hourly Pay and Annual Wage

All of the jobs I had when I was in high school were remunerated by the hour. If I worked 10 hours, I was paid for 10 hours. When I worked full time during the summer, I received a weekly paycheck based on how many hours I was on the job. Usually this was 40 hours, but if it rained it may have been 32 hours.

If you work by the hour and want to figure your wages for a year and not just a week, I have found a quick way to estimate it. Take your hourly wage, double it, then add three zeros to the end. If you work for $4.00 per hour, doubling it makes $8.00 and adding three zeros makes $8,000.00. Here is why it works. Generally, an average work week is 40 hours. That is five days per week and eight hours a day. This method does assume you work 50 weeks in a year which is less than the actual 52 weeks in a year but this is close enough to get a good estimate. Thus 40 hours per week times 50 weeks is 2,000 hours. So $4.00 per hour times 2,000 hours is $8,000.00. The 4 is doubled ($\times 2$), and multiplying by 1,000 is the same as adding three zeros.

Example 3

Rowan's wage was $7.50 per hour. If he worked all year, and did not receive a raise or a bonus, how much could he expect to receive annually?

Solution 3

$7.50 doubled is 15 and adding three zeroes makes $15,000. Or another way to think of this is $2,000 \times \$7.50 = \$15,000.00$

Overtime and Holiday Pay

A normal work week is 40 hours. If you work more than that, it is called overtime and your pay is computed differently. These numbers will vary, but generally it is 1.5, or one and a half times a normal hourly wage. If you receive $9.00 per hour and work overtime, you would get $13.50 ($9.00 + $4.50) per hour for the hours beyond 40. If Raleigh is paid $9.00 per hour and worked 46 hours last week, he gets 40 hr $\times$ $9.00/hr for the normal weekly wages. Since he works 6 hours more than 40, he will receive 6 hr $\times$ $13.50/hr for overtime pay. His total wage for the week is then $360.00 + $81.00 = $441.00.

If you work on a holiday you may receive "holiday pay," which is double your normal pay. If Raleigh worked 49 hours with 9 of those hours coming on Memorial Day, he would receive 40 hr $\times$ $9.00/hr + 9 hr $\times$ $18.00/hr, or $360.00 + $162.00 = $522.00.

Example 4

Savana is a diligent worker who decides to work 44.5 hours this week. Her normal pay is $8.50 per hour. How much did she make for the whole week's work?

Solution 4

40 hr $\times$ $8.50/hr is for the normal weekly wages. Since she worked 4.5 hours more than 40, she will receive 4.5 hr $\times$ $12.75 ($8.50 + $4.25) per hour for overtime pay. Her total wage for the week is then

$340.00 + \$57.38 = \$397.38.$

Salary

Certain jobs are paid a regular salary. This is like hourly pay, except the number of paid hours is specified in advance by an employee contract. For example if you have a contract for 40 hours per week at \$20 per hour, then you will be paid \$800 every week as if you worked exactly 40 hours every week, regardless of how many hours you actually worked. If you worked 39.5 hours one week, and 43 hours the next week, you would still be paid as if you had worked 40 hours on both weeks and would not receive overtime pay for the week you worked 43 hours. Salaried jobs are also called "exempt" jobs, because they are exempt from state and federal laws regarding minimum wage and overtime.

Example 5

Bill was a sales rep for MathUSee. Through the convention season (about 10 weeks) he worked an average of 50 hours per week. During the slow time between Thanksgiving and Christmas, he only worked 30 hours for those 4 weeks. How many hours did Bill work for the year, assuming 40 hours for all of the other weeks?

Solution 5

For 52 weeks, with 10×50 plus 4 times 30 plus 38 (52 weeks − 10 weeks − 4 weeks = 38 weeks) × 40 hours.
$500 + 120 + 1{,}520 = 2{,}140$ hours

Example 6

What was his average hourly salary if his annual salary was \$42,000.00?

Solution 6

$\$42{,}000 \div 2{,}140 = \$19.63$. We would assume it was \$21.00 per hour ($\$42{,}000 \div 2{,}000 = \$21.00$) but because of the longer convention weeks, it was less.

Piecemeal

Another way to earn money is what is referred to as piecemeal, per piece, or by the job. When you assemble block sets for me, I pay you by the piece. The faster you work, the more you make. My grandfather used to say you work by the (read slowly) hour . . . after . . . hour ... after . . . hour, or (read quickly) the jobbity-job-job. If you were paid by the hour, you would not get nearly as many block sets assembled as you would if paid by the piece—am I correct? It is human nature.

All of my early work experiences—mowing lawns and shoveling snow—were paid by the job. Delivering papers was by the paper, or by the piece. There are many jobs today that still operate this way and pay piecemeal. Those who hang drywall are often paid by the number of sheets hung on a job. Some delivery companies reimburse their workers by how many packages they pick up and/or deliver.

When MathUSee was in its infancy I used to pay families to assemble block sets for \$1.25 per set. Families sat around a table and put these kits together in their own home. In 2018 as I am writing this most of our assembly is done by adults affected with a disability. They are paid for how many sets they are able to assemble. Our manipulative blocks sets are now larger and assemblers receive $2.30 per set.

Example 7

Ephrata Area Rehabilitation Services has a team of workers who will be assembling block sets this week. By the end of the week, the team of five workers had put together 480 sets. How much was the combined pay for the team?

Solution 7

$480 \times \$2.30 = \$1,104.00$.

Commissions

Salesmen are generally paid according by how much they sell. Their wages are computed as a percentage of their total sales and are called a commission. The more they sell, the more they earn. Real estate salesmen are often paid a flat 1.5% commission for their work in helping someone sell or purchase a house. If they help sell a house that costs $53,000.00, their commission is $53,000.00 times 1.5% (0.015), or $795.00. They may sell one house per day in a good week. The flip side is that they may sell only one house a month during a rough stretch. Making a bunch of sales one week and then selling very little for a few weeks is called "feast or famine."

Example 8

Alex sold a house to Jeff and Fritha for $235,900.00. What was his commission?

Solution 8

$235,900.00 times 1.5% (0.015), or $3,538.50

Door To Door

One year I sold World Book encyclopedias and found they reimbursed me 20% for my commission on each set I sold. It was a larger ticket purchase, and customers would need to think a little bit before investing the first time they saw my presentation. I found that it took an average of five presentations to sell one set. I took a sample around to show the product and if a sale was made the company would send it directly to the customer. World Book is one of those companies that doesn't have middlemen. They produce the books then sell them through their sales force. You can't buy a set of World Book Encyclopedias in a Barnes & Noble bookstore. One advantage of this approach is I didn't need to fill my garage full of sets of encyclopedias and have a lot of money invested in them.

Example 9

The first week I began selling Encyclopedias I did 4 presentations in three evenings before I sold one set on the third evening. While there several different binding options from leather to faux leather, they chose a set which cost $789.00. What was my commission?

Solution 9

20% of $789.00 is $157.80

Commission Plus a Base Salary

Salesmen who work on a pure commission basis work harder than most, since their livelihood depends on their sales. An encyclopedia salesman might receive a 20% sales commission. On a set that runs $1,200.00, this comes to a check for $240.00. If he sells one per night, then sales are good, but if he sells one per week, then he is hungry. Often companies have a base salary for salesmen, with a commission added on. This way salesmen are not totally dependent on selling but still retain the incentive, since the more they sell, the more they make.

Example 10

Reedy's Real Estate firm pays each person in full time sales $1,500.00 per month as their base salary. They also receive a 1.5% commission on any properties they sell. Laura began working there in April and did not sell any homes during the first month. She continued to work diligently and in May she closed (sold a home) on three homes which sold for an average of $185,000 each. What was her combined income for April and May?

Solution 10

$185,000 \times 3$ homes $= \$555,000.00$ for her total sales.
$\$555,000 \times 0.015 = \$8,325.00$ for the commissions.
$\$8,325.00 + \$1,500$ (April) $+ \$1,500$ (May) $= \$11,325.00$

PERCENT

We'll begin this lesson with a review of what a percentage is and then study how to find a percentage. A percentage is a fraction with a denominator of 100. It is usually easier to change a fraction to a decimal before changing it to a percentage. We can change a fraction to a decimal by placing a tenth overlay on top of it. In this illustration $\frac{2}{5}$ becomes $\frac{4}{10}$ which can be written as the decimal 0.4. We can go a step further and place the other tenth overlay on top of the first one at a 90-degree angle. Four-tenths or 0.4 is now 40/100 or 0.40 or 40%.

Figure 1

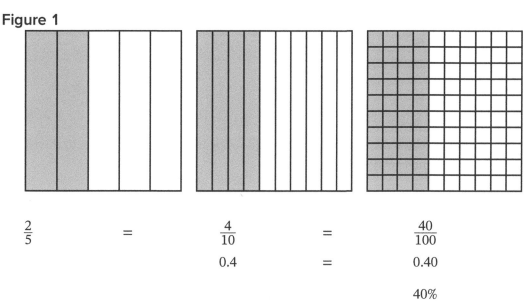

$$\frac{2}{5} \qquad = \qquad \frac{4}{10} \qquad = \qquad \frac{40}{100}$$

$$0.4 \qquad = \qquad 0.40$$

$$40\%$$

Fractions as Decimals and Percentages

Every fraction can be transformed to a decimal by dividing the numerator by the denominator. The fraction $\frac{1}{2}$ is 1 divided by 2, which is 0.5. The fraction $\frac{2}{7}$ is 2 divided by 7, which is 0.285. This can be rounded to the hundredths place and becomes 0.29.

Simple fractions such as $\frac{1}{2}$, $\frac{2}{5}$, $\frac{1}{4}$, and $\frac{3}{4}$ are relatively simple to rewrite as tenths and hundredths. For example, $\frac{1}{2} = \frac{5}{10}$ and $\frac{2}{5} = \frac{4}{10}$. Think of money as you do fourths: one quarter is the same as twenty-five pennies, so $\frac{1}{4} = \frac{25}{100}$ and $\frac{3}{4} = \frac{75}{100}$.

Once you have rewritten the fraction as its decimal equivalent, it is an easy process to convert the decimals into hundredths. The number written as 0.4 or $\frac{4}{10}$ is equivalent to 0.40 or $\frac{40}{100}$. Once you have hundredths, you have percent, since percent means "per hundred." 0.40 or $\frac{40}{100} = 40\%$. $\frac{1}{4} = \frac{25}{100} = 25\%$. $\frac{1}{2} = \frac{5}{10} = \frac{50}{100}$ or 50%.

Multiplication by a Decimal is the Same as Division by a Whole Number

Notice that when you multiply a number by 10, the digit does not change, but it appears to move one place to the left, making the number larger. Consider the following examples:

Example 1

$7 \times 10 = 70$

Example 2

$28 \times 10 = 280$

Example 3

$0.09 \times 10 = 0.9$

When you multiply a number by 100, once again the digit(s) remain the same, but the number is much larger, and the digits appear to move two places to the left.

Example 4

$34 \times 100 = 3,400$

Example 5

$5.01 \times 100 = 501$

Example 6

$0.0006 \times 100 = 0.06$

Similarly, when dividing by 100 the digits appear to move two places to the right, because the result is much smaller.

Example 7

$451 \div 100 = 4.51$

Example 8

$2 \div 100 = 0.02$

Example 9

$7,809 \div 100 = 78.09$

Now let's apply this simple concept to decimals. A decimal is a fraction written on one line. When you multiply by a decimal numeral it is the same as multiplying by a fraction. The denominator of a fraction is another way of expressing division, since the line separating the numerator and denominator means "divided by."

Multiplying by 0.1 is the same as multiplying by $\frac{1}{10}$, which is another way of expressing "divide by 10." Similarly, multiplying by a decimal is the same as dividing by a whole number. Observe the following problems that illustrate different ways of expressing the same operation.

Example 10

$$6 \times 0.1 = 0.6$$

$$6 \times \frac{1}{10} = \frac{6}{10} = 0.6$$

$$6 \div 10 = \frac{6}{10} = 0.6$$

Example 11

$$840 \times 0.01 = 8.4$$

$$840 \times \frac{1}{100} = \frac{840}{100} = 8.4$$

$$840 \div 100 = \frac{840}{100} = 8.4$$

When you are asked to find a percentage of a number, simply rewrite the percentage as a decimal or a fraction and then multiply. Remember what we have just observed and don't be surprised that when we multiply by a decimal (that is less than 1), our answer will be much smaller than what we began with.

Example 12

Find 25% of 36.

Solution 12

$25\% = 0.25$ or $\frac{25}{100}$ and $0.25 \times 36 = 9$

So 25% of 36 is 9.

Example 13

Find 7% of 409.

Solution 13

$7\% = 0.07$ or $\frac{7}{100}$ and $0.07 \times 409 = 28.63$

So 7% of 409 = 28.63.

Working with Tenths

One tenth is the same as $\frac{1}{10}$ or 0.1 or $\frac{10}{100}$ or 10%. We have observed that one tenth means 1 divided by 10. When you divide by 10 or multiply by 0.1, move the decimal point over one place to the left. Another word for a tenth is a tithe.

Example 14

Find $\frac{1}{10}$ or 10% of 6.53.

Solution 14

$\frac{1}{10}$ or 10% or 0.1 of 6.53 is $0.1 \times 6.53 = 0.653$

Once you have mastered 10%, you can use this trick to figure out 20% or any multiple of 10%. For example, to find 20% of 4.13, first find 10% by moving the decimal point to the left, making it $\frac{1}{10}$ of what it was. Ten percent of 4.13 is 0.413. To find 20%, double that answer or multiply it by two, since 20% is two times 10%. The final answer is 0.826. We know that 20% is the same as $\frac{20}{100}$ or 0.20 written as a decimal. We could have multiplied 4.13 by 0.20 (or 0.2) and gotten 0.826, but I am trying to teach you to do this in your head!

Example 15

Find 20% of 175.

Solution 15

$\frac{1}{10}$ or 10% or 0.1 of 175 is $0.1 \times 175 = 17.50$

20% would be 2 times as much or 35.00.

Five percent is half of 10%. If you are asked to find 5% of a number, just find 10% and cut the answer in half. If you are buying a washing machine which costs $350.00, and there is a 5% tax, take 10% of the price, or $35.00 and cut it in half to get $17.50. Then add the tax on to the original price. So, $350 + $17.50 is $367.50, which is the real cost for the washer.

Sales Tax and Strategies for Computing Percentages

Almost every day we each pay sales tax. This tax varies from state to state. Including sales tax in your calculations, particularly when you are purchasing a large ticket item like a washing machine or a used car, helps you calculate the real cost of what you are buying.

In most of Pennsylvania we have a 6% sales tax. There are two ways to figure it. The most direct is to multiply the total by 0.06. Another way is to do it in your head. First find 5% by taking half of 10%. We still need to find 6%, which is 5% plus 1%. To find the 1%, move the decimal of the total amount two places to the left. If the amount you are being charged is $120.00, 10% is $12.00, and half of that is $6.00. One percent of $120.00 is $1.20, so the tax is $6.00 plus $1.20, or $7.20. The direct way is to multiply $120.00 by 0.06 to get $7.20. You could also multiply $120.00 by 6 and then move the decimal point two places to the left for $7.20. Either way will work.

Example 16

Adam purchased a new paddle for his kayak. It cost $48.00. What was the total bill if the sales tax is 5%?

Solution 16

This problem may be figured a few ways.
5% is half of 10% and 10% of $48.00 is $4.80, so 5% is $2.40
$48.00 + $2.40 = $50.40
Or, multiply $48.00 times 5%, which is $48.00 \times 0.05 = $2.40
$48.00 + $2.40 = $50.40

Some cities and counties have a different sales tax than the state does, and the amount may be a mixed number like 8.25%.

Example 17

Teagan saw a nice sweatshirt at the mall. It cost $19.50.
What was the total bill if the sales tax is 8.25%?

Solution 17

$19.50 times 8.25% or $19.50 × 0.0825% = $1.60875 which rounds to $1.61.
The total is $19.50 + $1.61 = $21.11.

Tips

If you tip a waiter in an eating establishment, you have the opportunity to calculate percentages such as 15%. (The 15% is calculated on the amount of the food bill, not the food bill plus the tax.) I do this by figuring 10% and then taking half of that for the 5%. Here is an easy example. You get the bill and are ready to leave a tip. The bill is $24.00. So, 10% is $2.40 and half of that (5%) is $1.20. The $2.40 plus $1.20 is $3.60, which is the tip.

In real life, I like to round up or down depending on the service. If I got really good service, I would leave $4.00. If it was okay, but maybe not what it could be, a tip of $3.00 might do. I always leave something. Usually the waiters are paid a minimum salary plus their tips, so they do need to receive some tips. I have friends who will not leave any tip if the service was really bad. Everyone has to make their own decisions.

Depending on where you live, the standard tipping amount may vary. In most of the United States 15%–20% is considered standard. If you eat out for a special occasion with a number of guests, make sure you don't tip twice. Some restaurants automatically figure the tip into the bill when serving a large group.

In the past few years, the expected tip for servers in restaurants has moved from 15% to 20%. This is much easier to calculate. If the bill is $24.00, then 10% of 24.00 is $2.40, and you simply double that amount to arrive at $4.80 for the tip. The total for the food and a 20% tip is $28.80 ($24.00 + 4.80 = $28.80). Since I like to round up or down depending on the service, I would round up to $29.00 if it was good service. If the service was below average, I might make the final amount only $28.00, which includes a $4.00 tip. The lower tip is still over 15% (15% of $24.00 is $3.60).

Example 18

Darby's bill for lunch was $12.75. She had a wonderful server. The sales tax was 5%. How much was her tip and the final tally? How much could she add to make it a round number?

Solution 18

$12.75 × 20% = $2.55 for the tip
$12.75 × 5% = $0.64 for the tax
Total bill is $12.75 + $2.55 + $0.64 = $15.94
If you want it in even dollars, add $0.06 to make $16.00.

Example 19

Hannah took friends out to celebrate her first real estate sale. The price for breakfast was $46.25. The server was okay, but not special, and the sales tax was 6.5%. How much was the tip and the final tally? How much could be added to make it a round number?

Solution 19

$46.25 × 16% = $7.40 for the tip since the service was just okay.

$46.25 × 6.5% = $3.01 for the tax

Total bill is $46.25 + $7.40 + $3.01 = $56.66

If you want it in even dollars, add $0.34 to make $57.00.

Another Tip on Tipping

I have noticed that many eating establishments will now provide suggested tip amounts on the bottom of the check. The tip is calculated for 15%, 18%, and 20%. As I examined their computations, I discovered the percentage was figured on the price of the food PLUS the tax.

Example 20

The bill for the food was $40.00 and the sales tax was 8%. The total bill was $43.20. What is the difference between a tip computed on the price of the food alone and a tip computed with the tax included?

Solution 20

The percentages and resulting tip amounts on my bill were shown as:

15% $6.48	18% $7.78	20% $8.64

When I figured the tip based on the cost of food alone, the numbers were:

15% $6.00	18% $7.20	20% $8.00

At the Airport

When I am traveling, I carry several one-dollar bills with me. I tip the parking service if I leave a car at the garage because the driver helps me take my bags into his van and unloads them at the curb. I usually tip $1.00 per bag. If I use curbside boarding, I also tip the workers who help unload and check my bags. This service helps me avoid the line inside of the airport.

Example 21

Collin was flying to China and had three large bags with him. He first had to take a shuttle from the parking garage to the airport, and then have help checking his bags at the curbside baggage counter. How much did he spend in tips?

Solution 21

Collin tipped the shuttle driver $3.00 for his assistance. At the curbside baggage check-in, Collin gave the worker $5.00 for his help, since the bags were large.

Paying Bills

When you see "1% 10 Net 30 Days" on an invoice (an invoice is a bill for you to pay), it indicates two things. The "1% 10" means that if you pay your bill within 10 days, you can deduct 1% from the total. The "30" means that if you do not opt to make use of this discount, you still must pay within 30 days. Some companies will have a rate of 2% 15 Net 30 Days, which means that if you pay your bill within 15 days you save 2% of the total invoice.

Encouraging people to pay quickly is a positive thing for both those paying the invoice and those being paid. If you as the consumer could pay 1% or 2% less on items you purchase, it would mean significant savings over a year. To the business offering the discount, cash flow, or having cash on hand with which to do business, is vital. They may have the best product and lots of sales, but if they aren't being paid in a timely fashion, they can't pay their suppliers and workers and eventually may have to close-up shop.

Example 22

Seth's printing bill for $785.00 was dated December 9. On the invoice it read "1% 10 net 30." It is now December 14th. How much should Seth pay?

Solution 22

Since it has been only five days since the date on the bill, Seth can deduct 1% or $7.85. The amount to pay is $777.15.

Example 23

Adam has a bill on his desk for $540.00. It reads "2% 15 net 30." It has been 17 days since the date on the bill. How much is he expected to send?

Solution 23

Adam missed the 15-day bonus period, so he has to pay the "net" or total amount of $540.00.

Property Taxes

Where I now live, we receive two tax bills for our home or property. One comes in the Spring and is called the Spring Tax. The larger one comes in the Fall and is referred to as the Fall Tax. Since these are large bills, there are several options for paying them. If you pay within the first two months of receiving the bill, you can deduct 5% from the total tax. If you pay a little later, you can save 2%, or you can wait a few months and pay it in full. If you wait too long, you will have to pay an additional fee of 1%.

Example 24

The Lloyd's property tax bill is $2,687.15 and was received on March 15.
They have the following options:
If paid in April or May receive a 5% discount.
If paid in June or July receive a 2% discount.
If paid in August or September pay full amount.
If paid after September 30 accrue a 1% penalty.

Option A: If they choose to pay their property tax bill on May 22, how much will it be?
Option B: What is the total amount if they send their payment on October 29?

Solution 24

Option A: Since it is in May, they can deduct 5%.

$2,687.15 × 0.05 = $134.36.

$2,687.15 - $134.36 = $2,552.79

Option B: If they are paying after September 30, they pay an additional 1%.

$2,687.15 × 0.01 = $26.87

$2,687.15 + $26.87 = $2,714.02

Rounding

When performing math with money, the standard practice is to not round off the numbers when working electronically. However, when a payment will be made by check or cash, you must round off at the hundredths place (cents), because that is the smallest unit of currency in the US. In the examples and solutions in this book, our general practice will be to not round off numbers in the middle of a calculation. Instead we will wait until we write the final answer before rounding to the nearest cent. In the rare case where the final answer has exactly five thousandths (and is therefore exactly between two numbers in the hundredths place) we will round up instead of down. If you end up with an answer that is within a few hundredths of the solution, it is probably only due to a difference in when and how you rounded the numbers.

Example 25

Divide $1.05 by 2 and then multiply by 3. Round the answer to the nearest cent.

Solution 25A (rounding at the end of the problem)

$1.05 ÷ 2 = $0.525

$0.525 × 3 = $1.575

Rounding the 5 in the thousandths place makes the final answer $1.58

Solution 25B (rounding in the middle of the problem)

$1.05 ÷ 2 = $0.525 which rounds to $0.053

$0.53 × 3 = $1.59

Income Tax

My first real paying job was working at a local deli. When I was hired, I was told that my hourly wage would be $1.45 per hour. That may not seem like much, but this was the minimum wage at the time (a long time ago). I think I worked 28 hours the first week, and I thought I would receive a check for $40.60. I was surprised to receive much less than I expected because a whole bunch of taxes had been taken out.

Since then the minimum wage has increased, and so has the tax burden. If you are currently working and receiving a paycheck, you will have shared the unpleasant experience of seeing your take-home pay be much less than your gross pay. I am getting ahead of myself, so let's define some terms before we embark on this topic of taxes.

Your Earnings

Gross pay is what you earn, whether by salary, hourly wage, piecemeal reimbursement, or commission. It is what you think your income will be. Net pay, or take-home pay, is what you really take home after the government has taken its cut of your income. This tax on your income is called income tax.

Employer and Employee

Employers are those who hire you and pay you for your work. Those of us who are hired are referred to as employees. The employer and the employee have similar but different responsibilities for paying taxes on what is earned.

I am responsible to pay several different kinds of taxes: federal (United States), state (Pennsylvania), and county (Lancaster). Unless you are my next-door neighbor, your taxes will be different, since the taxes and tax rates vary from country to country, state to state, county to county, and school district to school district. Let's examine a few of these income taxes, so that you will better understand your paycheck.

Graduated Tax

There are two different ways of taxing income. One is called a graduated tax. This means that the more money you earn, the greater the percentage of your earnings you pay in taxes. For 2018, if your taxable income is less than $9,525.00, you are responsible to pay 15% of your taxable income in federal tax. If you make between $38,701.00 and $82,500.00, you are in a higher bracket (there are seven brackets which are listed below), and you will pay 24% of your taxable income. The greater the amount of your taxable income, the higher your percentage.

Flat Tax

A flat tax requires everyone to pay the same income tax rate regardless of how much or how little they earn. There is one rate for everyone. Forty-three states have a state income tax.

Thirty-five of them use a graduated tax formula while eight states have a flat tax. Seven states do not have any state income tax. Some people are proponents of a federal flat tax on income instead of a graduated tax. There are advantages to both, but the flat tax is much simpler and would drastically cut back on the cost to the Internal Revenue Service (IRS) of administering the graduated tax model.

Taxable Income (Federal)

As of January 1, 2018, a single person filing their own tax return receives a $12,000.00 standard deduction. This means that if you earn $62,000.00, you can deduct $12,000.00 and compute your taxes on only $50,000.00 ($62,000.00 − $12,000.00). This amount of $50,000.00 is called your taxable income.

Federal Withholding Tax

This tax is a graduated tax and therefore depends on how much you earn in a year. This is taken from your paycheck by your employer and is usually deposited in a local bank, and then transferred to the Internal Revenue Service, or IRS. When you are hired by your employer, you will be asked to fill out a W-4 form, which determines how many allowances you can claim. Having more allowances means you can have less taxes taken out of each paycheck.

Filing Individually or Jointly

When you fill out your tax return, if you are single, you will select the option to be considered as an individual. Someday when you are married, you and your spouse may each file individually, or you may file jointly. If you look at the tax tables for Federal Withholding Tax, notice these two options. The tax rates are graduated and computed on what your net income is. If you and your spouse each make $50,000 annually, examine whether it is better to file your taxes individually or jointly. In the first section you would fall into the 22% bracket. In the second section, your combined income would be $100,000 and you are still responsible to pay 22%. Until you reach the last two brackets for 35% and 37%, there is no difference between filing individually or jointly.

2018 Income Tax Brackets

Rate	Filing as an Individual	Filing Jointly
10%	$0 to $9,525	$0 to $19,050
12%	$9,526 to $38,700	$19,051 to $77,400
22%	$38,701 to $82,500	$77,401 to $165,000
24%	$82,501 to $157,500	$165,001 to $315,000
32%	$157,501 to $200,000	$315,001 to $400,000
35%	$200,001 to $500,000	$400,001 to $600,000
37%	over $500,000	over $600,000

Computing your Annual Federal Income Tax Using these Seven Brackets

If you are single and have a gross income of $47,000.00, how would you compute your Federal Income Tax? The first step would be to subtract $12,000.00, which is your standard deduction. Your taxable income is $35,000.00.

> The first $9,525 will be taxed at a rate of 10%, which is $952.50
>
> Subtracting $9,525.00 from $35,000 yields a balance of $25,475
>
> This amount is taxed at the 12% rate
>
> $25,475 \times 0.12 = \$3,057.00$
>
> Adding the two amounts: $3,057.00 + $952.50 = $4,009.50

Net Tax Rate

You did not pay any taxes on your first $12,000 because of the standard deduction. You paid 10% on your next $9,525.00 and 12% on your final $25,475.00, so you ended up paying $4,009.50, which is 8.53% of your gross pay. I calculated this percent by dividing $4,009.50 by $47,000 to get 8.53%.

Weekly Deductions Of Federal Income Tax

Federal income tax withheld is calculated using the Wage Bracket Method and is determined by the information on your W-4 form. The W-4 will determine how many allowances you can claim. I am including a few lines from the table for 2018 for an example.

		Witholding Allowances Claimed			
Wages are at least	but less than	0	1	2	3
890	900	103	86	76	66
900	910	105	88	77	68
910	920	108	90	78	69

State Income Tax

Pennsylvania is one of eight states that has opted for a flat income tax. It has a flat rate of 3.07%. If you live in Pennsylvania, this means that 3.07% of your gross pay is deducted from your paycheck by your employer, and then sent directly to the Pennsylvania State Treasury.

Since your income is $47,000, you also pay 3.07% for state income tax. This is a flat tax for PA residents and comes out to $47,000 \times 0.0307 = \$1,442.90$.

County Income Tax

In my county (Lancaster), the rate varies for each local school district. Our school district rate is 1.0%. This is one of the smaller taxes and is taken from the paycheck and sent directly to the Lancaster County Treasurer. The county then distributes the money to the school districts and local municipalities. I learned in my research that there is an additional tax in my county called the Local Services Tax, which is $52.00 a year per employee. Generally, if you are a full-time employee this amount is withheld at a rate of $1.00 each week. I called the county tax collection agency twice, and no one can tell me what it is for, but it is another tax I have to pay.

FICA

This acronym stands for Federal Insurance Contribution Act and is the first of several federally imposed payroll taxes. I call these taxes "double dips" because not only does the government take 6.20% from your paycheck for the Social Security portion, but the employer has to match the "contribution" and pay 6.20% as well. FICA funds both Social Security and

Medicare. The rate for the Medicare portion is 1.45%. It, too, is matched by the employer. Both of these taxes, Social Security and Medicare, are part of the money deposited at the local bank by the employer and then sent to the government. When you add them up, you have a FICA tax of 7.65%. There are maximum contribution thresholds, but this rate will apply to most of us.

SUI

State Unemployment Insurance (SUI) is put into a fund and then withdrawn by those who have lost their jobs or are out of work. The employee rate is 0.06% on all of his or her annual earnings. The employer pays anywhere between 2% and 10%. This tax is instituted when there are high unemployment rates, and varies from year to year. There are maximum contribution thresholds, but the 0.06% rate will apply to most of us.

A Paycheck

If you are an adult and are not being claimed as a dependent on your parents' tax returns, you will have to pay taxes. If you are earning an annual salary of $47,000, your weekly gross pay is $904. Here is what your paycheck might like after your taxes have been withheld, if you work in Lancaster County, Pennsylvania in 2018 and didn't claim any allowances on your W4 form.

Example 1

Federal	$105.00	(about 11%, could vary)
State	$27.75	3.07%
County	$9.04	1.00%
LST	$1.00	fee
FICA (SS + Medicare)	$69.16	7.65%
SUI	$0.54	0.06%
Total Deducted Weekly Tax	$212.49	
Net Take Home Pay	$691.51	

Employer Taxes

The employer also must pay taxes on what you earn. Those taxes don't come directly out of your paycheck. You may see them referred to as employer expenses. Most of the employer taxes have been mentioned, but here they are spelled out again. The one new tax is FUTA, which stands for Federal Unemployment Tax Act. It is 6% but is only computed on the first $7,000.00 of wages earned.

Example 2
(based on $904 weekly gross pay from Example 1)

FUTA	$54.24	6.00%
FICA (SS + Medicare)	$69.16	7.65%
SUI	$18.08	2.00%
Total Employer Taxes	$141.48	

Self-Employed Federal Estimated Quarterly Tax Payments

Your annual income will vary each year if you are self-employed. You are required to make estimated tax payments based on the previous year's income. These dates may vary from year to year, and depending on whether your fiscal year corresponds to the calendar year. Here are the due dates for the 2019 calendar year.

Quarter	Payment Due
January–March	April 15
April–May	June 17
June–August	September 16
September–December	January 15

Suppose you made $47,000.00 last year, reported this amount on your federal tax return, and paid $4,009.50 in taxes. Divide the total tax into four equal payments. You must pay $1,002.38 estimated tax per quarter this year.

Example 3

Ned and Leslie made a gross income of $81,700.00 last year as self-employed graphic designers. How much should they pay in estimated quarterly payments?

Solution 3

First we must determine how much they paid in taxes.

Since they are married and filing jointly, they can subtract their standard deduction of $24,000.00 from $81,700.00. Their taxable income is $57,700.00.

The first $19,050.00 of taxable income will be taxed at a rate of 10%, which yields $1,905.00.

Subtracting $19,050.00 from $57,700.00 yields a balance of $38,650.00, which is taxed at the 12% rate.

$38,650.00 × 0.12 = $4,638.00

Adding the two amounts: $1,905.00 + $4,638.00 = $6,543.00

$6,543.00 ÷ 4 = $1,635.75.

Self-Employed State Estimated Quarterly Tax Payments

If you made $47,000.00 the year before, reported this amount on your state tax return, and paid $1,442.90 in taxes, divide this amount into four equal payments of $360.73.

Example 4

Paula has a dog sitting business. She makes an average of $400.00 per month. Last year she showed a net taxable income of $5,000.00. How much should she pay in estimated quarterly payments if her state income tax is 3.07%?

Solution 4

$5,000.00 × 3.07% = $153.50

$153.50 ÷ 4 = $38.375, which rounds to $38.38

Plan For FICA

When you are self-employed, you are both the employer and the employee. Since each party normally pays 7.65% for FICA, as both the boss and the worker you will pay 15.3% (ouch). There may be some deductions which will impact this amount, but you should count on this tax being close to 15.3% of your income. If you make $47,000.00 a year, the FICA tax will be $7,191.00. Start setting aside money now so you can pay this when your taxes are due by April 15 of the next year.

Example 5

Paula (Example 4) wants to set aside money for her FICA taxes. How much should she have in her savings account by April 15 of the next year?

Solution 5

$5,000.00 × 15.3% = $765.00

BANKING

Banks are useful for holding your money, investing your money, facilitating the moving of your money, and lending money. Banks do not create money. The board of directors of a bank manages money by offering a variety of services to you and your neighbors. The money that is in a bank comes from people who deposit their funds in the bank.

One thing that has always struck me about a bank is the words associated with it. Notice how often you see words like fidelity (which means faith or faithful), trust, or security. We know that it is a temptation to put our trust in riches instead of in God. I am conscious of this as a Christian. Banks like to be thought of as safe places that you can trust to take good care of your hard-earned money. There are a few banks in our county called Sovereign Bank and Integrity Bank. Ultimately God is our refuge and strength, not a bank. That being said, let's examine some of the functions of a bank that can be helpful.

Banks Serve the Customer

As you transition through different seasons of life, your needs will also change. When I first began banking, I was looking for free checking and an ATM card. Then when I had a family, I was interested in a safety deposit box to store valuable papers. A few times I needed cashier's checks to make large purchases.

I chose the bank we currently use because of the excellent customer service, as well as for their checking, savings, and other services. A few years ago, I arranged to have my first home equity loan to enable us to move, as we were between two homes. Now that I am a seasoned citizen (old), I can also ask for investment advice and retirement input. As you think about your needs, I hope you will also think through how the bank can serve you through different seasons of your own life.

Checking

The first function we look at is checking. A checking account lets you give the bank your money to hold for you. This transaction is called making a deposit. As an example, I just opened a checking account at the local branch of Fulton Bank. I made an initial deposit of $500.00. With that amount of money in the bank, I can now use checks to make transactions just as if they were cash. I want to buy a new gas grill, so I drive to Bomberger's Store, pick one out, and write a check for $199.00. The store has my check, and I have the grill. Bomberger's Store deposits this check into their bank at the end of the day. Their bank and my bank communicate electronically, and $199.00 is transferred to their bank.

Perhaps I decide to buy a grill my neighbor is selling. I give him a check for $150.00, and he takes it to his bank where they take the check and give him $150.00. As before, his bank and my bank communicate electronically, and $150.00 is transferred to my neighbor's bank from Fulton Bank.

This service is a convenience for you and for the person you paid. The process of cashing and depositing checks is work for the banks for which they should be paid. How are they being paid for their checking services?

When you deposit your money into the bank's hands, they don't just sit on it; they use it to make money. Your next-door neighbor may need to borrow $5,000.00 for a new car. He goes to the bank, and they decide he is worth the risk (lending money is always a risk). The neighbor agrees to pay it back in 12 months at 8% interest. If he honors the agreement, the bank just made 8% on the $5,000.00, or $400.00. Simply put, the bank is lending out your money and making money with it. The more money that you deposit, or place in the bank, the more money the bank can make.

You can also make deposits in person, through the mail, or electronically by using your computer or smartphone. Now, the more the bank profits from holding your money, the less you should pay, since they are using your money very profitably. This affects your fees.

Each bank has separate fees and structures in place for the services they offer. If you put in a little money, say, $100.00, you may have to pay for your checking privileges. If you deposit a lot, like $2,000.00, you probably will qualify for free checking. In a best-case scenario the bank will even pay you for holding the money. They do this by paying you a percentage of what is in your account. Several years ago, I received 2% for the money in my checking account. I moved my checking account to this bank because of this bonus. The bank that had been handling my checking account began charging fees regardless of how much money was in my account. At the new bank, I not only get a 2% return, but free checking services as well. However, markets change, and currently I receive a very small percent that amounts to pennies each month.

Online Banking

My local bank pays me 0.02% interest on my balance in checking. All of the brick and mortar banks in our county are paying similar interest rates on checking and savings accounts. This is 1/50 of one percent. Peanuts! By working with my financial advisor, I learned of a bank in Atlanta that is paying 2.75% for money deposited in checking. I live in Pennsylvania but have arranged to electronically transfer funds via the internet. The new rate of 2.75% is 135 times as much as 0.02%. I have two accounts with the bank in Atlanta and now am receiving a much better return on my money.

Savings Accounts

Some banks used to be called savings and loan banks, which emphasizes the importance of these two functions. When I was a child, my brothers and I all had savings accounts at the local bank. With each account came a little book called a passbook, in which the bank would write the amount in your account. When you made withdrawals, they would subtract the amount. All of this was handwritten in the passbook. From time to time, they also recorded the interest earned. This was long before computers, which keep track of everything for us now. Banks provided a place for your money to grow. If you had $100.00 in your account and received 3% each year (annually), at the end of one year you had $103.00 in your savings account instead of $100.00. If the money was in a shoe box under your bed, you still had only $100.00. Savings accounts are still a function of most banks. These accounts might be special funds used for saving for college, or for an emergency fund, or for a new car. If the funds are not in your wallet, you have a better chance of not spending them.

Loans

Another service of a bank is offering loans. Smaller amounts, such as those needed for a car or a new kitchen, are usually referred to as loans. Larger amounts that are loaned for the purchase of a home are called mortgages. The primary components of a loan are (1) how much you must pay back, which is determined by the percentage of the loan, and (2) the time frame in which you must pay it back. These are our concern as the ones who are borrowing and receiving the money.

The bank—that is, the lender—has other concerns: such as how you are going to pay the loan back, and whether you have the means with which to pay it back. There will be quite an interview process with a loan officer, along with an application, to determine your ability to pay back what you are borrowing. This is done to establish what kind of a risk you are, or if you have good credit. For a house, the bank will look over your application carefully, because if you can't make your monthly payments (not paying is called defaulting), they can always take your house back (called repossessing) and then resell it to get their money back. They want to make sure the house is worth the price you have paid for it.

A car is different, because you may drive away and not return, and if you don't make your regular payments, it is hard to track you down. Usually you need some sort of collateral, or something worth the price of the car, that will replace the value of the car if you default on your payments. Remember, the money in the bank is your money as well money from your friends and neighbors. Everyone involved wants the bank to be careful about who is borrowing the money and when they will pay it back.

Another popular loan is the home equity loan. When you make house payments, you pay the interest and the principal. The principal goes toward paying for the house, and the interest goes to the bank to pay for your loan. Equity is the amount of your home's value that you have actually paid. When you take out a home equity loan, you are borrowing on the value of your home's equity, or what you own so far.

ATM

Most banks also provide access to cash in an ATM, which stands for Automated Teller Machine. If you get money from a machine owned by your bank where you have an account, there are usually no fees involved. But if you use an ATM where you do not have an account, there is usually a fee of $2.00 or $3.00. If you withdraw $100.00, that would amount to a 2% or 3% charge.

Wages as a Percentage of a Job

I knew a framing crew who had about five guys on their team. The owner paid each member of the crew a percentage of the total amount he received for the job. Since the owner had the most responsibility, he received the highest percentage. Based on their experience and expertise, every guy has a percentage allocated to him. Let me introduce you to all five workers to illustrate this arrangement. Jeff as the owner has the largest share at 40%, Chuck as the foreman receives 24%, Dan, Chris, and Mike are the carpenters, and they each get 12% each.

Example 1

This week they are stick framing a new 2,000 square foot home, and they are being paid $6.50 per square foot for their labor. How much does each worker receive?

Solution 1

2,000 × $6.50 = $13,000.00

Jeff's share is $13,000.00 × 0.4 = $5,200.00

Chuck is $13,000.00 × 0.24 = $3,120.00

Dan, Chris, and Mike's portion is $13,000.00 × 0.12 = $1,560.00 for each

The workers know that the harder and more efficiently they work, the greater their profit. If they work fast and complete the job in four days instead of five days, the three carpenters each make $390.00 per day instead of $312.00 per day. On the fifth day they can either begin a new job or take the day off.

Example 2

Jeff was wanting to work less, so he decreased his percentage and increased the percentage of each member of the team. Chuck's share became 30% and each of the three carpenters now received 16%. How much was Jeff's percentage now?

Solution 2

30% + 16% + 16% + 16% = 78%

100% − 78% = 22% for Jeff

Shortcuts with Percentages

I was shopping at a local department store this past weekend to buy some shirts for filming Stewardship. As I walked into the store, I noticed that everything in the store was 40% off. The normal way to calculate this discount is to take the retail price, and then multiply by 0.40 and subtract this from the retail price to discover the discounted price.

Example 3

If the shirt was $35.00, what is the new sale price?

Long Solution 3

$35.00 × 0.40 = $14.00

$35.00 − $14.00 = $21.00

Short Solution 3

Instead of taking 40% OFF, I take 60% OF. When I hear 40%, I subtract that in my mind from 100% and come up with 60%. Instead of multiplying and then subtracting, I do this in one step by just multiplying.

$35.00 × 0.60 = $21.00

Example 4

I also bought a sport coat that I discovered in the clearance section. The coat was marked down and was now 90% off the original price of $160.00. What is the new discounted price?

Long Solution 4

$160.00 × 0.90 = $144.00

$160.00 − $144.00 = $16.00

Short Solution 4

$160.00 × 0.10 = $16.00

In a previous lesson we discovered that we will multiply our bill at an eating establishment first by the tax percentage and then by another percentage for the tip. If the tax is 7% and our tip is 18%, this is two multiplication problems and two addition problems.

The shortcut would be to first add 7% and 18% to give 25%. Then add 100% for the original bill. The total amount we will pay is 125% of the cost of the meal. See how much of a timesaver this can be in the example:

Example 5

The bill at All Night Diner came to $46.80. The service was good, so we wanted to leave a tip of 18%. The tax is 7%.

Long Solution 5

$46.80 × 0.07 = $3.28

$46.80 × 0.18 = $8.42

Adding both, $8.42 + $3.28 = $11.70

Adding this to the original bill $46.80 + $11.70 = $58.50

Short Solution 5

7% (tax) + 18% (tip) + 100% (meal) = 125%

$46.80 × 1.25 = $58.50

Example 6

The gross wages for this week are $904.00. Based on what we have done in a previous lesson, here is the breakdown of the taxes:

Federal	$105.00	(from the table about 11.6%)
State	$27.75	3.07%
County	$9.04	1.00%
FICA (SS + Medicare)	$69.16	7.65%
SUI	$0.54	0.06%
Total Deducted Weekly		
Tax	$211.49	23.4%
Net Take Home Pay	$692.51	76.6%

In our work above, there are a plethora of taxes to multiply, and then add, and finally subtract from the gross wages to determine the net take home pay.

    If we divide the net pay by the gross pay, $690.51 ÷ $904.00 = 76.6%, and rounding the answer to the nearest percent, we observe that around 23% of the income is taken as a tax. We can multiply the gross wages by 77% to find the take home pay. This will not be totally accurate for each paycheck, since the federal taxes are not computed strictly as a percentage, but it is helpful to give an estimate.

Quick Solution 6 (estimated with our new shortcut)
    $904.00 × 77% = $696.08, which is close

CHECKING

Figure 1

Joe and Josephine Unit	**NEIGHBOR'S BANK**	**1556**

Joe and Josephine Unit
369 Decimal Street
Place Value, PA 17606

NEIGHBOR'S BANK   **1556**
12 Main Street
Goodtown, PA 17601
60-1234/0313   DATE _May 19, 2019_

PAY TO THE
ORDER OF _Manny Tens_ $ |_125.00_|

One hundred twenty-five and 00/100 _____ DOLLARS

MEMO _downpayment boat_   _Joseph B. Unit_
                                                                    AUTHORIZED SIGNATURE

⑈031312343⑈1556 0898765402⑈

Let's take a look at several items of note on the check. At the top you will find your name and address and the bank's name and address. The "date" space is in the upper right-hand corner. On the line that begins "Pay to the Order of," you put in the name of the person or institution that you want to receive your money. In the rectangle with the dollar sign in front of it, you write the amount you want to have paid using a decimal number, including cents. Below this, on the longest line, you write out that same amount using words. If you want to remind yourself what the check is for, you have the option of making a note in the "Memo" space. Then make sure you sign the check with your signature. The name on the check and the signature should be for the same person.

The numbers below the memo space are written in magnetic ink so that they can be read by a computer, and they help different banks communicate with each other. The number on the left is the routing number 031312343. The routing number is unique to your bank, and it appears twice on the check in different formats. The 60–1234/0313 below the bank's address is the routing number presented in another format. The next two numbers are the check number, which in this case is 1556, and your bank account number, which for Joseph is 0898765402. What order to put the check number and account number or whether to include them at all is up to the bank, so this section might be different for some checks.

On the back of the check, at the top after you have turned it sideways, is a place for the receiver of the check to endorse or sign for a deposit. This is the name of the same person as the one beside "Pay to the Order of." If you have a check made out to you, you have three options: (1) Cash it by signing your name on the back of the check and receive cash in exchange from your bank. (2) Deposit it by simply signing your name. It is also a good idea to include the number of your bank account into which the money is to be deposited. Then you will receive a receipt that verifies that the money is now in your account. (3) Endorse it to someone you want to give the money to. In that case, you write, "Pay to the order of So & So Jones," and then sign your name to show that you are transferring the check to So & So Jones and it is their money now.

When you write a check, make sure that you record all the information in the Transaction Register. If you have a computer for banking, this is done automatically. But if you don't use a computer, you need to compare what you have written on the check with what is entered in the register. I suggest you write your check and record it at the same time. Don't wait until later to enter this information. You may make mistakes and forget. You should also make an entry in your register when you put more money into your checking account. This is called making a deposit. Another idea for those who aren't doing this on a computer is to use checks with a duplicate copy underneath. That way you have a carbon copy of the exact check you have written. This register is crucial to knowing how much money you have in your account. If you don't know your ongoing balance, you will incur fees when you write checks for money that is not there. This is called an overdraft.

Whenever you write a check, you subtract that amount from your balance to show you have less money in your account. When you make a deposit, you are adding to your account, so you add this to your balance. An ATM withdrawal will also be subtracted from your account.

You can't go by what the bank or the bank statement tells you when determining your balance, because they don't know how many checks you have written. If you write a check to your cousin, for example, and he doesn't cash it for several weeks, it won't show up on the bank's records. But you have committed funds to your cousin by means of that check, and they are gone, as far as you are concerned, and you can't spend them on something else.

Reconcile

Each month you will get a statement from the bank (most banks will let you view it online) that you will want to compare with the records in your register. The first part is usually a summary of your previous balance, a total of the checks that have cleared, a total of your deposits, any fees, and then a current balance. Remember, this won't agree with your personal register unless all of the checks you have written have cleared by the time your statement goes out. This is very rare. The statement tells you which checks have been turned in to the bank. They are said to have "cleared" if they are on your statement. You need to go through your register and mark those checks that have cleared. Then there is a list of all the activity in your account listed chronologically. This is usually followed by a list of checks that have been paid by the bank, in numerical order. You may also get the checks themselves or photos of them. You may have noticed that I keep saying "usually" or "generally," because banks do things differently. Their statements don't look the same. The best thing is to take your first statement and your register to the bank and ask them to explain how to reconcile your account and how to read the statement. They are glad to help.

Figure 2

■AD-Automatic Deposit   ■AP-Automatic Payment   ■ATM-Teller Machine   ■DC-Debit Card   ■T-Tax Deductible   ■TT-Telephone Transfer

NUMBER OR CODE	DATE	transaction description	PAYMENT AMOUNT	☑	FEE	DEPOSIT AMOUNT	BALANCE	
							0	00
	9/7	Opened Account				575 00	575	00
1001	9/10	Newspaper Subscription	25 00				550	00
1002	9/12	Groceries	64 50				485	50
1003	9/15	Filled Gas Tank	33 20				452	30
1004	9/12	Missionary Support	50 00				402	30
	9/15	Deposited Bday money				60 00	462	30
1005	9/22	Phone Bill	30 00				432	30
1006	9/24	Water Bill	19 67				412	63

When you know how an account like this operates, it makes everybody's job easier. Figure 2 shows a register for one month with six checks written and two deposits. This account began with a $575.00 initial deposit. Figure 3 shows a statement for the same period.

Figure 3

ACCOUNT STATEMENT

Statement Date		09-18-2019
Beginning Date		08-19-2019
Previous Balance		$0.00

Date	Transaction	Deposits/Credits	Payments/Debits	Balance	Checks Paid		
					#	Date	Amount
9/07	Deposit	575.00		575.00	1001	9/14	25.00
9/13	Check 1002		64.50	510.50	1002	9/14	64.50
9/14	Check 1001		25.00	485.50	1003	9/16	33.20
9/15	Check 1003		33.20	452.30			
9/15	Deposit	60.00		512.30			

First get your register and put a check mark in the square that shows the check has been cleared (figure 4). Do this for the two deposits as well. Notice that the statement dates are from the 19th through the 18th, so the last two checks would obviously not have cleared. Also, it appears that the person we are sending the missionary support check to either did not receive it or did not get to the bank by the 18th. That is why there is a disparity between the register and the statement. On the back of the statement there is usually a place for you to "reconcile" this disparity (figure 5). First fill in the balance on the statement, and then add any deposits made since the statement came out. After you have listed the "outstanding" checks, add them up and subtract them from the balance. This should agree with your personal register as shown in figure 4.

Figure 4

■AD-Automatic Deposit   ■AP-Automatic Payment   ■ATM-Teller Machine   ■DC-Debit Card   ■T-Tax Deductible   ■TT-Telephone Transfer

NUMBER OR CODE	DATE	transaction description	PAYMENT AMOUNT		☑	FEE	DEPOSIT AMOUNT		BALANCE	
									0	00
	9/7	Opened Account			✓		575	00	575	00
1001	9/10	Newspaper Subscription	25	00	✓				550	00
1002	9/12	Groceries	64	50	✓				485	50
1003	9/15	Filled Gas Tank	33	20	✓				452	30
1004	9/12	Missionary Support	50	00					402	30
	9/15	Deposited Bday money			✓		60	00	462	30
1005	9/22	Phone Bill	30	00					432	30
1006	9/24	Water Bill	19	67					412	63

Figure 5

BALANCE THIS STATEMENT			512	30
	Add			
	Deposits made since this statement			
			0	00
SUBTOTAL			512	30
Checks issued but not on the statement				
Number	Amount			
1004		50	00	
1005		30	00	
1006		19	67	
TOTAL OUTSTANDING CHECKS			99	67
Subtract (total outstanding checks from subtotal)			412	63
CURRENT BALANCE			412	63

Additional Fees

Reconciling your checkbook regularly will help you to keep it accurate. Your check statements not only tell you which checks and deposits have cleared, it will also tell you if you have incurred any fees that month.

ATM Fees

One of fees I have received are foreign ATM charges. If I use my ATM card at my local bank or one of the branches across the county, there are no fees. If I use my ATM card to withdraw cash at another bank (if it is not mine, it is foreign) there is a fee of between $1.00 and $3.00. Usually the ATM machine will ask you if you are willing to pay this fee before it completes your transaction. If I have requested $300.00 and there is a fee of $2.00, I will be given $298.00 when the fee is subtracted.

Overdraft Fees

I learned about overdrafts the hard way. An overdraft occurs when a check is written for more than is in your account. My first experience writing checks was when I was in college. I did not understand the concept of checks being cleared at the bank. When I received my bank statement and saw the balance was higher than in my check book, I surmised I had made an error in my calculations and rejoiced that I had more money than I thought, so I spent it. Then I began receiving pink pieces of paper in the mail telling me I had been charged $15.00 for writing a check and not having sufficient funds in my account to cover the amount of the check. Sometimes these penalties are called insufficient fund charges. These overdraft fees are much higher now than when I was in college, and they are a significant deterrent to me even today. I reconcile my checking account each month to insure this will not happen again.

I am hoping you won't have any additional charges or fees, but if you do, the ATM fee or overdraft charge should be listed as a debit, or payment, and subtracted from your balance. If you accumulate interest on your account, it will be recorded as a credit, or deposit, and added to the balance. When in doubt, ask questions!

Credit Unions

A credit union is similar to a bank and offers many of the same services. Usually they charge less for services than a bank and offer a little better interest rate on a home mortgage or loan. That is because a bank exists as a business and is trying to make money for its shareholders. A credit union is a service offered to its members. They also want to make a profit, but when they do, the money goes back into the business. When a bank makes a profit, it issues dividends to its shareholders. When you open a checking or savings account, you may want to consider using a credit union.

BUDGETING

This is a subject that everyone must consider. How much money do you need to earn to care for your living expenses and have some left over for savings, emergencies, and giving? It will never be the same for any two people or any two families, because we are all uniquely designed and thus are all different. We have different priorities, different personalities, different spending habits, and, of course, different incomes. The goal is to identify your needs and make sure you have enough in-come to cover your out-go with enough left over, or a surplus, for savings, emergencies, and giving. Remember the title and object of this book. We want to be faithful stewards of God's resources.

Income or In-Come

Document your income. As we have seen, with all of the taxes taken from your paycheck, it may be less than you think. If you are on a fixed income, this will be easy to figure out. For several years I was a teacher and received a monthly check. I deposited it on the way home, wrote a tithe check, and then set aside money for groceries and our other needs for the month. It was the easiest time budgeting I ever experienced. I was on a fixed income. But if you are self-employed, it is more difficult. I was a self-employed painter at one time. In the summer and fall when it was dry, I had more work than I did in the spring when it was raining, or in the winter when it was cold. Unless there was indoor work available, I earned less in those seasons. For that job, I would try to average my income over 12 months and use that as a figure to determine my monthly income. An expression that is often used by those self-employed people whose jobs are seasonal is "feast or famine." You are either well off or broke.

Expenses or Out-Go

Identify your needs. Carefully and prayerfully make a distinction between your wants and your needs. Food, clothing, shelter, and transportation are needs. A new computer, midnight snacks, eating out, and an off-road dirt bike are most likely wants. But this is for you, your spouse, and your God to determine. My biggest advice along this line is to collect data. Consider keeping a note card in your wallet and recording every penny you spend for two months. Whether it is a cash purchase or something bought with a check or a credit card, write it down, and at the end of the day, record it in a notebook or computer finance program. This will provide solid data about your spending and help you to project what you will need. It will also reveal spending habits you may not have noticed before. You may be surprised at the results. When you have a credit card and checking account, your expenses will be easier to keep track of, but cash spent on a whim is harder to document. Write down what you spend when you spend it, either on a card or using an app on your phone.

Some expenses are monthly. I refer to these as recurring bills. Others are paid each year and are called annual expenses. Still other expenses arise (like a new refrigerator) that are not recurring or annual. Appliances eventually break down and will have to be replaced. This is also true of your phone, your car, and your computer. By setting aside money when you have a surplus, you can prepare for the unexpected.

Surplus

Out of our surplus, or money remaining after we have paid for our expenses, we can set aside money for emergencies, specific needs, other needs, and the future. You need money not only for daily expenses, but also for unforeseen needs that may arise. Designate an envelope, or a new savings account, for these situations, and then try to forget the money is there. This requires discipline, and there are no easy shortcuts. As you learn to control your spending and develop the habit of saving, you will be well on your way to being a faithful, godly steward.

Emergencies

You may get injured and be unable to work for a season. Since you don't know what could happen, it is wise and prudent to have some cash reserve on hand for unexpected and unplanned emergencies. You might call this your rainy-day fund.

Save for Specific Needs

I am not an enveloper. My wife is. I do not have the makeup conducive to setting up accounts in envelopes and then diligently adding to them over a period of time. At one time my wife had a drawer full of real envelopes, and she would regularly put funds in each one until a specific amount was reached. For example, she might have wanted to save $50.00 to buy a new toaster. She would write "toaster" on the envelope and put $5.00 or $10.00 in at a time until she got the money needed. Then she would go out and buy the toaster. This is one approach. My approach is always to spend less than I earn, and that has kept me in the black.

Save for Others

From your surplus, I hope you have a little left over for others. I say I hope, because it is a joy to be able to give to meet the needs of your "neighbor" that Jesus reminds us to love. We don't live for ourselves alone. Our first responsibility is to our family, but we also want to be able to care for others as we have the opportunity.

Save for the Future

Setting aside money for your future is not the responsibility of the government. It is your responsibility. Develop the habit of setting aside funds when you are just beginning to earn an income, and that habit will stay with you through the years. My father set aside $10.00 from every paycheck to invest for his retirement. If that amount were adjusted for inflation, it would probably be $50.00 from every paycheck today. He diligently stuck to this plan all of his life. When he passed away, my mother was able to live well off what my dad set aside all those years. That money could have been spent on other things, even legitimate needs. He told me of lean times when he was paying off significant bills at the local pharmacy. When I entered kindergarten, I acquired most of the communicable diseases in one year and took them home to my brothers. There were only two weeks that year when one of us wasn't sick. Dad still stuck to his plan and set aside $10.00 from every paycheck. That money grew and was there when my mom needed it.

Budget Categories

Many excellent resources have been developed for budgeting. I have personally taught a small group study using materials developed by Howard Dayton at Compass, www.compass1.org. I have also heard wonderful things about Dave Ramsey and his resources, www.daveramsey.com. I have friends who use YNAB, or You Need a Budget, www.youneedabudget.org. Talk to your friends and find out what works for them.

For many years I listened to a radio broadcast by Crown Ministries founded by Larry Burkett, www.crown.org. In his book The Financial Planning Organizer, published in 1991, he has two sections that I want to summarize as an example of one option for setting budget goals. In the section entitled "Divisions of Income" Burkett lists five categories: tithes, taxes, family needs, debts, and surpluses. In a subsequent section he gives guidelines for a budget, breaking these categories down into more detail. Using percentages, he suggests some guides for a family budget. These are not only helpful for setting a budget, but if you document your family spending habits (as suggested earlier) and figure out your percentages, it will be helpful in revealing possible problem spending areas. His chart lists the percentages for several different family incomes. I have chosen three examples to illustrate how helpful these categories and percentages can be in determining where you are spending your money. Remember that unless you track your spending for several months, you will not have a handle on where your money is going or how you can be a faithful steward of the money in your possession.

In figure 1, housing includes utilities, such as heating and electric service. Debts is for repayment of existing debts.

Figure 1

Gross Income	$15,000	$25,000	$40,000
Tithe	10%	10%	10%
Taxes	8%	15%	18%

Net Spendable Income Percentages (after returning tithes to God and rendering to Caesar what is Caesar's)

Housing*	35%	38%	30%
Food*	15%	12%	12%
Auto*	15%	15%	12%
Insurance	5%	5%	5%
Debts	5%	5%	5%
Recreation	5%	5%	7%
Clothing	5%	5%	5%
Savings	5%	5%	5%
Medical/Dental	5%	5%	4%
Miscellaneous	5%	5%	7%
Investments	0%	0%	8%

* Housing, Food, and Auto expenses should not exceed

65% of your spendable income

Wholesale and Retail Prices and Percentages

In many parts of the world, when a consumer seeks to purchase a good or service they are required to haggle or dicker about the price until they arrive at one that is agreeable to both the buyer and the seller. My first experience dickering was in Israel when I was offered a few hand carved olive wood camels. I didn't want them, especially at the starting price of over $20.00 for the set, but as I walked away the seller took that as a challenge and followed me as I continued to say no. Finally, he offered them to me at $2.00 for the set. I stopped and bought them. That was a great price, and my sons played with them for years. This practice of haggling rather than having set prices was the accepted way of conducting commerce in America until a committed Christian businessman introduced the price tag.

As a young man John Wanamaker (1838–1922) was torn between operating a business and entering the Christian ministry. He ended up merging both of these desires, and the result was a wonderful balance between an excellent businessman and someone who lived out his Christian principles in the world of commerce. Wanamaker was one of the first businessmen to offer price tags which was an extension of His faith. Quaker merchants believed that if we were all equal before God we should be equal before price. He was also a pioneer of the department store concept, where a variety of products were offered under one roof.

Wanamaker's faith spilled into every area of his business, from the way he treated his employees to how he communicated with the general public. He offered vacations, free medical care, pensions, paid for the ongoing education of his workers. He also demanded that management treat each worker with respect. These benefits are now considered normal but at the time his innovations were years ahead of other corporations.

Wanamaker was committed to truth in advertising. As the public discovered he meant what he said, they trusted him, and his stores prospered. When he was a young man, he tried to return a product for a refund but was denied. As a result of this experience, his customers were permitted to return merchandise for a cash refund.

Wholesale and Retail Prices

Even though we need to change percentages to hundredths to use them in an equation, percentages are still widely used in everyday commerce. Two words we should learn in order to more fully understand retail pricing are "wholesale" and "retail." When you purchase an item in a store, you are a retail customer buying at a retail store or retail outlet. The retailer purchases products at a wholesale price and then adds a markup for their profit. The result is the retail price.

Darby has a retail store called Darby's Emporium. One item she has on her shelves is backpacks. Darby projects that she will sell about 25 backpacks this year, so she places an order and buys them at $12.00 per backpack. This is her wholesale price. She then sells them for $20.00 apiece. For every backpack she sells, she makes a profit of $8.00. The $20.00 is the retail price and $12.00 is the wholesale price.

Now let's look at the percentages involved here. The wholesale price of $12.00 is 60% of $20.00, which is the retail price. This is a pretty normal markup for an item such as this in a store. A markup of 30%–40% is necessary to pay for the rent of the building, salaries, utilities, advertising, and other expenses necessary to operating a business. You are also paying for the service Darby is providing for you in letting you come in, examine the backpacks, see how they feel on your back, and buy one right in your hometown.

Sales

October comes around, and Darby still has three backpacks on the shelf, and they have been sitting there for two months. She decides to have a sale and marks down the price to $15.00. For every one she sells, she will still make a profit of $3.00, but you as the consumer now save $5.00 off the retail price. In November she discovered she still has one backpack and puts this in her clearance area, making down the price even further to $12.00 just to break even. This is an even better sale, because the retail price is now the same as the wholesale price.

Darby advertised this sale as 25% off of the retail price, because 25% of $20.00 is $5.00 and $20.00 − $5.00 = $15.00. When she discounted the price again in November this sale was 40% off the retail price and 40% of $20.00 is $8.00 and $20.00 − $8.00 = $12.00. Whenever I see a sale of 25% off the retail cost, I think this is pretty good. When I see 40% off, I know this is really good.

Pink Sport Coat

If you have watched the video instruction for this unit, you saw my classy pink sport coat which I purchased a few weeks ago for $11.79. When I first spotted it on the clearance rack, where I usually find the best buys and the deepest discounts, I assumed the retail price was originally $160.00 and the sale price was $16.00, which would be a 90% discount. When I arrived home, I looked at the sales receipt and saw the cashier had given me two more discounts as I was checking out.

This is what the receipt looked like.

cost	$16.00
discount	$1.26
subtotal	$14.74
20% off	$2.95
total	$11.79

I wondered what percentage of the original price the final cost of $11.79 was.

W_p of $160.00 is $11.79 or $W_p \times \$160.00 = \$11.79$

$$W_p = \frac{\$11.79}{\$160.00} = 0.074 = 7.4\%$$

I was blessed and grateful for being given the opportunity to purchase a snappy coat for 7.4% of the retail cost.

Our Family Resources

When I began selling curriculum, I was a reseller of several products. The name of this business was Our Family Resources. We had been using several educational products which we found effective and determined to make them available to others. I contacted the producers of each product and asked if I could resell their product. This was my first experience with the concept of wholesale and retail prices. Most of the products had a wholesale price between 30–50% of the retail price. Some of the companies required that I purchase items in case lots to receive the maximum discount. For example, if I bought five books to resell at retail for $10.00, the wholesale price would be 30% of this amount or $7.00. But if I were to order a case lot of perhaps 20 books, the wholesale price would be 45% of the retail. Then each item cost me $5.50 instead of $7.00. When I sold these items, I now made a profit of $4.50 instead of $3.00.

You may think I would buy all case lots to increase my profit margin, but I did not have much money to invest in inventory while providing for the needs of our family. I had to be judicious in how I purchased products to sell. This juggling act is called managing cashflow.

Cashflow

Someday when you begin your own enterprise, you will understand this concept. Having capital, or cash, on hand is essential to purchasing inventory, paying your employees, paying the utility bills, etc. I have never been comfortable borrowing money. For every business I operated, I began small and grew slowly to avoid having to go into debt. The challenge is how to use the available cash or funds to grow the business while still fulfilling your obligations and paying your bills on time.

Math Books

A few years later I began producing my own math books, and people began inquiring if they could sell these MathUSee books. I was now the manufacturer as well as the wholesaler. Since I had been in their shoes for a few years as reseller, I tried to treat them as I wanted to be treated, and I extended as generous a discount structure as I could. I had three wholesale prices for them to choose from.

The books cost me $4.00 to print and I set a retail price of $15.00. If the reseller wanted to buy just a few books, I charged them 60% of the retail price which is $9.00. They were to pay within 30 days of receiving the books or net 30. My profit for selling to the reseller was $9.00 − $4.00 = $5.00. Their profit from selling to the customer was $15.00 − $9.00 = $6.00.

If the reseller was able to buy the books in case lots at net 30, then the discount was 50% or $7.50. My profit for selling to the reseller was $3.50. Their profit from selling to the customer was $7.50.

Eventually I added another option. If the resellers sent a check along with their order, called prepayment, they received a discount of 55%. This helped with my cashflow and increased their profit another 5%.

Percent of What

When you are discussing the percentage markup or the percentage discount, you need to understand "what is a percent of what." In my new book business, I saw my cost of $4.00 as 27% of the retail price.

Example 1

What Percent of the Retail Price is the Manufacturer's Cost?

W_p of $15.00 is $4.00. $W_p = \$4.00 \div \$15.00 = 0.2666 = 27\%$

Solution 1

The resellers saw their profit as 50% of the retail price.

W_p of $15.00 is $7.50. $W_p = \$7.50 \div \$15.00 = 0.50 = 50\%$

I used to sell juggling equipment. The wholesaler who carried the equipment and sold it to me, the retailer, always said I made 100% on every item. This sounds a lot better than 50%. It is a manner of semantics. In my thinking, he sold it to me for 50% of the retail price. I could buy a set of three balls for $4.00 and sell them for $8.00. I viewed the profit of $4.00, as half of the retail, or 50%. However this particular wholesaler saw $8.00 as double the $4.00 or a full 100% markup of the wholesale price. I was taking a percentage of the retail (50%), and he was taking a percentage of the wholesale (100%). When discussing percentages, we need to know whether it is a percentage of the retail or wholesale price.

In applying this thinking to the backpack illustration, I saw the $8.00 profit on the sale of the backpack as 40% of the retail price, but I could have also said that $8.00 was 67% of the wholesale price. I hope these examples will clarify these concepts.

Example 2

W_p of the Retail Price is the Profit?

Solution 2

W_p of $20.00 is $8.00?

$$W_p \times \$20.00 = \$8.00 \qquad W_p = \frac{\$8.00}{\$20.00} = 0.40 = 40\%$$

Example 3

W_p of the Wholesale Price is the Profit?

Solution 3

W_p of $12.00 is $8.00?

$$W_p \times \$12.00 = \$8.00$$

$$W_p = \frac{\$8.00}{\$12.00} = 0.666 = 67\%$$

Grocery Stores

Supermarkets or grocery stores have a lower percentage markup on their products because they sell many more items, and they sell them more often. I only need a backpack once every few years, but I need eggs, bread, and yogurt every week. The store's profit may be only 4% to 5% of the retail cost. If a loaf of bread costs $2.50, the wholesale price is $2.50 minus 4%. Since 4% times $2.50 is 10¢, the wholesale price is $2.50 minus 10¢ or $2.40.

Example 4

Example: Which product makes the most profit in a week, a loaf of bread at Greta's Grocery Store or a backpack at Darby's Emporium?

What is the profit for each item? Which product provides the most overall profit at the end of the week if Greta's Grocery Store sells 295 loaves of bread and Darby's Emporium sells three backpacks.

Solution 4

Solution A: The backpack retails for $20.00 and wholesales for $12.00 for a net profit of $8.00. One loaf of bread retails for $2.50 and wholesales for $2.40 for a net profit of 10¢. One backpack is much more profitable than one loaf of bread.

Solution B: 295 loaves times 10¢ is $29.50 net profit for the week.

$295 \times \$0.10 = \$29.50$

3 backpacks times $8.00 is $24.00. $3 \times \$8.00 = \$24.00$

$29.50 is more than $24.00 and the bread wins!

Online Purchasing

In another unit we will discuss the pros and cons of shopping online. Since the internet, brick and mortar retail stores are suffering. There is still a retail cost and a wholesale price, but since there are fewer steps between the seller and the buyer, online prices are frequently lower than what a retail store is able to offer.

CREDIT CARDS

To understand the fees of a credit card, let's examine how one works. Another name we often use in referring to these cards is "plastic." Cash is affectionately called "paper," and credit cards are referred to as plastic, which makes sense, doesn't it? The expression "to buy on credit" used to mean that you purchased something and took it home with you. Then you made regular payments to the store until the debt was paid in full. You were borrowing from the store and paying back as you were able, or with arrangements agreed upon by the store. Today the phrase "buying on credit" means using a credit card. In a previous lesson, I mentioned how we had someone sick in our family one year for 50 of the 52 weeks. Throughout that year, my dad was making payments of $10.00 per month towards paying off the bill accrued during that one year of sickness. It took him a few years but he did it. During this time, the pharmacy was extending credit to my dad. They knew him personally and trusted him to pay the money back.

Retail Store Cards

Today, there are credit cards offered by specific stores. You may have a Sears card, a JC Penney card, a Home Depot card, or any number of other cards. When you buy something on credit using a store card, you are dealing directly with the store. These stores usually offer a significant percentage off your initial purchase as an incentive for signing up. These companies want your business!

The Major Players

The big credit card companies are Visa, Mastercard, American Express, and Discover. These credit card companies, in conjunction with banks, operate as a third party. They pay the store for the item you purchase and then bill you. They are extending credit to you instead of the store where you purchased the item extending it to you. In our family's situation, instead of dealing with the pharmacy directly, my father would have charged the bill using his Visa card and then made payments to Visa until the full amount of the debt was paid. When offering this service to the stores, the major credit card companies charge fees. Some of these fees are hidden, and others are not so hidden.

For this illustration, let's pretend you buy a paintball gun for $100.00 from Walmart with a Visa credit card. When you use this card, Visa immediately pays Walmart and then bills you. You may assume that Walmart gets the $100.00, but that is not quite true. There is a fee for this service that varies from company to company, but it is usually around 3%. The credit card company pays Walmart $97.00 at the time of the sale ($100.00 minus 3% of $100.00, or $3.00), and then bills you $100.00 in the form of a monthly bill, or credit card statement. Walmart has $97.00 in hand. When you pay your bill, the Visa credit card company divides the remaining $3.00 fee with the bank who issued the credit card. Walmart is willing to pay this fee in order to have their money right away. Walmart is a retailer, not a bill collector. Visa is a money lender and bill collector, and not a retailer.

Cash or Credit

I have been at gasoline stations where there are two prices offered, cash and credit. This is to make up for this hidden fee. If you pay cash, you get a better price because the gas station doesn't have the additional fee of 3%. Some states frown on this practice and discourage businesses from offering two prices, and some credit card companies also try to stop this practice.

Credit cards are convenient, no doubt about it, and they make buying much easier. It is generally known that they make it too easy. Studies have shown that you will spend less if you purchase only with cash instead of plastic. It is harder to part with cash than it is to painlessly and effortlessly charge an item to your credit card.

Unpaid Balance

Have you ever received several credit card offers in the same week and wondered why? Credit card companies are businesses seeking to make a profit for the services they offer. These companies not only make 3% on each transaction, they also make money on unpaid balances. When we study compound interest in another lesson, we will learn more about this subject. If you have a credit card and pay off the balance each month, as I do, then you won't have to understand this concept. But if you are one of the unfortunate ones who regularly carries an unpaid balance from month to month, buckle your seat belt for more on this unpleasant topic.

Shopping for a Credit Card

If you are over 18 years of age and gainfully employed (have a steady job), you should be able to find a credit card that suits your needs. When considering getting a credit card, make sure you are comparing apples to apples. Make a list of annual fees, finance charges, late fees, grace periods, and spending limits. Then make an informed decision. If you do get a credit card, keep a list of what you buy with it and compare it with the monthly statement; don't assume anything. I check the items on my credit card statement each month when I pay off the balance in full.

Why Have a Credit Card?

This is a good question. You may be able to get along without one in normal situations, but if you are going to travel, rent a car, stay in a hotel, use UBER or LYFT, or purchase items online, you will need a credit card. If you are going to buy a home and probably need a mortgage, you will need a good credit score, which is a result of using your plastic wisely.

Acquiring Your First Credit Card

If you are over 18 and having trouble getting that first credit card, you have a few options. You may wonder why it is so difficult to have your own card. Until you have demonstrated that you can make timely payments on your outstanding balance, you are a high risk. You may be able to pay the credit card company back, or you may not. Companies are going to need proof before they give you the ability to use their services. Visa, Mastercard, Discover, and American Express have a way of rating you which is called your credit score. The higher your score, the better chance you have of getting a card.

Credit Score or Report

This score, or report, is like a report card which measures how likely you are to pay back the credit card company. If you demonstrate that you will use your card and pay back the unpaid balance (which is a small loan the credit card company has extended to the retail store) in a diligent manner, your score will improve. However, if you do not pay off your balance, or at least make an attempt to do so, you will be considered a bad risk and receive a low score.

Building a Positive Credit History

One math technique that is used to calculate your score involves a ratio of how much you use your card (the amount of your balance) to your spending limit. If you have a card that limits your spending to $200.00, and you are using your card for an average of $30.00 each month, your credit utilization ratio is $30/200 = 3/20$. This is low and looks good to the powers that be.

But if you are using your card for an average of $150.00 each month, your credit utilization ratio is $150/200 = 3/4$, which is high and makes companies nervous.

Action Point 1: Keep your ratio low.

Ask your bank if they offer a secured credit card. You can build your credit score with one of these cards. In this scenario, you make a deposit and the bank now has your money. They will then set the limit on your card, so you will only be allowed to spend up to that amount. As you pay your balance in a timely fashion each month, you are contributing to your positive credit history.

Action Point 2: Open a secured card and pay off the complete balance each month.

You could also open a joint account with your mom or dad. This is not your account alone, but you will have a card. The bank knows your folks, but they don't know you. This is another way to introduce yourself to the bank! Make sure your folks have a good credit history, because it will reflect on your ability to get a card later by yourself.

Action Point 3: Open a joint account with someone who has an established positive credit history.

Consider opening a store account at a major department store like Sears or Home Depot. Then use your card regularly, always paying off the balance each month. You are acquiring a good discipline and demonstrating to the big guys that you are responsible and diligent.

Action Point 4: Begin with a retail store credit card in order to develop good paying habits and show the major players that you are a responsible adult.

College students are seen as good credit risks. If you are attending college or a post high school institution you may qualify for a student credit card.

Action Point 5: Go to college and fill out the application for a student credit card.

If you have had a checking and/or savings account at your local bank for several years, and are developing a positive relationship with said bank, perhaps they will help you receive your first credit card there. Once you have your foot in the door, you will receive lots of offers in the mail for other cards. Good news spreads quickly among all the major players, and they all want your business.

When you do have a card, use it regularly, or there will not be enough activity to produce a credit card score. Pay off your balance in full each month. Think of this whole process like courting or dating. You are trying to show these card companies that you are responsible and know how to play the game of credit.

Action Point 6: Talk to your bank and ask for a bank credit card.

Overdraft Fees

Another expression for an overdraft is "non-sufficient funds." This means that you may have charged a new coat which costs $75.00, but you don't have that much money in your secured bank account or in the bank account which is tied to your debit card. When an overdraft occurs, there is a lot of communication going back and forth between the retailers and your bank. You will be charged for this activity. The fee is normally at least $30.00. This is also a penalty of sorts, which acts as a deterrent for you repeating this mistake.

Debit Card

Another alternative to credit cards is debit cards. When you use a debit card, the money is immediately taken out of your bank checking account. This has the plus of not allowing you to spend beyond your means, but there are drawbacks here as well. Make sure you thoroughly investigate the fine print before using a debit card. An article appeared in the Lancaster New Era, (page 11, on December 27, 2004) about a local college student who used a debit card. "In one month this fall," the article read, "he used his Visa check card for 10 purchases and 8 withdrawals (ATM machine) totaling less than $250.00. But during this one month, he generated nearly $140.00 in fees (penalties), almost all for overdrafts. In one case he was charged $31.00 for an 11-cent overdraft." (There are ways to avoid overdraft fees. Speak to your bank about these, since they vary.)

The article continued, "Each of his (non-home-bank ATM withdrawals) generated a $1.50 fee, enough to trigger at least one of his overdrafts." "Another [pitfall] is the 'hold' that some merchants place on funds that you don't actually wind up spending. For instance, a gas station might put a 25 dollar or 50 dollar hold on your account the moment you swipe your card, to authorize a purchase before the bottom line is known. Holds should disappear when a transaction clears. But if you're not careful, they too can trigger overdrafts." Another area that tripped him up was the order of payment. The bank's practice was to pay the largest debits first. On one particular day his statement showed five purchases, two withdrawals, two ATM fees—and three 31-dollar overdraft charges. If the bank had paid the debts chronologically as they were listed, only the last transaction would have triggered an overdraft.

Perks and Rewards

Another factor in choosing a credit card is the rebate you receive or the perks for using it. I have a credit card with an airline that I fly frequently. If I use it to spend $19,200.00 during the normal course of spending money, I receive a free flight. Now that flight would probably cost $400.00, and the cost of having that particular card is $59.00 per annum, or per year. The $400.00 is approximately 2% of $19,200.00, so I look at it as a 2% rebate. My mom had a card that gave her a 5% rebate on gas and groceries. For the rest of her purchases, she received a 1% rebate. When choosing a card, choose wisely and consider the different incentives.

Debt

Personal debt is comprised of credit cards, student loans, mortgages, car loans, and personal loans. Most Americans have a combination of these sources of debt. According to the Northwestern Mutual 2018 Planning and Progress Study (news.northwesternmutual.com/planning-and-progress-2018) the average American now has about $38,000 in personal debt, excluding home mortgages. That's up $1,000 from a year ago.

In 2017, 27% of Americans surveyed claimed to have no debt. Thankfully, I am in this group. Sadly only 23% made that claim in 2018. Credit cards and mortgages tied as the leading source of debt, followed by student loans and car loans, according to the survey. The findings are based on a survey of over 2,000 U.S. adults, including an oversampling of more than 600 millennials.

Gen Z and younger millennials (ages 18–24) had an average debt burden of $22,000. For this group, student loans were the highest source of debt (28 percent), followed by credit card balances.

Older millennials (ages 25–34) had an average debt load of $42,000. Credit card balances were the leading source of debt, followed by student loans, and a small amount of mortgage debt.

Gen X (ages 35–49): Their average debt was $39,000 These folks had the most mortgage debt, with credit card debt in second place.

Baby boomers (age 50+): Their average debt was $36,000. This group had the second-lowest amount of debt, which is good news. Their top three sources of debt were mortgages, credit card bills, and car loans.

COMPARISON SHOPPING

There are three key ideas in this lesson. The first is making sure you are comparing apples to apples, the second is considering all of the factors involved in a purchase, and the third is not trusting your eyes. Let's consider several examples to illustrate these points.

Apples to Apples

Recently we had a water softener installed in our home. Periodically I need to buy salt for this unit. Martin's Appliance installed the water softener, and I can buy 50 pound (50#) bags for $5.29 at their store. One day I was at Home Depot and saw what appeared to be the same yellow bag for $4.79. My first thought was to buy the salt there and save 50¢ per bag, but upon closer examination, I noticed the bags weren't the same size. The Home Depot bag, which looked identical to the one at Martin's, was only 40 pounds (or 40#). When deciding between two similar products, I needed to compare apples to apples, or use a common unit of measure. I decided to find the price per pound. To do this, I divided the price by the number of pounds. When I worked it out, Martin's was $5.29 ÷ 50, which is $0.1058 or 10.58¢ per pound. Home Depot's 40# bag was $0.1198 or 11.98¢ per pound. So Martin's was the better buy, even though it didn't initially appear to be so.

Something else I have learned is that multiple stores will each offer a low price guarantee. I shopped at two building supply stores that each claimed to offer the lowest prices. I was curious how they could each offer similar products and yet both declare they had the lowest price. I pinned down a salesman and asked him how this could be true. He taught me that even though there are Makita Drills in both stores, they don't have the same model of Makita drill. Or if they seem to be the same drill, they might not be from the same manufacturer. Once again, when doing comparison shopping, make sure you are comparing the same product or the same model. If the product comes in different sizes be careful to divide to discover the unit pricing, as in price per pound, per ounce, or per hundred.

Transportation Factor

How far you have to drive to make a purchase is a significant factor involving time and expense. The Internal Revenue Service has a standard mileage rate of 54.5¢ in 2018. If you use your car for work purposes, you can use this rate for a deduction on your income taxes. Other sources say the cost of operating a car is 60.8¢ per mile. We have a unit devoted to the cost of operating a car in a subsequent lesson. For the purposes of this unit, I am setting the cost of driving to 50¢ per mile.

In the first example about the salt I measured and found that Martin's is eight miles from our home, while the Home Depot is four miles away. If I buy 200 pounds of salt, which is the best place to make this purchase?

Martin Water

200 pounds is four 50# bags plus 16 miles (roundtrip).

($5.29 × 4) + (16 × $0.50) = $21.16 + $8.00 = $29.16

Home Depot

200 pounds is five 40# bags plus 8 miles (roundtrip).

($4.79 × 5) + (8 × $0.50) = $23.95 + $4.00 = $27.95

You are probably thinking about other factors, but the winner based on price is Home Depot. On the other hand, if you happen to be driving right past Martin Water on another errand, then they have the best price, because you are not making a separate trip.

Dollars to Dimes

My mom and dad were very thrifty when it came to items like groceries, and they were big fans of coupons. Our family would often travel across the state to be with my folks for holidays. On one occasion my dear wife was taken shopping to help them buy groceries for the weekend. They went to four or five stores to find one that honored their coupons, which amounted to only pennies per can. On another occasion they bought an item and then drove back and returned it because they found they had a coupon at home for a different brand. My question was, "What about the dollars you spent driving around to save the nickels and dimes?"

Buying Clubs

I enjoy shopping at Costco, which is a buying club like Sam's and BJ's. Their prices are often lower, but there is a fee to join these clubs. A quick search revealed that the fees for these three clubs are all around $50.00 per year. The first question to ask yourself is whether shopping here will save money over the course of a year. In our situation, Costco is nine miles away and it takes me 16 minutes to drive there. Stauffers is our preferred supermarket and is 2.3 miles from home. If we drive, it takes us six minutes each way to get there. Stauffers is also near work, so we drive near it a few times each day. There is also a Target 2.6 miles and seven minutes away.

I think you can quickly see that considering the distance, the mileage expense, the extra time, and the annual fee, this buying club may not be the best place for us to shop unless we plan these trips well to make the trip profitable. Let me give one example which factors these different elements into our purchase. I am also assuming that we go to Costco twenty times a year.

Example 1

I like all-natural yogurt, cinnamon, and coconut oil. If I am about to make a fresh batch of my homemade granola, I need some of each of these items. Here is what I discovered on a recent scouting expedition to buy these items. RT stands for Round Trip.

	Yogurt	Cinnamon	Coconut Oil	RT Time	Mileage	Club Fee
Stauffers	32 oz $3.99	6.5 oz $4.99	23 oz $10.99	12 min	4.6 mi	$0
Target	32 oz $4.99	4.1 oz $2.19	54 oz $19.99	14 min	5.2 mi	$0
Costco	48 oz $5.79	10.7 oz $2.99	84 oz $13.99	32 min	18.0 mi	$55.00

I first break down the cost as price per ounce and then compute the mileage cost. I divided the club fee by 20, the estimated number of times I drive to Costco annually.

	Yogurt	Cinnamon	Coconut Oil	RT Time	Mileage	Club Fee
Stauffers	12¢/oz	77¢/oz	48¢/oz	12 min	$2.30	$0
Target	16¢/oz	53¢/oz	37¢/oz	14 min	$2.60	$0
Costco	12¢/oz	28¢/oz	17¢/oz	32 min	$9.00	$2.75

The mileage is computed as round trip, so nine miles each way to Costco is 18 miles @ $0.50 per mile which is $9.00.

If I purchase one container of each item at each store, here is the composite cost plus my time.

Stauffers: $3.99 + $4.99 + $10.99 + $2.30 = $22.27 with 12 minutes for travel time.

Target: $4.99 + $2.19 + $19.99 + $2.60 = $29.77 with 14 minutes for travel time.

Costco: $5.79 + $2.99 + $13.99 + $9.00 + $2.75 = $34.52 with 32 minutes for travel time.

This is surprising on one level, considering how much lower the price per ounce was for cinnamon and oil at Costco. Because of the larger size containers, I also have almost a tub of coconut oil, several ounces of cinnamon, and a pound of yogurt left over if I purchased these times at Costco. When shopping I hope this helps you to see how different factors contribute to the overall expense of your shopping.

Discount Stores

A few weeks ago, John and I were in a different part of town, and saw a Grocery Outlet store, so we popped in for a few items we needed. I discovered wonderful buys for some other products I knew we could use and I ended up spending over fifty dollars. One item was a tub of very good yogurt for 97¢. The expiration date was in a few days away, but that didn't bother me, and I was thrilled to not have to pay $3.99 for the same product. I went back a few days later to price out the nine items I had just priced at the other stores. As I found the price per ounce for each item I discovered that these prices were very good. There is no annual fee to shop there, and it is closer than Costco! We may be frequenting this store more in the future.

Larger Quantities

I have observed that buying clubs often package their products in larger quantities and in different sized boxes. And upon comparing the price per ounce I discovered the product packaged in those boxes costs more per ounce than it would in a regular supermarket. Be careful to not simply choose an item because it appears to be a good deal. Compare the price per ounce, or the price per item. Many years ago this required division, but now most stores offer unit pricing and they have already done the math for you. When there are different prices for different sizes, unit pricing will give you the price per ounce or price per 100 count. This makes it very easy to be accurate in your comparisons without having to calculate unit prices yourself. In our buying expedition notice that the price per ounce of yogurt was the same at the grocery store as at the buying club. One was a larger amount and may have appeared to be a better buy, but they were the same per ounce.

Example 2

What is the better buy for eggs?

Stauffer's eggs are $1.55 per dozen while the buying club is $7.99 for 60.

Stauffer's eggs are $\dfrac{\$1.55}{12} = \$0.1291\overline{6}$

Costco eggs are $\dfrac{\$7.99}{60} = \$0.1331\overline{6}$

Stauffers was slightly cheaper but they are close enough that the unit price doesn't matter.

As we know, it is a lot closer to Stauffers than Costco and there is the annual membership fee to consider. Another factor to think about is even if you do save on the price per ounce or price per item, if you purchase a large quantity of perishable items you may not be able to consume them before they begin to go bad. The experienced shoppers in your family will know this!

Don't Trust your Eyes

My first real job was at the Whitehall Dairy Mart. I had just turned 16 and my responsibilities included hand-packing ice cream, peeling potatoes for french fries, serving customers, and sweeping the floor at the end of the day. Once when I was waiting tables I had two customers order different sizes of soda pop. At that time a large drink cost 15¢ and the small one was 10¢, but the large glass looked much larger in comparison. The guy who had ordered the small took one look at his friend's large drink and asked me to take the small drink back and bring him a large one. I took it back and the cook smiled, picked up a large glass, poured the small into it, added an ice cube, and that was it. The drinks were virtually the same size, but the large glass, also used for milkshakes and ice cream sodas, had a fake glass bottom and gave the impression that the glass was much larger, even though it wasn't. If you are curious, you might ask how many ounces of liquid there are in each size so you can compare numbers and not be deceived by looks. When I get drinks in a restaurant I almost always ask for no ice. Ice is filler, and the drinks are usually cold anyway. I get a lot more drink for my dollar. Although I generally just ask for water with a slice of lemon.

Apple Juice to Apple Juice

One afternoon, when I was a high school teacher, I was shopping for frozen apple juice and noticed there were two cans of different sizes. The large can was 12 ounces for 84¢, and the small can was 8 ounces for 48¢. In most cases the larger can is the better buy, but I suspected this might not be the case, so I did the division to make sure. I found the price per ounce and was surprised to learn that the large can was 84 ÷ 12 = 7¢ per ounce, and the small can was 48 ÷ 8 = 6¢ per ounce and therefore the better buy. I looked around to share this exciting news and saw one of my students. I called to her and showed her my recent discovery and how math had helped me be a more efficient shopper! Beware of assuming that the larger can is the best buy.

No Apples To Apples, Or Sandy Apples

One of the strangest experiences I have had in comparing apples to apples was when I was buying sand for a sandbox. I borrowed a pickup truck and went to the local lumber yard where I knew the owners. They weighed the truck then sent me down to get a load of sand.

When I came I was weighed again with the load of sand. The difference between the weight of the empty truck and the full truck would be the weight of the sand, and I would pay by the pound.

It had just rained the night before and the sand was quite heavy. I mentioned this when I was checking out but was confidently assured that it didn't affect the amount of sand because you could add water without changing the volume of sand.

Do you see the flaw in their reasoning? I never was able to convince them of their error, and I finally dropped it. I recognize that you can have a five-gallon bucket of sand and still add a lot of water to the bucket and it is still the same amount of sand. But I wasn't paying by volume but by weight, and a five-gallon bucket of sand with water is much heavier than a bucket of sand without water. I paid for the sand AND the water.

Comparison Table (for Lesson 09 Worksheets)

	Sheetz	Stauffers	Target	CVS	Costco	Grocery Outlet
Miles from home	2.6	2.3	2.6	2.6	9	4.3
Eggs, Grade A large	12 for $3.29	12 for $1.55	12 for $1.69	12 for $2.49	60 for $7.99	12 for $1.49
Milk 2% Gallon	$4.99	$3.58	$4.49	$3.59	$3.58	$3.58
Cooked Round Pizza, with diameter	7" $2.99	10" $5.55	6" $4.29		18" $9.95	
Apples, price per pound		$.99 per #	$1.53 per #		$2.00 per #	$.99 per #
Honey Nut Cheerios	1.6 oz for $1.79	15.4 oz for $3.99	19.5 oz for $3.99	19.5 oz for $5.99	55 oz for $6.79	55 oz for $6.99
Almond Butter		12 oz. for $9.79	19 oz for $6.99	12 oz for $7.49	27 oz for $7.99	16 oz for $4.99
Yogurt	5.3 oz for $1.79	32 oz for $3.99	32 oz for $4.99	5.3 oz for $1.79	48 oz for $5.79	5.3 oz for $.59
Coconut Oil		23 oz for $10.99	54 oz. for $19.99	14 oz for $10.49	84 oz for $13.99	54 oz. for $9.99
Cinnamon		6.5 oz for $4.99	4.1 oz for $2.19	2.37 oz for $1.99	10.7 oz for $2.99	3.25 oz for $.99

Best Value

Value includes more than price. Value includes customer service and a company that stands behind its product. It has to do with quality, dependability, and reliability. It is intrinsic or intangible, and not easy to measure. When I was younger, I looked almost exclusively at the price tag when deciding where to shop. If I needed to buy paint, I knew that I could buy good quality paint at a low price at a large department store. As I have grown older—and I hope wiser—I don't mind spending a little more and buying it at a small paint store because of the information and help I receive from the employees who are specialists. They are a resource that may not always be available at the megastores.

Intangibles

Shopping is not all about dollars and cents. For some families, going to Costco can be an experience. It is for me. I enjoy shopping at our local store. When I show my card to the folks at the front door, we exchange pleasantries as we greet each other. I have been going there for years and am recognized. I like the way the store is laid out without fancy displays, just good products and plain concrete floors.

I enjoy sampling products as I walk up and down the aisles. If we went as a family, we usually bought a pizza and perhaps a salad to share at the little red tables. We have discovered this is a cheap place to share a meal! Then we could partake of a few frozen yogurts as an inexpensive dessert for the drive home. These intangibles are a part of the shopping experience and need to be considered.

One of my favorite fast food establishments is Chick-fil-A. Besides having excellent food and reasonable prices, the atmosphere created and fostered by the employees is unique. I feel welcomed, valued, and respected. The workers will say things like, "It is my pleasure to serve you." This attitude of service and respect imbues every aspect of the dining experience. While other fast food eateries treat me like a number, Chick-fil-A makes me feel like a valued customer. It is refreshing.

President Dan Cathy was speaking to a "packed auditorium at SAS Headquarters in Cary, NC, when he shared the company's approach, which is summed up in their corporate purpose statement: To glorify God by being a faithful steward of all that is entrusted to us. To have a positive influence on all who come in contact with Chick-fil-A." https://www.sas.com/en_us/insights/articles/marketing/a-lesson-in-customer-service-from-chick-fil-a.html

Buy Local

There are also intangibles and value at the local hardware store where I buy many things to maintain our home. The people working there possess a wealth of practical information. I have been going there for years, and many of the same people still work there, which provides comfort and continuity. I know who to ask when I have specific questions. When I spend a few bucks more for a product, I am also paying for their knowledge. When I had a bad leak in the basement, I went to the hardware store, and they told me which part I needed and how to fix the problem. It is one thing to buy a gizmo for my well pump and another thing to know how to replace it. That is value. And if the part they had recommended had turned out to be the wrong one, they would have swapped the part and given me the proper one. If there had been a defect in the gizmo, they would have replaced it without any hassle. All of this information and customer service adds up to great value for me.

Here is a plug for the local hardware store. When I only need to purchase a few items, I prefer to give my business to the local store. If I have a large remodeling job, then I hook up the trailer and make my way to the large lumber yards. If I make a habit of running to the large stores indiscriminately, pretty soon there may not be a local hardware store to help me when I need it. When I give my business to a "mom and pop" store in my town, I am investing in the future of the town and the small business owner at the same time.

Lifetime Guarantee

Most automobile mechanics I have known have a Sears Craftsman story. Sears Craftsman tools have a lifetime guarantee. If they break or don't work as expected, they are replaced free of charge. My friend Jim was helping me replace the engine in my Buick when we had a fire in the garage. The handles on his new Craftsman tools melted and were unusable. Since he was helping me, I offered to purchase replacement tools. Instead he went into the local Sears and told them what had happened. They replaced the damaged tools. Now guess where Jim and I continue to buy our tools—Sears! That kind of customer service is above and beyond the call of duty, and it engenders tremendous consumer loyalty.

There is another factor to consider when buying a product with a lifetime guarantee. This may seem confusing at first, but stick with me. I have also seen hand tools that carried a "lifetime guarantee," but I knew they would probably break when they were put to serious use. If I am under a car and using one of these tools, and it breaks in the middle of a job, that guarantee isn't very attractive at that moment. I need the tool now and not in a few weeks after I have shipped the tool back to receive a replacement. Some guarantees have their limitations.

Warranty

When you make a purchase, consider all of the factors and not just the price on the tag. Consider the warranty from the company that makes the product. If the product is faulty, will they replace it in a timely fashion or will you have to wait six months? Then factor in what kind of customer service they have and the ongoing technical support. A warranty is the pledge of the company to stand behind their product or service. It is like buying insurance on your product. Remember to register your product and keep track of your warranty papers, especially more expensive purchases.

According to a study in Consumer Reports, most people do not buy warranties. In this article, I discovered that stores promote warranties because they receive 50% of the amount we pay for their warranty. Only 20% of people buying a large appliance purchase a warranty or service plan, and only 3% will buy a similar plan for a small appliance. If you do want to set aside the money you would pay for a warranty, you will have some cash for a possible repair in the future. For more information, read the entire article; it is eye opening. https://

www.consumerreports.org/cro/extended-warranties/buying-guide/index.htm

Electronics

I have found warranties to be particularly important when buying anything electronic. I have purchased a few computers from a local guy who is happy to make sales, but who is almost impossible to reach for any kind of customer support. I won't do business with him anymore because of this. He isn't there when I need his expertise. On the other hand, I have bought several used computers from Walt down the road because of his knowledge and willingness to support what he sells. When there have been repair issues or questions about the computer, he is there to help me or to replace the product. As a result I have dealt with him for years.

When you are buying a used electronic product, in particular, be extra careful to make sure of the warranty and what to do if there is a problem. Because computers and other similar products are so intricate and complex, I suggest the following advice: when in doubt, buy it new. Unless you know the person or company you are buying from, get a new product. There is so much that can go wrong, and you often have no way of knowing until it is too late.

Large Ticket Items

Twelve years ago, we moved to a house with a large yard to mow. It is about three-quarters of an acre. I had a cheap lawn tractor and used it for a few years, but it began breaking down and needed to be replaced. I narrowed down my search to a John Deere riding mower and began pricing them at local stores. Home Depot had the best price, and Bomberger Store was a close second. As I looked closely at the model at Home Depot, I noticed a sticker on it which read, "Assembled at Bombergers Store." I decided to pay the few extra dollars and buy it directly from Bombergers. If they were the local experts and knew how to assemble the mower, they would probably be the best place to have it serviced when it needed repairs. I have had this mower for eight years (I just asked the folks at Bombergers) and they have done a wonderful job of serving and maintaining our green and yellow lawn mower. The value their customer service adds to the original price is hard to measure, but it is a big part of the buying experience for me.

You may wonder why I am still mowing my own grass. There are several reasons, not all of which are related to money. I think caring for our yard is like Adam tending the Garden of Eden. It is good for me to mow and maintain the yard, prune the shrubs, fertilize the plants, trim the trees and seek to make our home look pleasant. I can afford to pay someone to do this, but I feel like it is my responsibility. I feel productive. My son John also helps in mowing the grass, and in shoveling the snow when the weather turns cold. It gives him a sense of purpose, of being a contributing member of our family, and of sharing in the upkeep of our home, which are all good.

I have calculated the cost of what I save doing the mowing ourselves. We mow from April through November. That means about 30 times in a season. If I were to hire others, they would charge at least $75.00 per visit, or a minimum of $2,250.00 per year. Gasoline costs me about $45.00 per year, and an annual service to the mower (tuneup, sharpen blades, etc.) is another $150.00. The John Deere riding mower cost $2,300.00 initially, so you can see that we paid for the initial cost of the mower in a little over one year.

My Favorite Airline

I am a big fan of Southwest Airlines for several reasons. They may not always have the lowest fare, although they are usually competitive, but they have so many other pluses that contribute to the overall value of what they are selling. There a few new low-cost airlines who advertise the cost of their fares, so I thought I would try one and see what it was like. I went to the website and discovered that I had to pay an extra charge for an aisle seat. Being 6' 5" this is important to me. I also discovered there was a fee for my luggage AND for my carryon items. When I compared this to Southwest, which allows you two free bags to check in, as well as a free carry-on, and does not charge extra for the aisle seat, I decided not to fly with the alternate company.

There are more reasons why I like Southwest. If you have a problem and call the company, you speak to a person and not a computer. They are friendly and have wonderful customer service. You can also cancel and rebook a flight for no penalty fee. Yes, that is correct, no fee. I have called the airlines the morning of a flight and cancelled the flight. The cost of the flight was credited to my account, and the next time I flew (within 12 months) I used those funds to pay for the new flight. I am not aware of any other airline doing this. Sandi and I had tickets on another airline once and one of us was too sick to travel. The cost to rebook the flights and use the credit on another flight was $200.00 per ticket, which was close to the original cost of the flight. We ended up not receiving any value from these fares; and they were lost. When you make an airline reservation, look at the big picture and the overall value, not just the advertised price.

Flight to Tampa

I checked fares and fees to fly three different airlines to Tampa in January to visit family. I wanted to fly down on Thursday and return on Tuesday. The first airline was a low-cost option, called ACME AIR. The second is an old established airline which will henceforth be known as GAMMA GO, and the third was my favorite airline, SOUTHWEST, or SWA. I have one carry-on item and one bag to check. Since I am tall, I either need an aisle seat or to be in the main cabin. Each of the prices and fees listed below are for two segments, which is a round trip.

	Flight	Carry-On	One Bag	Aisle Seat	Cancel Fee	Speak to Agent
ACME	$161.00	$32.00	$44.00	$46.00	$150.00	$14.99
GAMMA	$271.60	free	$60.00	$60.00	$200.00	free
SWA	$318.96	free	free	free	free	free

There are additional items to consider; the SWA flights are nonstop (1 hour and 30 minutes) on the exact dates I selected to fly. ACME does not fly on those days, so I had to pick different dates. GAMMA GO does not fly directly to Tampa, so I had longer flights of at least 4 hours, with layovers in other airports. If you are hungry, you will have to pay for snacks on ACME. I have flown GAMMA GO several times and the flight attendants are polite and helpful. I have not flown ACME, so I cannot speak from experience. I do fly many times per year on SWA and enjoy interacting with their fun and friendly employees. Do you see why I like SWA?

Amazon

I was having lunch with a friend who works for Christian Book Distributors (CBD). I asked him how they were doing since Amazon was growing so large, and it seemed like it was becoming a monopoly in the world of online shopping. I learned something interesting. He said that several of their prices are lower than Amazon's, even with the cost of shipping added, but people assume that Amazon is lower priced and no longer compare prices. It only takes a few minutes to do a quick search and examine your options for a book or other item. CBD did a study and marked down some of their best-selling items at significant discounts so they would be much less expensive than the same item Amazon. They found that most people are no longer doing their homework. It seems Amazon has effectively convinced most of the general population that they are the cheapest and quickest place to purchase anything. They have marketed this thinking and people mistakenly believe they are receiving "FREE" shipping, but we know that is only IF you are a member, and this means an annual fee. As of June of 2018, the annual student fee is $59.00 and the adult yearly fee is $119.99. These fees are similar to the membership fees at buying clubs, which we have already discussed. A few questions to ask yourself are "How much shopping do I do online?" and "Will this amount of activity justify paying the annual fee?"

What are the perks for shopping through your computer or smartphone? One advantage is that there is no transportation cost incurred by driving to the store. If you shop on Amazon, there are a wide variety of products all at one place, like an electronic department store. It is convenient and easy. Once you have logged in all your personal information, with just a few clicks, and the product is at your door in a few days.

One disadvantage is that you can't try on shoes. I have tried to buy shoes online and they have never fit so I stopped trying. Another disadvantage is that to be a member of Amazon, or other similar online companies, you are required to pay an annual fee for the convenience of shopping with them.

Networking

Before I make a large purchase, I do my homework. I know how to find a price but how do I discover the value and intangibles about a product? I am thinking about purchasing an electric bike. I test rode one in a bike shop and really liked it, but I didn't like the price, as it was more than I had ever spent for a bicycle. While I was in the store, I learned a lot of information about the bike by asking questions and listening to the salesman. I also asked the owner of the store how he got into this line of work. He told me his grandfather had started this business 59 years earlier, and he had grown up in the business. This conversation conveyed two messages to me: he was going to be there to service the bike for many years, and he was quite knowledgeable about the product.

I then talked to one of my sons who does a lot of cycling. He told me about a bike shop which specializes in electric bikes. I drove there, asked questions, listened, sat on a few bikes, and added to my knowledge about how they operate. I also discovered that this owner had begun assembling e-bikes from kits and liked it, so he started his own shop. He informed me that in Pennsylvania electric bikes have only been legal for three years.

Then I watched a few youtube videos about e-bikes and read some more information online. While I was in the first bike shop a customer came in who had just purchased an electric bike. I asked him what he thought from a consumer's point of view, which was very helpful. A week or so later I bumped into a couple while my wife and I were hiking. We learned that he and his wife had been on a long trip out west, and had ridden electric bikes. In the course of our conversation, I gathered more information from his perspective.

I am a little distrustful of online reviews as the only source of information, since they may be false or placed there by the company's employees. So I like to balance what I read on the internet with information from people that I know and trust.

Banks and Mechanics

One of the reasons I like my bank is their customer service. I know the manager personally and have his cell phone number. Whenever I need a cashier's check, a safety deposit box, or need to deposit funds from out of the country, or have other special requests, having this relationship make the process so much easier.

Whenever I move into a new area, finding a mechanic whom I trust is also important to me. I am not a fan of a big dealership. I feel I am charged too much because of the "certified professionals," the fancy waiting room, and all the folks I need to speak to just to repair my vehicle. I much prefer a local mechanic whom I can count on when I need to have my car repaired without all the unnecessary frills. Good prices are an important factor in choosing a mechanic, but honesty and expertise have equal value. Cars can be expensive (as we will see in another unit), so if I have confidence in the mechanic and his diagnosis, that contributes to my piece of mind.

Beds and Boots

I don't spend very much money on clothes, and I rarely enjoy shopping for them. There are a few items that I do like to think about before purchasing, and those are shoes and a mattress. If I spend eight hours a day on a bed sleeping, I want to have a good one. If during most of my waking hours I am going to be wearing shoes, I want them to be quality footwear. In both scenarios, I don't mind spending a little extra to find a reliable, quality product. My brother discovered a wonderful mattress company and we now have one of their mattresses. We like the product so much that we have purchased them for our children as wedding gifts.

When I am planning on buying shoes and boots, I don't skimp on the price as I search to find a good dependable product. When I am speaking at a conference, I am on my feet for long stretches of time. I also walk a good bit and have wonderful outdoor hiking shoes. I have them on right now as I type.

PURCHASING AND OWNING A VEHICLE

I purchased my first car when I was twenty years old and was about to leave for college to begin my junior year. A man I knew was given a car from a fellow employee for nothing. He invested one hundred dollars into making the car run and sold it to me for the same amount. This car was a nine-year-old Plymouth Barracuda with push button gears on the dashboard, four bucket seats, and a large sloping rear window. I had to buy a new front fender for $75.00 and then purchase four new tires in order to pass inspection. The tires were retreads (recycled older tires with new tread glued on) and cost about $35.00 each. After adding all the costs, I had a nice gold 'Cuda for $315.00. I drove this little car for two years without needing to make any other repairs and sold it for $35.00 when I graduated from college.

Over the next fifteen years, with a few exceptions, most of the cars I acquired were from family, friends, or relatives. Unless you have some help from others, most young folks reading this book will be driving hand-me-down cars from their parents, older siblings, or grandparents.

Thoughts to Consider Before Buying a Car

Do you really need one? My oldest son was 18 before he received his driver's license. He did not think he should try and buy a used car for his needs at that point in his life. It is a good idea to make a list of times you really NEED to have a car. When I turned 16, I worked diligently to get my license as soon as I could. My second son also was anxious to get his license when he was 16. But both of my boys had access to our second car until they went off to college when they were 20.

If you need a vehicle to get to a job or other commitment on a regular basis recognize that there are several options to owning your own car. Where I live, there is a local bus service that is within walking distance of our house. This form of public transportation is much cheaper than owning and operating your own car. Walking is another option if you live in a town or city, as is riding a bicycle. Our Demme Learning office is only 1.8 miles away from our home, and I like to ride my bike there.

Looking for Used Wheels

If you are looking for a used vehicle from someone other than your friends and family, here are a few tips to consider. First, pray and ask God to direct your steps and lead you to just the right vehicle. If you see a used car in someone's yard, or find it on Craigslist, or notice a sign on the bulletin board in town, and purchase this vehicle, this is called buying from a private party. When you are considering purchasing a car that you know nothing about, ask the person who is selling it why they are selling. You can be assured that in most cases, a car is being sold because it has had some problems. If it was a sweet running machine with no issues, the owner would most likely keep it. I would! Keep in mind that, when we buy used, we often buy someone else's problems. Definitely ask for your parent's help and insight when you go to look at the car and test drive it.

Another place to look for a used or pre-owned car is from a reputable dealer. We have a used car business in our community where I am planning on buying my next car. They have demonstrated honesty and integrity in our previous dealings with them, and my mechanic, whom I trust, thinks highly of them. If you or your parents know of someone like this, who buys and sells cars for a living, they are worth considering.

Talk to your family's mechanic, if you have a good one. He may know of someone who is looking to sell their car. He will also have a good idea of what kind of shape it is in, since he may have worked on it. Perhaps you have a mechanically minded friend who has a gift for working with cars. I know very little about cars compared to some of my friends, and I lean on their advice when I am shopping for a car.

Research

When you have found a car that you are interested in, look online for reports about the car and customer reviews. One source I frequently consult is https://www.kbb.com. I am also a member of AAA, and they have other helpful resources. Thirteen years ago, I bought a vehicle on EBAY. I had been researching Yukons for over a year and I found one on EBAY with the right color, the right year, and the interior I wanted. I bid on it, but didn't get it, even though I was the highest bidder. I did not reach the seller's minimum amount that they wanted for the car. I emailed her and asked her what she was looking for in a price. We compromised and met in the middle of what I was wanting to spend, and she was willing to sell it for, but I still had not driven it. She was in Kentucky, near Cincinnati, and my mechanic friend was vacationing nearby. I called him and offered him $100.00 if he would make a trip to her place, drive it, and look it-over. He called and gave me a thumbs up, and I bought it. It was a wonderful vehicle for our family for many years.

Before purchasing a used car, I recommend obtaining a Carfax report. These are available online and can tell you how many people previously owned the car, any accidents which were reported, and possibly the service records. You can get these at https://www.carfax.com. Just for fun, consider putting in the information for your current car and see what comes up!

My Current SUV

Because of how quickly cars depreciate in the first few years, I have found that the best time to buy a car is when it is three or four years old. I made an exception in 2015 when I purchased the vehicle I am currently driving. I was researching online at a reputable used car dealer's site in hopes of finding a 2012 or 2013 Ford Explorer. I was surprised to find a 2015 Explorer just like I wanted, for almost half of the price of a new model. The reason it was priced so low was because it had 40,000 miles on it. Often new cars are released at the end of the previous year. This one obviously was placed on the market at the end of 2014, even though it was a 2015 model.

Even though the price was attractive, I still talked to my mechanic about it and discovered he also drove an Explorer and was very happy with his vehicle. Before I made my final decision, I called the local Ford Dealership and asked them what was the best price they could offer for a 2015 Explorer. Their price was much higher than what I had found. I asked the used car business if I could drive this car to my mechanic so he could examine it. After a test drive and a thorough going over, we found a few minor issues. After discussing the pros and cons, I decided it was a bargain and bought it. Three years later it is still running well with over 95,000 miles on it.

New Car

I have never purchased a new car, and probably never will. If I do, I know that I will have to drive it for at least seven years to make it worth the initial investment. New cars have the advantage of no hidden problems. Since they are new, they depreciate, or lose their initial value, very quickly. Depreciation is the opposite of appreciation. Often when you buy a home, the value of your home will increase in value over time. This increase in value is called appreciation. A car is the opposite. When you drive a new car off the lot, it drops in value several thousand dollars. Different cars have different rates of depreciation, but all cars will depreciate, or lose value, once they are not "new." Someone wisely observed that once you drive a new car off the lot, it is a used car with payments.

A friend had a son who won a new car in a contest. This new Dodge was worth $35,000.00. When the car arrived, he thought he would drive it for a month and put a few hundred miles on it. After thirty days he decided to sell it back to the dealership. For his one-month-old car, he was given $21,500.00! This is a true story.

Do your Homework First

As I have been researching the cost of buying a new car, I have discovered some interesting information. As I write in 2018 I learned that 2016 was the best year ever for new car sales. The top selling sedan was the Toyota Camry with over 387,000 sold. The vehicle which had the most sales was a pickup truck by Ford. There were over 850,000 F-Series trucks sold. I chose to focus on the Ford F-150 with a regular cab XL, with two-wheel drive, and an eight foot bed.

In the following chart, I am listing the average price for this truck assuming it is being driven 15,000 miles each year and has been kept in reasonably good condition. As we look at the chart, we can deduce that the 2017 truck would have been driven 15,000 miles, the 2016 model 30,000 miles, etc. Notice the additional fees, especially when you first buy a car, which are comprised of registration fees, title costs, and sales tax to be paid. In our example, they were paid when the new truck was purchased. Even when you buy a used car, you still have to pay fees for transferring the title, registration, sales tax, etc.

Year	1	2	3	4	5	Total
Average Price	$27,300	$21,200	$20,000	$19,000	$18,050	
Mileage	15,000	15,000	15,000	15,000	15,000	75,000
Fees	$1,600	$35	$35	$35	$35	$1,740
Depreciation	$6,100	$1,200	$1,000	$950	$850	$10,100

Cost to Own

In the next unit we will look at operating expenses. For now, consider the cost of owning a new Ford truck for the first year by adding the depreciation and fees for buying it, $1,600 + $6,100 = $7,700. If we divide total cost by days, weeks, and months this may help us gauge the real cost of owning a car.

Example 1

How much does it cost to own a new pickup truck per day, per week, and per month?

Solution 1

$7,700 ÷ 365 = $21.10 per day

$7,700 ÷ 52 = $148.08 per week

$7,700 ÷ 12 = $641.67 per month

If I keep the same truck for another year, note how the costs would be significantly less.

Example 2

How much does it cost to keep the same pickup truck per day, week, and month for a second year? The costs for the second year are $1,200 + $35 = $1,235

Solution 2

$1,235 ÷ 365 = $3.38 per day

$1,235 ÷ 52 = $23.75 per week

$1,235 ÷ 12 = $102.92 per month

Since I kept the truck for two years and drove it 30,000 miles, I am assuming I can sell it for $20,000.

Example 3

What is the cost per mile for depreciation and fees for the first year?

Solution 3

$7,700 ÷ 15,000 miles = $0.51 or 51¢ per mile

Example 4

What is the cost per mile for depreciation and fees for the first two years?

Solution 4

$7,700 + $1,235 = $8,935

$8,935 ÷ 30,000 miles = $0.297 or 30¢ per mile

Ownership Costs are Easily Forgotten

It is easy to forget the initial cost of a vehicle, plus the fees and depreciation. Generally, we are more cognizant of the regular fees which we see leaving our wallet, checkbook, or on our credit card statement for regular maintenance, insurance premiums, repairs, and gasoline. However, as you have seen, the initial cost, fees, and depreciation add up to a significant part of the cost of owning a vehicle.

OPERATING EXPENSES FOR A VEHICLE

Fuel Expense

You may be surprised to learn that fuel cost is not the largest part of the cost of keeping a car on the road. The only way to know how much you spend on fuel is to estimate how many miles you will drive in a year and divide it by your miles per gallon (mpg). This will tell you how many gallons of gas you've used. Then you can multiply that number by the price of a gallon of gas to estimate the annual cost of gasoline.

My Ford Explorer shows me my average miles per gallon as I am driving. Every time I fill up my tank, I select "trip 1" on my odometer and reset it. Then I know how many miles I have driven on a full tank of gasoline. I learned from reading the Owner's Manual, that my fuel tank has a capacity of 18.6 gallons. Thus when I am averaging 20 mpg, I can drive 372 miles per tank. Of course, with modern technology, the lights on the dashboard begin telling me I am low on fuel about 60 miles before I am actually on empty.

Before I had this option of selecting "trip 1" from the oometer, I used to compute my gas mileage by using math! I would note the odometer reading before I filled up the tank. Then when I needed gasoline again, I would read the new odometer reading. When I subtracted the first number, from the new number I knew how many miles I had traveled on that tank of gas. Then I noted how many gallons of gas I had just put into the tank to fill it up. I found this number on the gas pump. Then I divided the total miles by how many gallons of gas were required to fill up the tank, to discover the average miles per gallon.

Example 1

What was my miles per gallon on the trip I took this past weekend to the Poconos?

Solution 1

My odometer read 92,585 when I pulled into the Turkey Hill gas station. The gauge showed I had about a quarter tank of gas left. I filled the tank and drove up to the camp. On the way home I saw a low price for gasoline and stopped at the Sheetz station for a fill up. The mileage on my odometer now read 92,824. By subtracting, I found how many miles I had driven: 92,824 - 92,585 = 239 miles. When I was done filling the tank, the number of gallons on the pump read 11.3. I divided 239 by 11.3 and discovered I had averaged 21.15 miles per gallon.

Red VW versus Gold Plymouth

Our first car when we were married was a red VW Hatchback that got 22 miles per gallon. Our next vehicle was a Plymouth Sedan that was twice as large but only got 15 miles per gallon. That year I kept meticulous records of each expense and at the end of the year I found I had spent the same amount on the Plymouth as I had for the VW the year before. I recall the cost of a muffler being $19.00 for the Plymouth which was easy to replace. That same part for the smaller VW was $99.00 and was much more difficult to replace. The annual cost for operating both cars was the same, but the comfort and safety of the larger car was much better. Assuming I drove the same number of miles each year, let's look at these costs. This was in 1980 and 1981 when gas was $1.25 per gallon. Prices have increased, but I still learned a valuable lesson by keeping track of my expenses. Round to hundredths.

Example 2

What was the cost of fuel for both the VW and the Plymouth if I drove 16,000 miles each year?

Solution 2

VW: 16,000 m ÷ 22 m/gal = 727.27 gallons times $1.25 per gallon = $909.09

Plymouth: 16,000 m ÷ 15 m/gal = 1,066.67 gallons times $1.25 per gallon = $1,333.34

Example 3

What was the cost for repairs for both the VW and the Plymouth, during that same year?

Solution 3

VW - Muffler, brakes, tires, came to $590.00

Plymouth - Muffler, brakes, tires, came to $165.00

Notice that the fuel expense was less for the VW but the mechanical expenses were lower for the Plymouth.

The data on the following table comes from information gleaned online for a F-150 Ford pickup truck. Since we are assuming the total mileage per year is 15,000 miles and that our truck averages 20 miles per gallon of gasoline, we would need 750 gallons of gas each year (15,000 miles divided by 20 mpg is 750). The price of gas is currently about $3.00 per gallon, so we will be spending $2,250 per year on fuel (750 gal × $3.00/gal = $2,250).

Maintenance Expense

This is the cost of oil changes, annual state inspections, new belts, fluids, wiper blades, and other items. If we figure an oil change every 3,000 miles, then there are five in a year. If the cost is around $30.00 each time, that is an annual cost of $150.00 just for this part of the total maintenance expense category.

Repairs Expense

As you would assume, repairs are almost non-existent for a newer vehicle, but they increase based on the age and number of miles on a car or truck. The older the vehicle is, the more it will cost to keep it running well. As the car gets much older, the repairs may become more serious in nature, such as needing a new engine or transmission. This is the dilemma facing every car owner: When is the right time to stop fixing the old car and go purchase a new one?

Insurance Expense

My cousin has been in the insurance industry for decades. I asked him what the current situation was for rates for a young adult between the ages of 16 and 25. His advice was to stay on your parent's policy as long as you can. Actuaries are the people who study statistics and trends. They know that teens are more likely to get into an accident than older, more experienced drivers. Thus, rates will be higher because this group has a greater risk of being in an accident.

In the past, if you had good grades or had taken a driver safety class, you qualified for discounts on your rates. It seems the industry is changing rapidly, and quotes for the cost of a policy can change from day to day. As you consider being insured on your parent's policy, check back with your insurance company several times to see what is the best rate.

When it comes to buying insurance, there are several kinds of insurance available. I recently had lunch with two men who had been in accidents. Neither one of them had collision coverage. When you speak with an insurance agent, ask about the costs for each component and what components he recommends you need. Remember that you are buying the insurance and will make the final decision yourself. It is my experience that, since insurance sales folks make a percentage of what they sell, they want you to buy more than you may need. They also tell you scary stories of people who were not adequately covered. When I have driven old junkers, I did not carry collision and comprehensive coverage. By law I did have the minimum coverage, which was liability. Now that I have a nice vehicle, I have collision, comprehensive, as well as what is required. In the following table, I have listed the cost for insurance at between $750 and $870, which is probably a little low.

Operating Expenses (for the 2018 F-150 from Lesson 11)

Year	1	2	3	4	5	Total
Fuel	$2,250	$2,250	$2,250	$2,250	$2,250	$11,250
Maintenance	$230	$350	$650	$1,750	$1,810	$4,790
Repairs	$0	$0	$110	$260	$380	$750
Insurance	$750	$770	$800	$835	$870	$4,025
Total	$3,230	$3,370	$3,810	$5,095	$5,310	$20,815

Ownership Costs

Year	1	2	3	4	5	Total
Fees	$1,600	$35	$35	$35	$35	$1,740
Depreciation	$6,100	$1,200	$1,000	$950	$850	$10,100
Total	$7,700	$1,235	$1,035	$985	$885	$11,840

Operating Expenses and Ownership Costs

In the above table of data, look at the first four categories: fuel, maintenance, repairs, and insurance. These are ongoing costs that you experience every time you go to the gas station and fill up your tank, take your car to the garage for the scheduled oil change, buy a new a battery, replace worn brake pads or threadbare tires, and pay for insurance. These expenses are what most of us think about when we consider the cost of owning a car. But never forget the cost of buying the car in the first place. I call the regular ongoing expenses, "Operating Expenses." I refer to the initial costs, plus depreciation and fees, as the "Ownership Costs." The total ownership cost plus ongoing operating expenses for owning a truck for five years is $11,840 plus $20,815, which is $32,655.

Cost per Mile

If we keep this truck for 5 years our cost per mile will be 44¢ per mile ($32,655 ÷ 75,000 miles = .435). This would be closer to 50¢ per mile if we had borrowed money from the bank to purchase the truck or financed it with a dealer. There would have been a finance charge each month which we escaped since we decided to save up and buy it with cash.

Now that we have done all this work, I can see why my mechanic Ron says to figure at least 50 cents per mile for the cost of operating a car. Unless you have a job where you have a long commute to work, and put high miles on your car every year, having a small car with better gas mileage is not going to save you much money.

Horse and Buggy

I have heard people say, when faced with the cost and responsibility of owning a car, "I am going to buy a horse and buggy and sell my car!" So I interviewed an Amish friend who has owned and driven a buggy for many years to get some numbers. Here they are, minus the vet bills, which vary widely but are significant.

Used Buggy	$3,000.00	
Horse	$2,000.00	
Liability Insurance	$90.00 per year	
Hay and Feed	$912.50 per year	$2.50 per day
Maintenance	$150.00 per year	wheels, etc.
Depreciation	$500.00 per year	
Horse Shoes (tires!)	$280.00 per year	$43.00 per 8 weeks
12 V Battery	$50.00 per year	Night driving

If my friend drives it 30 miles per week, times 52 weeks, 1,560 miles is his annual distance on the road. The depreciation of a buggy and horse is $500.00 per year. Add this to the other annual expenses to reach $1,982.00 per year. Dividing this number by 1,560 miles, we find the cost per mile is $1.27. It is not as idyllic as it seems, is it? This is almost three times the cost per mile of operating a 2018 Ford 150 pickup truck. One downside of having a horse is that even if it is not pulling your buggy, it still needs to be fed. An upside is that a horse has baby horses. That being said, it is difficult to compare road apples to road apples when comparing a horse and buggy with a car.

Alternatives to a Car or Truck

Now that you have learned about depreciation and the costs of upkeep for a vehicle, you may be more open to catching a ride on a bus or paying for a ride with UBER, LYFT, or a taxi. While the costs of these forms of transportation may seem pricey at the time, they may be a savings in the long run. Think about buses, trains, and planes as well!

I would be interested to hear how your thinking has changed now that you know more about the cost of owning and operating a vehicle. Perhaps you might consider helping your parents out with the cost of the family car, especially if you are using it to drive to work on a regular basis. Maybe the next time a friend offers to drive somewhere, you may want to give them a few dollars for taking you along. You might even offer to keep the car clean and vacuumed in exchange for using it once in a while. Perhaps just a thank you to the devoted family that is paying for you to have a roof over your head and a car or truck to use once in awhile, would be a nice touch. Gratitude goes a long way :-)

Example 4

If you live in Harrisburg and are attending a college in Pittsburgh, what are some of the ways you can get to school?

Solution 4A Busing

Greyhound bus has a one-way fare of $22.00. The trip takes four hours and four minutes.

Solution 4B Shuttling

Megabus has a shuttle between for $29.99 between Harrisburg and Pittsburgh.

Solution 4C Driving

The tolls on the PA Turnpike are 26.75 or 18.97 if you use EZ Pass. It is 191 miles to Pittsburgh. If your car gets 24 mpg, that cost alone is 8 gallons at $3.00 per gallon, or $24.00. Just the expense for gas and tolls on this one trip is about $50.00. As we now know, the real cost is much greater since figuring $0.50 per mile comes to $95.50. In light of what we are learning, consider helping your friends pay for their costs when they drive their car, by pitching in. If there are four of you in the car, each of the three non-car owners should this about contributing at least $20.00. Do unto others as you would have them do unto you.

Solution 4D Training

Amtrak has a one-way fare of $53.00. It takes between six and seven hours.

Solution 4E Flying

The cost of flying one-way is $203.00.

BUYING A HOUSE AND UNDERSTANDING MORTGAGES

The American Dream

Many people believe that owning a home is part of the American dream, but houses are not cheap nor easily acquired. The average price for a house purchased in 2018 was over $200,000. Most of you will own your own home some day, but there is a lot of information to be digested before you make this significant purchase. Buying a home will most likely be the largest investment you ever make.

Real Estate Agent

One of the best things you can do when you begin hunting for a house is to enlist the help of a qualified agent. As in all professions, there are good ones and not so good ones. Find a good one. Pray, network, ask questions of your friends, and interview a few before picking one. You don't have to marry the first one you meet :-)

In Pennsylvania, the listing agent, or the one selling the property, receives a 3% commission. The agent representing the buyer, or buyer broker, gets 3% as well. This is negotiable and may vary from agent to agent. On a $100,000.00 house, each agent would receive a commission of $3,000.00. These fees are usually paid by the seller, and they are received at the closing.

Mortgage

Unless you inherit a fortune, or your parents help you buy your first home, you will need to get a mortgage. A mortgage is a loan that enables you to buy a house. Principal is the amount of the loan. Interest rate determines the amount the lender is charging you to borrow their money. In exchange for the lender giving you the money, you agree to pay them back a portion of the principal and the interest payment each month until your debt is paid in full.

For example, you locate a house that you like at a fair price. The cost is $150,000. Now you go to the bank (the lender) and ask them for a mortgage (a loan) so you can buy it. The bank checks your credit score (which is why it is important to have a good one) and looks over your loan application. Assuming you have been approved, the bank agrees to lend you the money. The amount you need is determined by the price of the house minus a down payment.

The down payment is the amount the lender requires you to pay up front. The lender wants you to be invested in this mortgage process with money of your own and not only their money. This is usually 3, 10, or 20 percent of the amount of the loan. The higher the percentage, the less you will have to pay back. Sometimes having a large down payment will also lower your interest rate. If you had saved 20% of the cost of the house, then you would have $30,000 for your down payment (20% x $150,000). The bank lends you $120,000 dollars (the principal), which is the cost of the house minus your down payment ($150,000 - $30,000 = $120,000).

Mortgages also have a term, which is the length of time we agree to pay back the loan. Most mortgages are for 15, 20 or 30 years, with different rates for different terms. Today I checked the rates and discovered they fluctuate daily. The current mortgage interest rates are 4.7% for a 30 year term, 4.4% for a 20 year, and 4.0% for a 15 year term. For this example, I chose a 15 year term at an annual interest rate of 5% (rate).

There are a few kinds of mortgages: fixed, interest only, and adjustable. For simplicity, all of the mortgages we will study are fixed rate mortgages, which means the initial rate which we negotiate with the lender remains the same for the term or length of our mortgage.

Monthly Payment

Now you will figure out how much you agree to pay back to the bank each month. This will be your monthly payment. The formula for calculating the monthly payment is interesting math, and I will explain it later. Most people simply use a loan calculator to determine the monthly payment. When using a loan calculator to determine the monthly payment you will need to know the amount being borrowed, the interest rate, and the length of the loan. Using our new vocabulary, this is the principal, the rate, and the term. When using a loan or mortgage calculator, the term needs to be changed from years to the number of months. Since we have a 15 year term, that is 180 months (15 years times 12 months per year). We have a loan calculator which you can access here: https://mathusee.com/e-learning/stewardship-calculators/

Using the MathUSee Loan Calculator

When you click on this link, a page will come up saying, "Stewardship Calculators."

Select "Loan Calculators."

Enter the Loan Amount (principal) on the first line.

Then type in the interest rate on the second line.

Enter how many monthly payments (the term times 12).

Then click on the orange box which says, "Calculate Monthly Payment."

An amount will appear in the second column next to "Amount of Monthly Payment."

When I enter $120,000 as the loan amount, with an interest rate of 5% for 180 months, the calculator tells me my monthly payment is $948.95. The monthly payment is a combination of the interest payment and the payment on the principal.

You can see all of this information on an amortization table, which is another part of the loan calculator. On the right hand side of the page you will see an orange box which reads "Show Amortization Table." When you click on this orange box another page will pop up on your screen which shows where your interest payments and principal payments have been allocated over the term of the mortgage.

Amortization Table			
Payment number	Principal	Interest	New Balance
1	448.95	500.00	119,551.05
2	450.82	498.13	119,100.22
180	945.01	3.94	0.00
Total Principal & Interest	120,000.00	50,811.42	

When we look at the first payment of $948.95 on the amortization table, we see that $500.00 is going to the bank as the interest payment, and the remainder of $448.95 is being applied to your initial principal of $120,000. The bank receives the interest first. Since we have an annual rate of 5%, you divide this by 12 to find the monthly rate. 5% ÷ 12 is 0.41$\overline{6}$% (which rounds to 0.417%).

Since you have paid $448.95 on our principal the first month, the next month the bank is calculating interest (0.41$\overline{6}$%) based on the remaining principal (or new balance in the table) of $119,551.05 or $120,000 minus $448.95. The second month's payment looks like this: Principal $450.82, Interest $498.13, new balance or principal remaining, $119,100.22. For the next 178 months, the interest amount continues to decrease while the principal payment increases until there is no more principal. The 180th payment has a principal of $945.01 with an interest payment of $3.94.

By scrolling down to the very bottom of the amortization table, you can see that you have paid $120,000 in principal and $50,811.42 in interest. The combined cost for the original $150,000 home is $120,000 (principal) + $30,000 (down payment) + $50,811.42 (interest) = $200,811.42.

At the end of 180 months, or 15 years, you now own our own home free and clear. You have joined the one-third of Americans who have no debt, obligation, or mortgage on their home. The word amortize means to kill, as in killing a debt. The amortization table shows us the monthly progress of paying off a debt over a specified period of time by making regular payments, in this case, monthly payments.

Extra Monthly Payment

There is another section on the Loan Calculator page on our website on the line below "Amount of Monthly Payment." It is called "Extra Monthly Payment (optional)". Since the bank or lender has already received their interest payment, if you add a few more dollars to the amount paying down your principal each month, you can pay off your loan more quickly. In the example, $948.95 is the monthly payment. If this amount was to be rounded up to an even $1,000 per month by adding $51.05, you will see how much interest can be saved, and how much sooner you can pay off your mortgage. To observe this process, enter 51.05 in "Extra Monthly Payment (optional)" and then print out a new amortization schedule and compare this table with the original table.

	Amortization Table	With Extra Payments	
Payment number	Principal	Interest	New Balance
1	500.00	500.00	119,500.00
2	502.09	497.92	118,997.91
167	698.62	2.91	0.00
Total Principal & Interest	120,000.00	46,701.92	

Notice that you now make our last payment in 167 months instead of 180 months. The total interest you pay over the course of our term is $46,701.92 instead of $50,811.42, for a savings of $4,109.50. Before you being adding extra payments, make sure you talk to the lender before officially entering into an agreement. Ask if you are able to prepay the loan and make additional payments on the principal. When my father loaned me money to buy our first home, I was able to make prepayments to him and we paid off our mortgage in six years instead of the 15 years on our original agreement.

Private Mortgage Insurance

Until you make that final payment, you don't technically own our home, the bank does. If you stop making your monthly payments, that are your obligation and responsibility, the bank can take back possession of your home until you have paid your debt in full. This right to repossess your personal property is called a lien.

If your down payment was less than 20%, then the bank may have required you to purchase insurance, in case you are unable to keep making your monthly mortgage payments. This is referred to as PMI, which stands for private mortgage insurance.

Monthly Payment Formula

M is the monthly payment, P is the principal, r is the monthly interest rate, n is the number of monthly payments.

$$M = P \times \frac{r(1 + r)^n}{(1 + r)^n - 1}$$

In our example this would be:

$$M = \$120{,}000 \times \frac{0.0041\overline{6}(1.0041\overline{6})^{180}}{(1.0041\overline{6})^{180} - 1}$$

$$M = \$120{,}000 \times \frac{0.0041\overline{6}(2.11370393244)}{(2.11370393244) - 1}$$

$$M = \$120{,}000 \times \frac{0.00880709971}{1.11370393244}$$

$$M = \$120{,}000 \times 0.00790793625$$

$$M = \$949$$

Points

Points, or mortgage points, or discount points, are 1% of the amount of the loan. They are prepaid interest on the amount you are borrowing. For example, by running the numbers from our $120,000, 15 year mortgage at 5%, you can see how much you can lower the percentage rate of the loan by prepaying the interest. The idea is if you pay more up front, your monthly payment will be lower. This money you are paying up front will generally lower the rate of your loan $\frac{1}{8}$ of a percent per point. If you pay one point, then the 5% loan will drop to $4\frac{7}{8}$% (4.875). That will lower the monthly payment from $948.95 to $941.16 for a saving of $7.79 per month.

To find out if this is a good deal, divide $1,200 (the 1% cost of one point) by $7.79, the amount you would be saving on the monthly payment. $1,200 ÷ $7.79 = 154. It will take 154 payments or about 13 years, to recoup the upfront cost of the one point. This is not much savings for a 15 year loan and I would probably not prepay a point in this case.

Figure 1

Rate	Interest Points	Loan Monthly	Payment	Save per Month
5%	0	$120,000.00	$948.95	
$4\frac{7}{8}$%	1	$120,000.00	$941.16	$7.79

Lesson 14

COST OF OWNING A HOME

Closing Costs

Remember when we bought that first car and then were surprised by the fees and taxes which accompanied this transaction? In real estate, when the buyer and seller sit down at a table to finalize the sale of the house, there are several taxes and transaction fees called closing costs. Some of these fees are percentages and others are fixed. Whether you buy a $150,000 home or a $200,000 home, you will pay the fixed fees and you will only save a small amount on the percentage costs.

These costs vary from state to state and county to county, but when in doubt—ask! I researched what I could online, thought about what I had learned from my own experience, and then had breakfast with a friend who has spent 40+ years in this industry. Here is a list of the costs that are due for a $200,000 house at the closing, or settlement, in my county. Two families, the Jacksons and Hills, bought similar homes. The only difference between the two columns is the amount of the down payment.

Cost of House	Jacksons	Hills	
Purchase Price	$200,000	$200,000	
Down Payment	(5%) $10,000	(20%) $40,000	
Principal	$190,000	$160,000	
Term	30 years	30 years	
Interest rate	5%	5%	
Monthly Payment			
Principal/Interest	$1,019.96	$858.91	from amortization table
Property Taxes(PT)	$300.00	$300.00	Held in escrow by lender
Home Insurance(HI)	$75.00	$75.00	Held in escrow by lender
PMI	$140.92	0	Private Mortgage Insurance
Monthly Payment	$1,535.88	$1,233.91	
Closing Costs			
Prepaid Reserves	$4,500.00	$4,500.00	PT & HI in advance for the next year
Transfer Taxes	$2,000.00	$2,000.00	2% divided between buyer and seller
Title Insurance	$1,500.00	$1,500.00	$750 per 100,000, or 0.75%
Fixed Fees	$3,191.00	$3,191.00	These are listed below*.
Total Closing Costs	$21,191.00	$51,191.00	

*Fixed Fees

Appraisal, credit report, processing, underwriting, wire transfer, notary, courier, title endorsement, owner's title insurance, closing letter, title Edoc, document preparation, government recording and mortgage fees. There are optional inspections for the house, pests, well, plus a flood certification fee. These add up to $3,191.00 for our example.

Down Payment Perks

As I look over the table, I wondered how much is saved in the long run by making a larger down payment. I found that the amount of total interest saved, by consulting the amortization tables for each loan, and subtracting $177,185.99 - $149,209.25 = $27,976.74. This is the difference between the total interest on the Jackson's mortgage of $190,000 with 5% down and the Hills' of $160,000 with 20% down. There is an additional savings of $1,691.04 per year because the Hills' will not need to pay the PMI fee each month of $140.92. PMI is private mortgage insurance that protects the lender in case the borrower is unable to make his monthly payment obligations.

Good Faith or Earnest Money

When you and your spouse have found a house that you want to buy, you will make an offer to show that you are serious. This monetary deposit is called Good Faith or Earnest Money. It demonstrates that you are in earnest and want to buy the house. A check is then written for a significant amount (1% or more), and the seller's agent will hold it until the closing. Since the check does not go to the seller directly, but is being held by a third party, we say it is "going into escrow." The money is in limbo until the official signing of the deed, when it will be credited to your account.

You may offer more earnest money to influence the seller to accept your offer over other offers they are considering. This practice is more prevalent in a seller's market when several people may be bidding on the same house. If you want to put yourself at the front of the line, and demonstrate how serious you are, make an offer of 2-3%. This money is used as a deposit, and assuming a successful transaction, it will be credited towards the purchase price upon settlement or closing. If you back out beyond a reasonable time, you may lose this deposit.

Prepaid Reserves in Escrow

The concept and practice of escrow pops up again at closing when prepaid reserves appears as a part of your monthly payment. One of the obligations of the buyer is to prepay a year's worth of home insurance and property taxes. As a part of the monthly payment, one-twelfth of the property taxes (PT) and one-twelfth of the home insurance (HI) is given to the lender, who stands to lose the most if these bills are not paid in a timely fashion. They are received and placed in an escrow account until the bills are due. Think of this as paying a year in advance for these necessary bills. In this table, this is $300 for property taxes and $75 for home insurance. $300 + $75 = $375 times 12 months is $4,500 per year.

More on Liens

It is the responsibility of the buyer to insure there are no liens on the property. He does this by contracting with a title company to verify that the title is clear. These title firms often research back as many as 80 years looking for liens.

A lien is the right of a creditor to collect money from the sale of your real estate. It is an obligation that the owner of the house has been unable to pay. Since the lender has not been receiving their money payments, they place a lien on the house. When the house is sold, the creditor receives the money that was owed to them.

An example of a lien that is different from someone not paying their mortgage payments might be the government collecting back taxes which have not been paid, or a hospital trying to collect payment for outstanding fees. If there are liens, the title is not free and clear. If you aren't careful, you may end up buying the seller's house and having to pay his debts! Since liens can take time to work their way through the bureaucratic red tape, title insurance (approximately $750.00 on a $100,000.00 loan) covers you and the title company in the event there are outstanding obligations. Since this is probably your largest investment to date, I suggest buying the title insurance; it is worth it.

Budget

You may not have thought much about a budget, but as I researched this unit, I noticed that almost every article assumed the buyers had a budget and knew how much they were spending on utilities, car expenses, food, utilities, etc. Some experts recommended that you not commit to over 30% of your take home pay or 45% of your gross pay when looking at a home to buy or a place to rent. Count the cost and figure out how much you can afford to pay each month before house or rent shopping.

Ongoing Expenses

In addition to the price of the house and the fees at the closing, there are ongoing maintenance and utilities expenses. Some of them are billed monthly and others quarterly.

My monthly expenses include electricity, natural gas, phone, and internet. My quarterly bills are for water, garbage removal, and sewer.

We have discussed the concept of property taxes in general. Our bills arrive in the spring and the fall. The spring bill, which is referred to as the spring tax, is for the county and the local township, while the revenue from fall tax goes to the local schools. After you have paid these for a year or so, you will have a good idea how to budget for them. If you have an escrow account, you don't have to think about your insurance or tax payments, as your lender will be responsible to pay them.

Some folks suggest setting aside 1% of the cost of your home for repairs and maintenance. I just checked my accounting program for 2018, and that is pretty close to the amount our home requires for normal maintenance. In addition to those normal expenses, we also had to replace our air conditioning unit, which was not expected. That is why it is a good idea to have funds in savings for these unexpected costs.

Rent or Own

This brings me to an important question. When is it better to rent, and when is it better to buy? At some time in your life you will wrestle with this question. There is not one correct answer for everybody, but here are some issues to consider when trying to decide.

I found a map of the United States that gives a great overview of the issue. There is a table with the average cost of renting on one side and the cost of ownership on the other side. If the cost of renting is higher than the the cost of buying, then this state would be assigned the color pink, indicating it is better to buy than rent. The whole country is shown with each state either pink, blue, or yellow. Thirty-seven of the states are pink, since it is economically a good idea to buy there, instead of to rent. Seven states are blue, because it is more cost efficient to rent there than buy a home. Six were yellow, indicating these states are a toss-up or neutral.

1. Consider the Cost of Closing

Since you have learned more about the closing costs required to buy a home at the closing, you don't want to do that frequently. One question to ask yourself is, "Are you planning on staying in one area for several years?" If you will be moving every two years, renting may be the better option, so that you will not incur these closing costs every time you buy and sell another home.

2. Stability

If you are planning on beginning a family you may want your children to have the stability that comes from being in one area or living near your relatives.

3. Retirement

Home ownership can be thought of as forced retirement savings. If you are not a good saver, you may need the pressure of making a mortgage payment each month to help you set aside money for the future. Owning your own home is the primary way most people develop a nest egg for retirement. Your home becomes your personal estate and will help provide for your needs in the future. Real estate will probably be one of your safest investments, and one that has historically appreciated over time.

4. Building Equity

As you make house payments you are putting the money into something that you own. When I examined the amortization table for the Jackson's $190,000, 5%, 30-year mortgage on page 1 of this lesson, I discovered the amount of equity they accumulated during the first three years by adding the amounts in the principal column, beginning with $228.29 and stopping at $264.06. The sum of these payments is approximately $8,900. This is not the interest, but the principal. This principal is what you own, or your equity. The lender gets their interest, but you own the equity. If you rented during this same three-year period, you would have no equity.

If you live in an area with a strong economy, the house you buy will most likely increase in value, or appreciate, while you are living in it. If your mortgage payment is comparable to what your rent in a similar area would be, you will be investing in an appreciating asset which increases in value over time. Even if the rent payment is $600.00 and the mortgage payment with taxes and insurance is $725.00, the amount you can write off on your taxes will offset the $125 difference.

5. Being Careful

If the economy is weak, consider renting unless you find a super deal. A weak economy means your home will probably not increase in value, and you won't be able to recoup the costs associated with buying and selling a home. When the economy is strong a home will most likely appreciate. Perhaps the primary reason for renting is that the landlord has all the responsibility for fixing plumbing problems, painting the exterior, repairing damage after a storm, etc. It is his house. He also is responsible to pay the property tax bill. On the other hand, no matter how long you stay there, when you leave, the landlord still owns the house.

6. Mobility

If you are just beginning your married life or career and are not sure where you will end up living, you may want to rent until you are more settled. Even when you do decide to settle in a specific area, renting for a season gives you a chance to learn more about the town and county before you invest in a home.

Positive Saving Habits

If you are younger than twenty as you are taking this course, it will probably be several years before you consider purchasing your new home. You may wonder why we are learning all this information about home ownership now. One reason is so you can see the big picture and begin making plans. You won't be able to save up a chunk of cash to drop a 20% down payment in a few months, but you can begin to develop the necessary habit, or discipline, of regularly and systematically setting aside money, and not waiting until you surmise you will have more money in the future. If you are saving now, it will be easier to establish this discipline of saving when you have more money coming in.

Tortoise and the Hare

We will be discussing compound interest in a separate unit, but let's use the other calculator on our website and put in some numbers to get a feel for this idea of investing now. The average return on the investment of people in the stock market in 2016-2018 was a little less than 10%. For our example, let's choose 9%. The question for you to answer first is whether it is better to invest $10.00 per week (or $42.00 per month) now for 10 years at 9% (like the Tortoise) or invest $139.00 per month for three years after you have a better paying job (like the Hare). Tortoise and Hare are both investing at least $5,000.00.

Tortoise: $42 × 12 = $504 per year for 10 years = $5,040
Hare: $139 × 12 = $1,668 per year for 3 years = $5,004

Using the Investment Calculator https://mathusee.com/e-learning/stewardship-calculators/, enter the data and compare the results. The Tortoise's slow steady investments increased to $8,128 ($5,040 + $3,088), while the Hare's $139.00 model has grown to only $5,720 ($5,004 + $716). I hope this reveals why it is more profitable to begin saving now instead of postponing your investing until you have more income in the future!

Down Payment

While you are saving for your down payment, build your credit score that a bank, credit union, or some other lender, will loan you the money when you need it. When I was eating breakfast with my real estate expert, I asked what one piece of advice they had for our class. Their answer was to have a nice amount saved up for a down payment. Having a significant amount in the bank, gives you more flexibility when making an offer on the house, lowers your monthly payment, and eliminates the need for PMI payments each month.

Wedding Bells

I am going to make suggestion that may offend some of you. If you are planning on having your parents spend several thousand dollars for a big expensive wedding, here is another idea. Perhaps you could have a simple wedding, and ask your mom and dad if the money they were planning on spending at the wedding could be set aside to be used in helping you purchase your first home. These funds would be a great asset as you save for your down payment.

Contracting, Painting, and Roofing

There are certain home maintenance jobs that I have felt my family and I could take care of ourselves. They include painting, landscaping, cutting the grass, washing cars, and washing windows. There are construction projects that we learned how to do, like building vinyl fences, wood decks, stone retaining walls, and storage sheds. There is a sense of satisfaction that comes from doing home maintenance and simple construction yourself. Each family will have to determine what they can and cannot do themselves. There are other jobs, such as electrical wiring, plumbing, and gas line installation, that I do not feel comfortable doing because of the potential danger if not done properly. Fortunately, God has provided trustworthy and qualified men to do this work for us, and I am glad to hire their services. There are other skills, like hanging and finishing drywall or sheetrock, that I can do; but professionals—guys who do it every day—are so much quicker and more efficient that it pays to hire them.

For example, in our current home, I mudded, sanded, and finished the drywall in our living room. It took me several evenings, was a lot of work, and it still wasn't smooth. Then I found a neighbor who finishes drywall for a living. When I had him finish the game room, he came down for a few hours in total (spread out over several days) and did a great job for $100.00. That was the end of my drywall finishing. Even though I can do it, I can't do it well, or efficiently.

When you do hire contractors, here are some tips to keep in mind:

1. Remember that you are hiring them and have the authority to make the final decision. If they are not willing to do the job exactly as you specify, then politely and firmly say, "No thanks," and interview someone else to do the work. It is your house. Don't give in to any pressure from workers that you are hiring.
2. Check with your friends and neighbors to find reliable workers and construction firms.
3. If you need to hire someone that neither you nor your friends and family know, ask for references from previous customers. Follow through and call these people or drive over and inspect his work. If this offends him, say good-bye. Better to do your homework first and not have to learn a painful lesson.
4. Check with your state government about the credibility and competence of a contractor. Ask if he is certified. Not all contractors have to be, but most professions require certification.
5. Whether you know them or not, make sure the workers are insured or bonded. Otherwise, if they get hurt on the job, you are responsible for their medical bills. If they have no insurance, even if they say they will accept responsibility, you are still responsible.
6. When you choose a contractor, don't assume anything. Put your expectations

in writing. By expectations, I mean write out what you want to have done. An estimate is somewhat flexible, but a bid is similar to a contract and is fixed. Any estimate or a bid from the contractor should also be spelled out in writing. Get several estimates to help you get an idea of how much the job will cost.

7. Make sure you both understand how you will pay. Is it half up front for materials and the rest when the job is done, or is it payment in full after the job is completed? There are many different ways to pay the worker. If his proposed payment schedule sounds fishy, tell him you'll get back to him and check it out with some of your experienced friends who can give you sound counsel.

8. Decide whether you are paying by the job or by the hour. If it is by the job, and you have agreed on the price, make sure there is a date of completion also specified. I would suggest you never pay for work in full until you have inspected it and are completely satisfied that it is done. If the workers have been paid in full, you have no leverage, and you will probably never see them again.

9. If you are paying for labor plus materials (which means you pay for the materials and an hourly rate for the contractor's time) find out when the time clock starts. A team of carpenters did some work for me and billed me from the time they left their home, till they got home that evening. I received eight hours of work, but was billed for 10 hours. They only worked one day!

10. Don't be afraid to ask questions. If you and your spouse have any concerns, remember, you are doing the hiring. If you are uncomfortable, don't get involved with a contractor in the first place.

11. If you are unable to reach the contractor on his phone, that is a warning signal to me. If all of your calls go to a voice mail, and your calls are not returned in a timely fashion, it will only be worse when/if you hire him. I appreciate a contractor who communicates well, and calls to tell you when he is coming or when he is being delayed.

Everyone has sad stories as well as glowing reports of working with contractors. I hope these tips help you have more positive than negative experiences.

Estimates

When I was finishing some improvements on my warehouse, I asked for an estimate of what it would cost to put metal siding on two sides. The contractor gave me a figure of what he thought it would cost him to do the work. He figured how much time it would take him to do the job and how much the materials would cost, and then he gave me a price, or quote. This was his estimate—the amount he estimated the job would cost. If he wanted to call it a bid, he would put it in writing and that would be his fixed price for doing the job. A bid, or contract, is what he will be paid regardless of how long it takes. When the contract is signed, he is committed to his bid. The positive aspect of a fixed bid to the contractor is that if all goes well, he may do very well. But, if the job runs into a snag, or the weather doesn't cooperate, or the price of materials goes up, he could lose money on a project.

During the course of our warehouse renovation project, I got to know several of the contractors very well and developed a relationship of trust with them. Even though I had their bids and estimates, I told them to charge me the fair value for their time and materials if the final bill was significantly more than what they expected due to unforeseen problems. This way I didn't pay too much, and they don't lose any money either.

I learned firsthand about estimates and bids as a painting contractor. After my initial experience as a painter of gutters and high trim, I decided to pursue painting full-time the next summer, so when I came home after my first year in college, I began painting houses. I hired some local guys to work for me. I figured the estimates and gave the homeowners my price and then paid my workers an hourly wage. I got paid by the job. My workers got paid by the hour. They had no risk and were paid regardless of how long it took to complete the job, but the better we worked, the more I made per job. As the contractor I had the potential to make more, and also to lose more. I was paid for taking that risk.

Paint

My father was a salesman who sold paint to department stores, . He often reminded me that there is a lot of information on a paint can. Besides telling you what kind of paint to use and how to prepare the surface before painting, you also learn about coverage. Coverage, or how many square feet the paint will cover, depends on the surface. If you are painting a rough surface, the paint will not cover as much as on a smooth surface. For smooth interior walls you can expect at least 400 square feet per gallon. Make sure you find out if the paint will require one coat or two. My rule of thumb for buying paint is to buy the high-quality brand. The difference between cheap paint and high-quality paint is only a few dollars compared to the time for your labor in getting ready to paint and then actually doing it. Plus, a good paint may need only one coat, or application, of paint, whereas a cheaper brand will probably take at least two coats. Paying a few more dollars for paint is worth the savings in labor. The same applies to painting the exterior of a house. Buy good paint and good brushes and don't cut corners in that department. The time you save will more than offset any savings in inferior materials or brushes.

When you are buying paint, you may find that two or three individual quarts cost the same as one gallon. If a gallon covers 400 square feet, then a quart will cover one-fourth of that, or 100 square feet. Two quarts will cover 200 square feet, which is enough to do a ceiling 12 ft × 15 ft. If my ceiling had been 250 square feet, I would have had to decide whether to buy two quarts or one gallon since the job would require a little over half a gallon of coverage. Sometimes you can stretch paint to cover 125 square feet per quart, but you don't want to run short, so I would opt for the gallon. If a quart of paint is priced at $18.00, then a gallon would be two and one-half times that, or $45.00. This is not necessarily true in all stores. Be sure to check this when buying paint.

Example 1

If you are painting a bedroom that is 12 ft × 15 ft with 8 ft ceilings, how much paint will you need for the walls and the ceiling?

Solution 1

You will need about one gallon for the walls and one-half of a gallon for the ceiling. Study figure 1 to see how we calculated the area for each flat surface, and then found the amount of paint needed for the ceiling and the four walls.

The area of the ceiling is 12 ft × 15 ft = 180 ft²

The area of four walls are 96 ft² + 120 ft² + 96 ft² + 120 ft² = 432 ft²

Figure 1

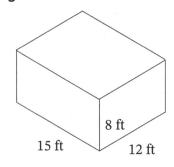

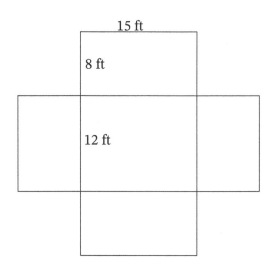

A Square of Shingles

Shingles are generally figured by the square. A square of shingles covers 100 square feet, or 10 ft × 10 ft, or 100 ft². If your house has a roof that is 40 ft × 18 ft on each side, as in figure 2, the area would be 40 ft × 18 ft = 720 $\frac{ft^2}{side}$ × 2 sides = 1,440 ft². We find 1,440 ft² ÷ 100 $\frac{ft^2}{square}$ = 14.4 squares. You will need 15 squares to cover 1,500 square feet, since 14 squares would not be enough.

A Square of Siding

Siding is also measured by the square. In figure 2, the area of the walls is 8 ft × 22 ft on each end and 8 ft × 40 ft on the long sides. Each triangular gable end is 22 ft wide and 14 ft high, and has an area of
$\frac{1}{2}$ft × 22 ft × 14 ft, or 154 ft². Since there are two of these, they add up to 308 square feet. 176 ft² + 176 ft² + 320 ft² + 308 ft² = 1,300 ft². When you divide this by 100 square feet (a square of siding is 100 square feet) you get 13, so you need 13 squares of siding to complete the job. Vinyl siding is sold in cartons which cover two squares, or 200 square feet per carton. Since there is more waste on the triangle shaped gable ends, and we can only buy in cartons, we will need seven cartons. Each carton has 24 pieces of vinyl siding with the length of a piece being 12′6″ long (or 12.5 ft) with a finished height of 8″ or $\frac{2}{3}$ ft. 24 × 12.5 ft × $\frac{2}{3}$ ft is 200 square feet.

Figure 2

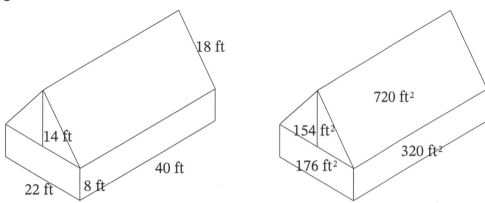

Conclusion

It is worth repeating that the cost of materials in the twenty-first century is usually less than the cost of labor in the twenty-first century. When I painted houses for several summers, I observed that homeowners who grew up in the Depression era were very frugal but unwise when they tried to save money on paint. Most of the homes I painted in Pittsburgh had brick, stone, or aluminum siding. The materials needed to paint a house with mostly windows, a few doors, some overhang, and a garage door only amounted to two to three gallons of paint. A good-quality paint when I was painting homes was about $20.00 per gallon, and the total cost of materials would be $60.00. The labor to do this job would be $400.00 to $500.00. Often the homeowner would buy a cheap brand of paint and save $15.00 to $20.00. That paint would not last as long as the good stuff, and the house would need to be repainted a year or two sooner. Saving $20.00 in materials actually cost them a few hundred dollars in increased labor charges.

Seventy-five years ago the cost of materials was a large part of the job. Materials are still a significant part of any job, but today the cost of labor has risen so dramatically that the cost of materials is not as important as it once was. My advice is to try not to skimp on quality paint, shingles, or siding. You will be better off in the long run!

HAGGLING, RENT OR BUY A TOOL, FLOORING AND FABRIC

Men have been borrowing tools for a long time. "As one was felling a log, his axe head fell into the water, and he cried out, 'Alas, my master! It was borrowed.' Then the man of God said, 'Where did it fall?' When he showed him the place, he cut off a stick and threw it in there and made the iron float. And he said, 'Take it up.' So he reached out his hand and took it." (2 Kings 6:5–7) I don't know what the message is from this story, but it is an interesting way to begin the lesson on borrowing tools, don't you think?

Guideline #1

If you need a tool or appliance that you will use frequently, but just haven't gotten around to purchasing, buy it now. Determining the quality of the item needed and how much you will spend depends on your situation. My brother used to make his living with tools, so if he needed a certain tool, he spent the extra money to make sure he had a high-quality one. I, on the other hand, like to have tools on hand for handyman jobs, but know that I don't need the best available. Middle-of-the-road is good enough for me.

Guideline #2

If it is an expensive item that you use only occasionally, rent it. I power wash the siding on my home twice a year. To rent a high-pressure power washer costs $70.00 a day. To buy the same one would cost over $2,000.00.

Dividing the $70.00 into $2,000.00, you can see that I would have to use the power washer 28 times for this to be a good investment. Plus, when I rent it, the rental company stores the machine, maintains it, and keeps it running efficiently. The power washer rents for $49.00 for four hours, $70.00 for a day, and $177.00 for a week.

While I was getting these figures from our local Grand Rental Station, I asked Mike and Steve which item was rented the most frequently. Their answer was the carpet cleaner, which rents for $19.00 for four hours, $29.00 per day (24 hours), and $87.00 per week. A new carpet cleaner retails for over $1,000.00. Think about how often you clean your carpets, and you can see what a great deal it is to rent instead of own. There are less expensive models you can buy, but I am pricing the same model as the one in the store.

Guideline #3

Here is a final thought on purchasing items for your home and family use. When you are considering buying a bed, remember that you will spend one third of your life using it. If you are considering buying a tuxedo, take into account the fact that you may wear it only once a year or once every five years. Identify the items that you use every day, like a bed and shoes, contrast them with tuxedos and carpet cleaners, and purchase accordingly. Some items are made to be rented.

Guideline #4

If you do borrow tools from a friend, make sure you return them in the same or better condition as soon as you complete your job. If you break the tool, buy a replacement tool whether they ask for it or not. Relationships are more important than things.

Bob was continually borrowing tools from George, who lived across the street. Bob had a bad habit of not returning the tools when he was finished with them. Instead, he left them in his garage. One day Bob looked out the window and saw George carrying his table saw from his home and putting it into Bob's garage. Bob was puzzled and came outside and asked George why he had moved his nice table saw into Bob's garage. George said, "I just want to keep all my tools in the same place." Bob took the hint and returned all of George's tools that evening.

Fabric

Recently I visited a local department store to see how mathematics was used in the fabric department. An associate named Patti graciously took me through the different rows of material. The first thing I noticed was how they were presented on the shelves. A bolt of fabric was wound around a cardboard center. There is also a good bit of material that is on sale, and not on a bolt. This fabric is lying in stacks on a shelf or table and is referred to as flat fold.

Cloth is sold by the yard, which is 36 inches, or 3 feet, in length. While the length of a yard is consistent, the width of the fabric varies. The most common width is 45 inches, but there are also 54-inch, 60-inch, and even 72-inch widths. A yard of 45-inch fabric is 36 inches by 45 inches. A yard of 60-inch material is 36 inches by 60 inches. This difference in width makes a big difference when considering the amount of area of a yard of fabric.

I'm going to focus my attention on the three most common fabric shoppers: quilters, crafters, and seamstresses (those who make clothes to wear). According to Patti, quilters usually look first at the flat fold material, which was sale priced at $1.99 per yard (45 inches wide). Then they go to the broadcloth, or calico prints, which are 100% cotton and were priced at $5.89 per yard. Crafters often buy felt, which goes for $4.19 per yard and is 72 inches wide. This material has a variety of uses, such as posters, banners, and boards for teaching children in a classroom setting. Seamstresses tend to purchase a fabric blend of polyester (65%) and cotton (35%). This was priced at $3.69 per yard and comes in 54-inch widths.

Figure 1

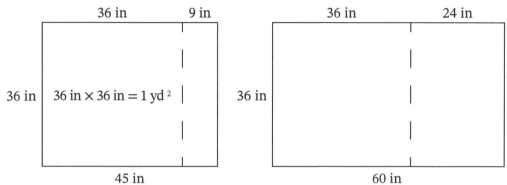

Carpet

My wife and I have bought carpet several times from Sam's store in town. He has been in the business for a long time and understands it well. Besides possessing a wealth of information, he is also a consummate salesman.

As with the other lessons in this book, I am simply going to take a quick look at this topic. Carpet quality is determined by its face weight, or the weight of the nylon in one yard. A good face weight is 35 oz. This is not wool carpet, but nylon, which is the material most commonly used for carpet. One question to ask when shopping for carpet for your home is whether the nylon is a continuous thread. If it is 100% continuous nylon, it will be as long wearing as steel (according to Sam).

To learn about the quality of carpet and the proficiency of the installer, it is worth developing a rapport with a local dealer. The average price for a good quality carpet can vary, but Sam's best-selling carpet goes for $15.00 per yard. Since most of us don't know how to install carpet, we must also pay the price for installation, which is 60¢ per square foot (or $5.40 per square yard) at Sam's. Notice how 60¢ per square foot sounds better than $5.40 (9 × 60¢) per square yard. Sam's store recommends a good-quality padding, which is 90¢ per square foot or $8.10 per square yard. Carpet is measured by the yard. This means a square yard, which is 3 feet × 3 feet, or 9 square feet, or one square yard.

Example 1

Find the cost of carpeting a room that is 12 ft by 15 ft

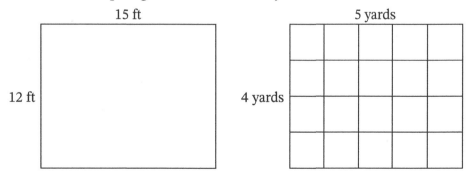

The total cost, $370.00, when divided by 20 square yards, is $18.50 per square yard. This in turn can be divided by 9 $\frac{ft^2}{yd^2}$ to find $2.06 per square foot. Now you will find carpet that is cheaper than this and some that is more expensive, but this is a good benchmark. May your carpet always lay flat and last long!

Haggling or Negotiating

Negotiating the cost of an item is very difficult for some and like breathing for others. I have some friends who are so good at it, I am embarrassed to go shopping with them. I have other friends who wouldn't think about doing it. I am in the middle. First, here is a little history.

In many parts of the world today, haggling or dickering, is still the way you do business. It also used to be the way to conduct business in the United States. The first businessman to print prices on price tags was John Wanamaker in Philadelphia. As a Christian, he believes that if we are equal before God, then we should be equal before price. Soon, other merchandisers like Woolworth, followed suit. We take price tags for granted, but you won't find them in much of the world. I took a trip to Thailand, where dickering is the accepted way of purchasing, but there is a certain way to do it. Now, I don't pretend to be an expert in the art of dickering, but here are a few points that I have learned.

Tip #1

Be polite and treat the sales staff as you would like to be treated. Avoid being rude and contentious. "The Lord's servant must not strive, but be gentle towards all." (2 Timothy 2:24)

Tip #2

Find out the approximate price of the item by going to several vendors and shopping. I found a wide range of prices for the same item on the same street in Thailand, from 290 bahts to 480 bahts. In US dollars that is $7.70 to $12.70. Know what the standard starting price is before you begin to dicker. In other words, do your homework. You aren't trying to cheat them. You just want to arrive at a place where you are both happy. This should be a win-win situation!

Tip #3

Talk to the locals to find a good place to begin bidding. Where I was recently, if you make too low an offer, sellers are offended. On the other hand, if you bid too high, then you have no room to negotiate. The rule of thumb was that you should pay a third less than they were asking. So if the price they ask is $300.00, then you should aim at $200.00. Your starting price might be $150.00 or $160.00. Then they make a counteroffer, and thus begins the haggle.

I was in Jerusalem years ago and was leaving the city when a boy offered me three hand-carved olive-wood camels. I didn't want them and kept walking, smiling, and telling him no thanks. He persisted until the price lowered to $2.00. Now for that price I couldn't refuse, and I bought them. They made a nice gift. The next day I was in the

Old City where there were shops selling the same camels. I innocently asked what the price was and was told something like $15.00–$20.00. To this day I still wonder what the real cost of a set of camels is.

My first experience haggling in the US was when I was renting a large moving truck. I went to a Ryder Truck rental place and got their offer. It was so much per day, plus a price for each mile. Then I called U-Haul and Hertz-Penske. All I remember is that I got prices from all three and eliminated one. Then I called the first place back and told them I was going with another bidder. He then asked me what price I had received and lowered his price to beat it. These two companies went back and forth a few times until I got the best price. I saved hundreds of dollars with just a few phone calls.

Shop Around

One fall I had a remodeling project. I made a list of exactly what I needed, then called five lumberyards to get quotes. I requested prices on the items I needed, plus the cost of the delivery options. When I found the best price and I was ready to buy, one of the lumberyards called me and said they would match the lowest price, and deduct another 10%. That was pretty tough to beat. The savings were significant.

Pray

When we were finishing off our current home, we had two experiences where God multiplied our dollars. The first was when we were looking for flooring. We wanted some kind of hardwood floor for health reasons but found it quite expensive. As we shopped and searched the newspaper, we found a furniture factory that had odds and ends of maple in different sizes and lengths. We bought skids of this wonderful wood for $5.00–$10.00 per skid. That is about the price of one square foot. A skid, or pallet, is normally 40" by 48" and ours were stacked about 40" high with pieces of maple. We bought about a dozen skids for $105.00. We had to load it into our van and unload it when we were home by hand. When I was calculating the cost of our flooring, I discovered we spent more for the floor adhesive, stain, and polyurethane than we did for the wood. We ended up with about 2,600 square feet of beautiful hardwood flooring for a few hundred dollars and a lot of manpower.

The second blessing had to do with trim. All of the doors and windows in our house had no casement trim, nor was there any baseboard trim. Someone told us of a place that sold trim in six- to seven-foot lengths for $1.00. That is about 16¢ per foot. The going price for the same material new was at least 69¢ to 79¢ per foot. We backed our good old van into the lumberyard and loaded hundreds of sticks for a fraction of the price. We had to do some piecing, but we received significant savings, and the different shapes and thicknesses of the trim added character to our home.

CONCRETE AND STONE

As of November, 2018 the price for a cubic yard of concrete where I live is $100.00. A cubic yard is 1 y × 1 yd × 1 yd, or 3 ft × 3 ft × 3 ft, so there are 27 cubic feet in one cubic yard, as you can see in figure 1. When talking with someone in this field, you will not hear them say "cubic yards." Instead they will say "yards," even though they are referring to cubic yards. A tri-axle truck typically holds 11 yards of concrete, or 11 cubic yards, or 11 yd^3.

If you want to pour a foundation using one yard of concrete and make it one foot deep, you will have a surface of 27 square feet, as shown in figure 2.

If you want it six inches (one half foot) deep, you still have 27 cubic feet, but now you have 54 square feet on the surface. See figure 3.

Figure 1

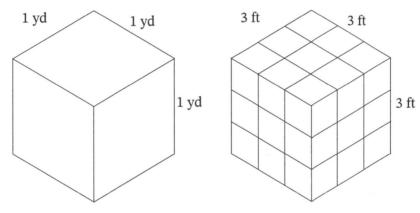

Figure 2

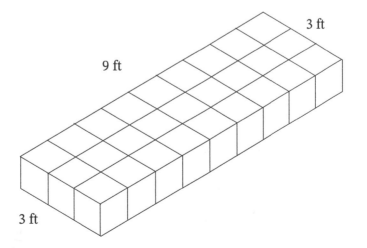

Figure 3

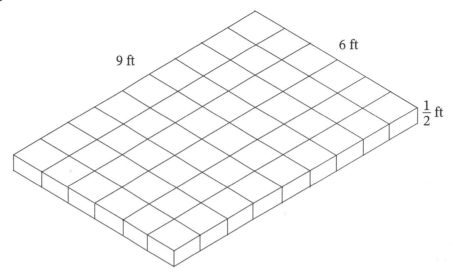

A yard of wet concrete mix weighs about 3,750 pounds. If the yard of concrete mix is dry, with just the cement, sand, and stone, it weighs 3,500 pounds. A standard concrete mix uses 500 pounds (500#) of cement, 1,200 pounds of sand, and 1,800 pounds of crushed stone or gravel. Gravel and sand both weigh about 100 pounds per cubic foot. Therefore, a ton is about 20 cubic feet of sand and gravel mix. (20 cubic feet times 100 pounds equals 2000 pounds or one ton.)

Concrete Mix

When you call to order the concrete mix, you will be asked to specify a number for the type of concrete you need. This number measures pounds per square foot, or the amount of weight the concrete will bear. The higher the number the more cement you get in the mix, which increase the weight capacity and makes it more durable. The increased amount of concrete also makes the price higher. The numbers in our table go from 3,000 to 5,000 in increments of 500. A grade of 3,000 is strong enough for sidewalks and patios, but 3,500 is recommended for driveways and garage floors. Here is a table with the grades and their prices per yard.

Grade	Price per Yard
3,000	$95
3,500	$100
4,000	$105
4,500	$110
5,000	$116

Gravel

I called a company that delivers gravel to job sites to ask questions about weight and volume. I learned that they use a ratio for figuring this relationship. The ratio they use is 1.4 tons per cubic yard. (Note that this is slightly more than the 100 lbs/ft³ we used on the previous page for the gravel used in concrete.) With this information, I was able to estimate the reverse ratio, or yards per ton, simply by applying what we know about fractions and unit multipliers from Algebra 1. There are 1.4 tons per one cubic yard, and one cubic yard per 1.4 tons, since both ratios are equal to one. To change yards to tons use the first ratio, and conversely, to change tons to yards, use the second ratio.

$$\frac{1.4 \text{ tons}}{1 \text{ yd}^3} = \frac{1 \text{ yd}^3}{1.4 \text{ tons}} = 1$$

Example 1

Change 21 tons to yards.

$$\frac{21 \text{ tons}}{1} \times \frac{1 \text{ yd}^3}{1.4 \text{ tons}} = 15 \text{ yd}^3$$

A truck designed for transporting heavy weights can carry 11 yards of concrete. If one cubic yard weighs 3,750 pounds, then 11 yards will top the scales at 41,250 pounds. With this information, consider the next example.

Example 2

How many truckloads are needed to carry 35 yards of gravel to a job site?

$$\frac{35 \text{ yd}^3}{1} \times \frac{1.4 \text{ tons}}{1 \text{ yd}^3} = 49 \text{ tons}$$

Since one ton equals 2,000 pounds, 49 tons is 49 times 2,000 pounds per ton, or 98,000 pounds. 98,000 ÷ 41,250 pounds per truck equals 2.38 trucks. To carry 98,000 pounds, we will need two full truck loads and one more truck carrying a partial load. The answer is three truckloads.

Water

In our former home we were blessed to have an in-ground pool. Each spring I would call a water delivery service to fill up our pool. The name of the company was Jacob's Well. It was not named after the biblical Jacob, but after the owner, Jacob Glick. Jacob's Well had trucks with the capacity to carry either 4,000 gallons or 6,500 gallons of water. There is a saying that "a pint is a pound the world around." Since there are 8 pints in a gallon, we expect a gallon of water to weigh 8 pounds. That is close, but the actual weight is about 8.35 pounds. There are 7.48 gallons of liquid in a cubic foot. Now we can figure out how much a cubic foot of water weighs.

7.48 gallons times 8.35 pounds per gallon equals = 62.458, or by rounding up, 62.5 pounds.

Example 3

How many cubic feet of water are in a 4,000 gallon truck?

$$\frac{4,000 \text{ gal}}{1} \times \frac{1 \text{ ft}^3}{7.48 \text{ gal}} = 534.76 \text{ ft}^3$$

Example 4

How many gallons of water will my tub hold if it is 4 ft long by 2 ft wide by 9 in deep?

(9 inches is $\frac{3}{4}$ of a foot or 0.75 ft)

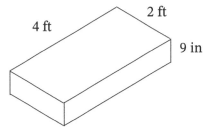

$4 \text{ ft} \times 2 \text{ ft} \times 0.75 \text{ ft} = 6 \text{ ft}^3$

$$\frac{6 \text{ ft}^3}{1} \times \frac{7.48 \text{ gal}}{1 \text{ ft}^3} = 44.88 \text{ gal}$$

Example 5

How much will the water weigh?

$$\frac{44.88 \text{ gal}}{1} \times \frac{8.35 \text{ lbs}}{1 \text{ gal}} = 374.5 \text{ lb}$$

PLUMBING AND ELECTRICAL

In plumbing, when you are moving liquid, the size of the pipe determines how much liquid can move through it. And even though you may think this is a volume issue, it is really the area of the circle, or the cross-section of the pipe, that determines the flow.

In the first example we are comparing the areas of two circles, one with a diameter of two inches and the other with a diameter of three inches. The formula for the area of a circle is πr^2.

Example 1

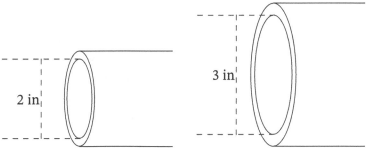

$$A_2 = \pi r^2 \approx (3.14)(1 \text{ in})^2 = 3.14 \text{ in}^2$$
$$A_3 = \pi r^2 \approx (3.14)(1.5 \text{ in})^2 \approx 7.07 \text{ in}^2$$

Notice that even though three inches is only 50% larger than two inches, the area of the three-inch diameter circle is almost double the area of the two-inch diameter circle. This is because we are squaring the radius before multiplying by pi, which is represented by π and has a value of approximately 3.14.

I recently made a trip to our local hardware store to confirm that with a two-inch pipe, the two inches is the measure of the opening. It is not the external measure of the pipe, but the internal measure of the opening.

In heating and air conditioning, the area of the cross-section of the duct—which could be a circle, oval, or rectangle—also determines the flow. My brother is an HVAC technician. The initials HVAC stand for Heating, Ventilation, and Air Conditioning He would sometimes call me from a job to ask how much more air could go through different size ducts. In the next example, we will compare the area of a six-inch air duct with an eight-inch air duct. In the six-inch duct the radius is three inches or half of the diameter. In the second duct the diameter is eight inches, so the radius is four inches. We may be tempted to think there is not much difference in the area but watch the math!

Example 2

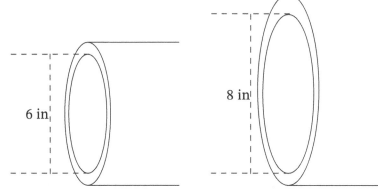

$A_6 = \pi r^2 \approx (3.14)(3 \text{ in})^2 = 28.26 \text{ in}^2$
$A_8 = \pi r^2 \approx (3.14)(4 \text{ in})^2 \approx 50.24 \text{ in}^2$

Using a pipe just 33%, or $\frac{1}{3}$ larger, yields an air flow that is 78% greater. Don't trust your eyes; use what you know about finding area to see that this is true.

Electricity

Electricity is both a source of energy and a convenience. Many Americans heat their homes with electricity (instead of oil or gas) and have come to rely on these little electrons moving through wires for everything from lights to computers and even cars. In this section we will be studying a formula for the basic electricity used in your home and learn how to make sense of an electric bill.

A very useful formula I use for understanding electricity is $V \times A = W$. Volts (V) is the electric potential, amperes (A) is the electric current, and watts (W) is the power. Amperes or amps measure how fast the current of little electrons is moving, volts represent how much push there is behind those little electrons, and the resultant power is measured in watts.

(The standard formula used to represent this relationship is $P = VI$, where P stands for power, I stands for current, and V stands for potential. I prefer to represent the power with W since watts are the unit used to measure power and I prefer to represent the current with A since amperes are the unit we use to measure current. I also changed the order to put power on the right side instead of the left.)

A home in the U.S. generally has 120 volts moving along the wires to the outlets, appliances, and light fixtures. The number on the top of your light bulbs is the number of watts. The larger the number, the more watts and the brighter the light. In our home we use mostly 60 watt bulbs and occasionally 40 watt and 75 watt bulbs. Twenty-five watt bulbs are used for decorative fixtures. One hundred watt lights are used in our basement fixtures. Here is a one-sentence simplified description of the three components: amps, watts, and volts. Amount of electricity (amps) pushed by the pressure (volts) yields the power usage or quantity (watts). For a 100 watt light bulb, you would use $0.8\overline{3}$ amps since the voltage is a constant 120. See the equation in example 3.

Example 3

$$V \times A = W$$

$$120 \text{ V} \times A = 100 \text{ W}$$

$$A = \frac{100 \text{ W}}{110 \text{ V}}$$

$$A = 0.8\overline{3} \text{ A}$$

To check if this is the correct solution, we can substitute $0.8\overline{3}$ A into the original equation.

$$V \times A = W$$

$$120 \text{ V} \times 0.8\overline{3} \text{ A} = 100 \text{ W which works}$$

Home Service

Most homes in my part of the U.S. are set up with what is called a 100-amp service. Older homes may have a 60-amp service. We certainly use more electricity today than 50 years ago. This also varies by where you live, since homes in the southern US use more electricity for air conditioning.

If you are an electrician and are planning the circuits in a home to run from a breaker box, you will need to add up the watts and find out how many amps are needed. Most appliances will have this information on a panel somewhere. If there is too much current running through a line, it could overheat and potentially cause a fire. When the line is overloaded, the breaker box "breaks," and then you know you have a problem. Another factor to consider is that appliances use much more electricity when they start up than while they are running. Therefore it is a good idea during a black-out or a brown-out (power failure), to turn off major appliances and then turn them on one at a time, so they do not turn on simultaneously and overload your circuits.

In your service panel, where the electricity enters your home from the power company, you will see several breaker boxes. Some will say 15, others 20, and a few 30. These numbers are measured in amps. The big ones, 30 for example, are for appliances that use large amounts of electricity, such as an electric range, an electric dryer, or a heat pump/air conditioning unit. The smaller 15-amp breakers are for regular usage around the home and are connected to the many outlets in your walls.

A 15-amp breaker has a maximum capacity of 1,800 watts.
$$V \times A = W$$
$$120 \text{ V} \times 15 \text{ A} = 1,800 \text{ W}$$
A 30-amp breaker has a maximum capacity of 3,600 watts.
$$V \times A = W$$
$$120 \text{ V} \times 30 \text{ A} = 3,600 \text{ W}$$

Safe Capacity

To be safe, we do not want to overload a 15-amp breaker before it flips or breaks the breaker, so we want to determine what a safe capacity is. The rule of thumb is to take 80% of the maximum capacity (or 20% less than 100%) to determine the safe capacity. See example 4.

Example 4

$$A_{max} \times 80\% = A_{safe}$$
$$15 \text{ A} \times 80\% = A_{safe}$$
$$12 \text{ A} = A_{safe}$$

Using 12 amps as our starting point, for safety concerns, and recognizing that most of our home uses 120 volts, the number of watts on this circuit would be 1,440. See example 5.

Example 5

$$V \times A = W$$
$$120 \text{ V} \times 12 \text{ A} = W_{safe}$$
$$1,440 \text{ W} = W_{safe}$$

Using what we have learned, would a 15-amp circuit be safe enough to provide electricity to a refrigerator which draws 500 watts, a toaster that uses 1,050 watts, and a microwave that draws 800 watts? If all three of these appliances are plugged in and operating, how much current would be flowing through our 15-amp breaker? 15 amps is the maximum capacity, but the safe capacity is 12 amps. Twelve amps allow for 1,440 watts. See example 6 for our calculations.

Example 6

Refrigerator	500 W
Toaster	1,050 W
Microwave	800 W
Total	2,350 W

Since 2,350 W is greater than 1,440 W, it would be unsafe to run all these appliances on a 15-amp circuit. The electrician will have to put one of these appliances on another circuit. Many building codes will require a separate circuit for the refrigerator. A lot of math is used in the electrical field. Hopefully this study will whet your appetite for more. Interview an electrician yourself and see if he can show you more applications of math!

My Electric Bill

The following chart is a copy of a recent electric bill. The two main numbers and symbols you will see as you read it are cents and kWh. Cents are given in large decimal numbers. The abbreviation "kWh" stands for one kilowatt hour. Kilo means 1,000, so a kilowatt hour represents 1,000 watts per hour. Think of the electricity required to power ten 100 W light bulbs for one hour.

Charges for PPL Electric Utilities

Residential Rate	
Distribution charge:	8.00
Customer Charge:	
200 kWh at 2.193¢ per kWh	4.39
600 kWh at 1.984¢ per kWh	11.90
518 kWh at 1.862¢ per kWh	9.65
PA Tax Adj. Surcharge at 0.088%	.03
Transmission Charge:	
1,318 kWh at 0.564¢ per kWh	7.43
Transition Charge:	
200 kWh at 1.329¢ per kWh	2.66
600 kWh at 1.178¢ per kWh	7.07
518 kWh at 1.088¢ per kWh	5.64
PA Tax Adj. Surcharge at 0.064%	.01
Generation Charge:	
200 kWh at 5.182¢ per kWh	10.36
600 kWh at 4.554¢ per kWh	27.32
518 kWh at 4.178¢ per kWh	21.64
PA Tax Adj. Surcharge at 0.088%	.05
Total PPL Electric Utilities Charges	116.15

Notice the breakdown of the charges. The first 200 kWh are computed at the highest rate (2.193¢/kWh), then 600 kWh are a little lower (1.984¢/kWh), and the 518 kWh are the lowest rate (1.862¢/kWh). There is a flat monthly distribution charge for your electrical service. The distribution charge and the customer charge pay for billing costs, reading the meter, equipment, and maintenance. The customer charge is tied to your usage amount. The transmission charge is what you pay to get the electricity to your electric provider from the company generating the power. The transition fee (which may eventually disappear) is the charge to recover your utility company's investment in power sources. The generation expense is for the production of electricity and is the most expensive charge on your bill.

To find the price paid for each kWh, add up the total kWh, in this case 1,318, and divide it into the total charges, which are $116.15.

$116.15 ÷ 1,318 kWh = $0.088/kWh or 8.8¢/kWh

This is the average price per kWh for the month. 8.8¢ is almost nine cents per hour. If you have ten 100 watt light bulbs turned on for one hour, then each one is using one kWh. The electricity to power each of these 10 bulbs costs about nine cents.

LUMBER, INSULATION, AND COMMON METRIC MEASURE

Lumber

When you purchase lumber for a construction project, you will find that the name or size of the piece does not match the actual dimensions. One of the most popular pieces of wood used in building is the 2 × 4 (called a two by four). You would think it would be 2 in × 4 in but it is really $1\frac{1}{2}$ in × $3\frac{1}{2}$ in. When it was first cut at the lumber mill it measured 2 in × 4 in, but after planing and finishing on all four sides, it arrived at a finished dimension of $1\frac{1}{2}$ in × $3\frac{1}{2}$ in. Think of taking $\frac{1}{4}$ in off of all four sides to smooth out the rough saw marks.

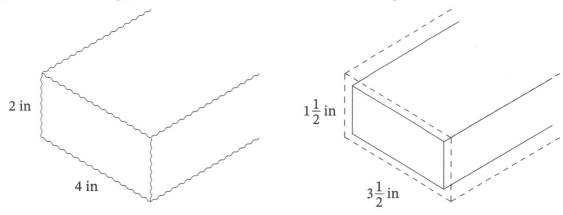

Similarly, a 1 × 4 (one by four) turns out to be $\frac{3}{4}$ in × $3\frac{1}{2}$ in.

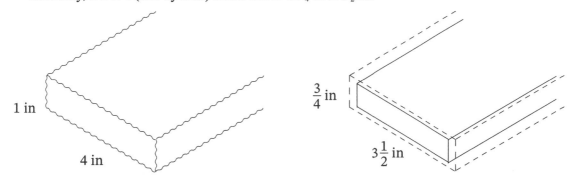

Another popular size is a "four by four," which begins as 4 in × 4 in when it is cut and becomes
$3\frac{1}{2}$ in × $3\frac{1}{2}$ in after it has been planed and smoothed out.

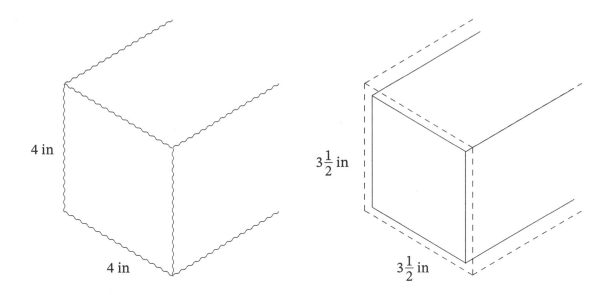

A "two by six" (2 × 6) is actually $1\frac{1}{2}$ in × $5\frac{1}{2}$ in. Look through the chart for other popular sizes and their actual dimensions.

Name of Size	Real Dimensions
1 × 4	$\frac{3}{4}$ in × $3\frac{1}{2}$ in
1 × 6	$\frac{3}{4}$ in × $5\frac{1}{2}$ in
2 × 4	$1\frac{1}{2}$ in × $3\frac{1}{2}$ in
2 × 6	$1\frac{1}{2}$ in × $5\frac{1}{2}$ in
2 × 8	$1\frac{1}{2}$ in × $7\frac{1}{4}$ in
2 × 10	$1\frac{1}{2}$ in × $9\frac{1}{4}$ in
4 × 4	$3\frac{1}{2}$ in × $3\frac{1}{2}$ in
6 × 6	$5\frac{1}{2}$ in × $5\frac{1}{2}$ in

Example 1

How high is a stack of five 1 × 4s if they are all lying flat?

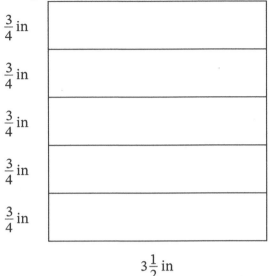

$\frac{3}{4}$ in

$\frac{3}{4}$ in

$\frac{3}{4}$ in

$\frac{3}{4}$ in

$\frac{3}{4}$ in

$3\frac{1}{2}$ in

Solution 1

The height is $5 \times \frac{3}{4}$ in $= \frac{15}{4}$ in $= 3\frac{3}{4}$ in

Example 2

How long are one 1 × 4, one 4 × 4, and one 2 × 6, when they are lying side by side?

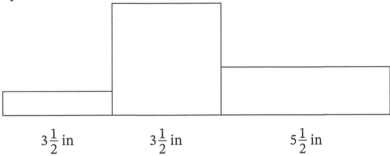

$3\frac{1}{2}$ in $3\frac{1}{2}$ in $5\frac{1}{2}$ in

Solution 2

The length is $3\frac{1}{2}$ in $+ 3\frac{1}{2}$ in $+ 5\frac{1}{2}$ in $= 12\frac{1}{2}$ in

You will also find man-made building materials that are called by the same sizes or names as wood products. I like to use vinyl for fencing since I don't have to paint it. It is close in price to wood and a lot easier to maintain. A vinyl piece that measures $\frac{3}{4}$ inch × $3\frac{1}{2}$ inches is still called a 1 × 4, and if it is $3\frac{1}{2}$ inches × $3\frac{1}{2}$ inches it is called a 4 × 4. The same is true of pressed board materials used in construction that are composed of man-made substances or wood chips.

Insulation

Another set of numbers you encounter in most building or remodeling projects is R-value. This is a measure of the effectiveness of your insulation. According to the Department of Energy, 50%–70% of the energy used in the average American home goes to heating and cooling. Twenty percent is used for heating water, and 10%–30% is used for appliances, lighting, computers, and everything else. R-value stands for thermal resistance, or the resistance to heat flow. The higher the R-value, the greater the effectiveness of the insulation. When you buy insulation you will see this number on the packaging. If your attic has a blown-in substance that gives you an R-value of 27, but you want more R-value, you can either blow in some more or lay fiberglass sections on top of the existing material. If the fiberglass gives you R-13, then you add the values to get an overall R-40 for your attic.

There are several different materials and options for insulation. The most common is fiberglass, which is usually pink and has been advertised by the Pink Panther. You will also find yellow fiberglass insulation. It comes in flat pieces (called batts) or in long rolls. Since the opening between the lumber is generally $14\frac{1}{2}$ inches, the rolls and batts come pre-cut to 15" wide so they will make a tight fit when you push them between the studs in your walls, between the ceiling rafters, or between the floor joists. The advantages of fiberglass are that it does not absorb moisture and is noncombustible. A $9\frac{1}{4}$ inch thick piece has an R-value of 34, or 3.7 per inch. See the chart for other values and thicknesses. The R-values are rounded to whole numbers.

Another popular insulation material which we have used in our home is cellulose. This is ground up recycled newspaper coated with chemicals to prevent a fire hazard. It is blown in with a machine and usually needs a professional to install. It can be wet (walls) or dry (attics) when first installed and fills up the cavity between the boards. The R-value is similar to fiberglass. Since it is blown in there are very few open spaces, which is a plus. Since fiberglass and cellulose are so close in R-values, I am going to estimate they are the same and have one table for both substances.

Fiberglass and Cellulose

Thickness	R-Value
$3\frac{1}{2}$ in	R-13
$5\frac{1}{2}$ in	R-20
$7\frac{1}{4}$ in	R-27
$9\frac{1}{4}$ in	R-34

Another amazing kind of insulation is polyurethane foam, which I have had put in my warehouse. It dries almost instantly and is pretty hard when it does. There are no air pockets, since it fills up all of the space as it expands when it dries and hardens. One inch of this material gives an R-value of 9 when it is installed and 7 after 20 years. I chose R-8 as the average to compute the values for our chart.

Polyurethane Foam

Thickness	R-Value
$3\frac{1}{2}$ in	R-28
$5\frac{1}{2}$ in	R-44
$7\frac{1}{4}$ in	R-58
$9\frac{1}{4}$ in	R-74

Example 3

The ceiling had no insulation and the rafters were 2 × 10s. If $9\frac{1}{4}$ in fiberglass batts were laid in the cavity, what is the R-value?

Solution 3

One 2 × 10 is $9\frac{1}{4}$ in thick.

$9\frac{1}{4}$ in fiberglass is R-34.

Example 4

At the construction site $\frac{3}{4}$ of an inch of polyurethane foam was sprayed first, and the rest of the 2 × 6 wall was filled with cellulose. What is the R-value of the walls?

Solution 4

$\frac{3}{4}$ times 8 equals R-6 for the foam

2 × 6 is $5\frac{1}{2}$ in thick, minus $\frac{3}{4}$ in (foam) equals $4\frac{3}{4}$ in

$4\frac{3}{4}$ in times 3.7 for cellulose equals R-17.6

R-6 plus R-17.6 equals R-23.6

Meters and Liters

Some of the metric measures I use the most are centimeters (cm), meters (m), kilometers (km), and liters (l). Accurate measures are shown in the first table while rough approximations that I find easier to remember are shown in the second table. In this unit I am not focused on being accurate as much as I am interested in conveying some short cuts which have helped me in remembering and using these measures.

Exact equivalents

Metric	US Customary
2.54 centimeters	1 inch
30.48 centimeters	1 foot
0.9144 meters	1 yard
1.609344 kilometers	1 mile
0.946352946 liters	1 quart (US liquid quart)

(You really only need the first one since all the rest can be derived from inches or centimeters)

Approximate equivalents

Metric	US Customary
1 cm	0.4 in
2.5 cm	1 in
1 m	39 in or 3.3 ft or 1.1 yd
1 km	0.62 mi
1.6 km	1 mi
1 liter	1.1 qt
0.95 liter	1 qt

Using the tables we can identify the following unit multipliers.

Exact

$$\frac{2.54 \text{ cm}}{1 \text{ in}} \qquad \frac{1.6109344 \text{ km}}{1 \text{ mi}} \qquad \frac{0.946352946 \text{ l}}{1 \text{ qt}}$$

Approximate

$$\frac{0.4 \text{ in}}{1 \text{ cm}} \qquad \frac{0.62 \text{ mi}}{1 \text{ km}} \qquad \frac{1.1 \text{ qt}}{1 \text{ l}}$$

$$\frac{3.3 \text{ ft}}{1 \text{ m}} \qquad \frac{39 \text{ in}}{1 \text{ m}} \qquad \frac{1.1 \text{ yd}}{1 \text{ m}}$$

$$\frac{1.6 \text{ km}}{1 \text{ mi}} \qquad \frac{0.95 \text{ l}}{1 \text{ qt}}$$

Example 5

30 feet is how many meters? Round to tenths.

$$\frac{30 \text{ ft}}{1} \times \frac{1 \text{ m}}{3.3 \text{ ft}} = 9.1 \text{ m}$$

or

$$\frac{30 \text{ ft}}{1} \times \frac{12 \text{ in}}{1 \text{ ft}} \times \frac{2.54 \text{ cm}}{1 \text{ in}} \times \frac{1 \text{ cm}}{100 \text{ m}} = 9.1 \text{ m}$$

Example 6

15 centimeters is how many inches?

$$\frac{15 \text{ cm}}{1} \times \frac{0.4 \text{ in}}{1 \text{ cm}} = 6.0 \text{ in}$$

or

$$\frac{15 \text{ cm}}{1} \times \frac{1 \text{ in}}{2.54 \text{ cm}} = 5.9 \text{ in}$$

Example 7

A "5k" or 5 kilometer race is how many miles?

$$\frac{5 \text{ km}}{1} \times \frac{0.62 \text{ mi}}{1 \text{ km}} = 3.1 \text{ mi}$$

or

$$\frac{5 \text{ km}}{1} \times \frac{1{,}000 \text{ m}}{1 \text{ km}} \times \frac{100 \text{ cm}}{1 \text{ m}} \times \frac{1 \text{ in}}{2.54 \text{ cm}} \times \frac{1 \text{ ft}}{12 \text{ in}} \times \frac{1 \text{ mi}}{5{,}280 \text{ ft}} = 3.1 \text{ mi}$$

Example 8

A 26.2 mile marathon is how many kilometers?

$$\frac{26.2 \text{ mi}}{1} \times \frac{1.6 \text{ km}}{1 \text{ mi}} = 41.9 \text{ km}$$

or

$$\frac{26.2 \text{ mi}}{1} \times \frac{1.6109344 \text{ km}}{1 \text{ mi}} = 42.2 \text{ km}$$

Example 9

Two gallons is how many liters? Estimate first.

I am going to treat this like a two-step problem. You may be able to do the first step in your head, but if not here are both solutions. The first step is to change gallons to quarts. There are 4 quarts in a gallon and 8 quarts in 2 gallons. Then change quarts to liters. Since liters are larger than quarts, there will be fewer liters per gallon than quarts per gallon, and the answer should be less than 8.

$$\frac{2 \text{ gal}}{1} \times \frac{4 \text{ qt}}{1 \text{ gal}} = 8 \text{ qt}$$

$$\frac{8 \text{ qt}}{1} \times \frac{0.95 \text{ L}}{1 \text{ qt}} = 7.6 \text{ L}$$

Humble Pie, Tips for Eating Out, Making Change, Travel Conversions

Humble Pie

A tried and proven way to save money is to not buy new. There are certain things that you will want to purchase brand spanking new, like shoes and underwear, but if you can eat a little humble pie and buy used, you will find some great buys. Here are some suggestions, after you pray. Remember, a man's life consists not in the abundance of the things which he possesses (Luke 12:15).

Garage sales, yard sales, and estate sales are wonderful places to find used items. When our children were younger, we would be praying for a bicycle or cowboy boots, and then we would see a sign or an ad for a garage sale. More often than not, we would find just what we were looking for at a very affordable price. It was so remarkable that I had to remind our kids that our faith was in God and not in yard sales, but God did use them a lot in our experience. We also found it to be helpful, if we had some time and could plan ahead, to shop at yard sales in upscale neighborhoods. For us this meant an hour drive or more, but it was worth the effort. We observed that there are two types of people that hold sales: those who are trying to make money from their junk, and those who are trying to clean out their houses and are happy to make a few bucks in the process. We found more of the latter in the nice suburbs. They would sell nice name-brand stuff at a fraction of the price. When you go to a yard sale, don't be afraid to dicker a little. Make an offer; the worst that can happen is that they say no.

We also found a lot of our larger items such as appliances and furniture in the classified section of the paper and in the Penny Saver or Advertiser in our area. Many people want to upgrade and will sell their used items that have plenty of life left in them for a bargain. We did this for years and found that we saved thousands of dollars in the process. We were blessed to see God guide our steps, and we enjoyed the adventure.

Don't overlook the many thrift, new-to-you, or consignment stores, and established stores such as Goodwill. These have regular hours and also carry nice things. Marketplace on Facebook and Craigslist are accessible online and are other good places to find used items.

Tips for eating Out

As you may have figured out, we lived on a pretty tight budget for many years while raising four boys. During that time, we made many long car trips attending church functions, visiting relatives, and going on vacations. For a while we made sandwiches, put them in the cooler, and ate in the car. Finally I decided that didn't make for much of a trip, especially for my wife, so we began eating out. Here are some tips we found that made it possible for us to afford it.

1. Drink water, not soft drinks. I haven't seen the profit sheets of a restaurant, but I am willing to bet that most of their profit is in the drinks they offer. Carbonated drinks cost pennies, yet they are sold for upwards of a dollar and are half ice. (Recently, I spoke to a lady who used to work in a nice, well-established local restaurant. She was told that they made 25 cents on the entrees and the rest of the profit came from drinks and desserts.)

2. If you do get lemonade or a soda, request no ice.

3. Forego dessert, which is an expensive item with little or no nutrition. If you must have one, share a large one among your family. Desserts are pricey!

4. An obvious tip is to buy items on sale. Many times we would walk into an Arby's and get 10 regulars and six waters. They used to run a special of five regular sandwiches for $5.55. Our family of six ate for $11.10. That is hard to beat even if you make your own food.

5. I think the best deal for a large family today is Boston Market. It is a cross between a restaurant and a fast food joint. You order your food, sit down, and eat it right there. The food is excellent: they have chicken, turkey, and meat loaf. You can choose from a wide variety of vegetables. It will feed the lot of you, and you won't pay more than $25.00—less if they are having specials. If you go to a McDonald's and each of you orders a combo meal for around $4.50, you will spend more money for burgers, carbonated drinks, and deep-fried cholesterol sticks. Another big savings in each of these choices is not having to pay tips.

6. For those special times when you do get to eat at a nice place, remember points one through three. When you are figuring your costs, add at least another 20% to the cost of what you order because tips are 15% to 20%. Then you have to add food tax, which can be from 4% to 8%, depending on where you are eating. If there are six of you and each of your meals is $12.99, your final bill is six times $12.99 or $77.94, plus 5% tax which equals $3.90, plus a 16% tip equaling $12.47, for a total of $94.31. That total is assuming you are all drinking water. If you add drinks at $2.49 each and a dessert at $6.99 apiece, then you will be adding $56.88 for a new total of $134.82 for food, plus $6.74 for tax and $21.57 for the tip, for a grand total of $163.13. There is quite a difference between $163.13 and $94.31. If you eat frugally, you can dine at a restaurant two times at $94.31 for almost the same price as dining once when you choose to order drinks and desserts.

	Frugal	Splurge
6 Waters @ $0.00	$0.00	$0.00
6 Entrees @ $12.99	$77.94	$77.94
6 Drinks @ $2.49	$0.00	$14.94
6 Desserts @ $6.99	$0.00	$41.94
Subtotal	$77.94	$134.82
5% Tax	$3.90	$6.74
16% Tip	$12.47	$21.57
Total Bill	$94.31	$163.13

Making Change

Recently, I visited our local farmers' market. A hundred years ago there were seven in our town, but now there is only one, which is open three days per week. When you go there you will notice the absence of computers and even cash registers in many of the booths. When you sell an item from a stand with no electronic machinery, you should to be able to "make change." In talking with a few different enterprises there, I found this skill is becoming a lost art. If you ever get a job and have to make change, you should know how to do so. By the way, I was in a Wendy's one day for lunch when there was a power failure. No one at the front counter knew how to figure change without the aid of a machine. Finally, they located a girl in the back who was peeling potatoes and she came to their rescue. It is a useful thing to be able to add and subtract without the aid of a cash register or calculator, and then make change.

Example 1

Let's playact. You are a worker at Shenk's Poultry when someone buys an assortment of chicken that comes to $3.27. They give you a 10-dollar bill. What do you do?

You could subtract $3.27 from $10.00 and get $6.73 and give them back their change. Or you could count it back to them by saying, "Three twenty-seven, three thirty, three fifty, four, five, and five is ten." What you are doing is starting with the amount they purchased and adding up to $10.00 in increments of coins and dollars.

Start with "three twenty-seven."

Place three pennies in their hand and say "three thirty."

Place two dimes in their hand and say "three fifty."

Place two quarters in their hand and say "four."

Place a one-dollar bill in their hand and say "five."

Place a five-dollar bill in their hand and say "and five is ten."

Example 2

This time the amount of the sale is $1.83, and it is paid with a five-dollar bill.

$5.00 − $1.83 = $3.17.

Start with "one eighty-three."

Give two pennies and say "one eighty-five."

Give one nickel and say "one ninety."

Give one dime and say "two" or "two dollars."

Give three one-dollar bills and say "three, four, and five."

You begin with $1.83 and add up to $5.00 in increments of coins and bills.

Example 3

The next customer checking out owes $14.08 and pays with a 20-dollar bill.

$20.00 minus $14.08 equals $5.92.

Start with "fourteen oh eight."

Give two pennies and say "fourteen ten."

Give one nickel and say "fourteen fifteen."

Give one dime and say "fourteen twenty-five."

Give three quarters and say "fifteen."

Give a five-dollar bill and say "and five is twenty."

You begin with $14.08 and add up to $20.00 in increments of coins and bills.

Temperature Conversions

If you visit Canada or another country that uses Celsius, you might be interested to know the temperature and notice it is 20°. To convert, you first have to decide between accuracy and speed. The specific formula for converting Celsius or Centigrade to Fahrenheit is for every 5°C, there is a corresponding 9°F plus 32°. In our example, we divide 20° by 5, which is 4°, multiply that by 9 to get 36°, then add 32° for 68°F.

The quick estimate method is to double 20°C and add 30° to find the approximate value in Fahrenheit. So 20° × 2 = 40° and 40° + 30° = 70°F, which is pretty close to 68°.

Accurate

$$t_c \times \frac{9}{5} + 32° = t_F$$

$$20° \times \frac{9}{5} + 32° = t_F$$

$$\frac{180°}{5} + 32° = t_F$$

$$36° + 32° = t_F$$

$$68° = t_F$$

Quick

$$t_c \times 2 + 30° = t_F$$
$$20° \times 2 + 30° = t_F$$
$$40° + 30° = t_F$$
$$70° = t_F$$

To see how we reached this answer, consider the formula. The fraction $\frac{9}{5}$ is 1.8, which is almost 2, and 30 is a little less than 32. The little bit you are over in multiplying by 2 instead by 1.8, you compensate for by adding 30, which is a little less than 32.

Distance Conversions

In the country we are visiting, we rent a car and are driving down the road when we see a sign informing us that the local speed limit is 100 kph. How fast is this in mph, or miles per hour?

A helpful ratio you can use to estimate how many kilometers are equal to how many to miles is 8 kilometers to 5 miles. Eight kilometers is very close to five miles although the two aren't exactly equal. An easy way to remember this is to look on your car's speedometer. Find where it reads 50 mph, and you'll see an 80 km/h almost exactly above or below it.

Using this same ratio we can divide both 80 and 50 by 10 to arrive at $\frac{8 \, km}{5 \, mi}$. Then we could change the fraction $\frac{8}{5}$ to 1.6. We have discovered that $\frac{8 \, km}{5 \, mi} = 1.6 \, \frac{km}{mi}$. This is an approximation, since the actual ratio of kilometers to miles is 1.609344 $\frac{km}{mi}$. You could also memorize the ratio 1.61 $\frac{km}{hr}$ to make the calculations a little more accurate.

Since unit multipliers are equal to one, or a unit, we can flip them and still have the same value. For miles to kilometers the ratio becomes $\frac{5 \, mi}{8 \, km}$. This fraction reduces to 0.625 miles per kilometer, which is an approximation, as the exact decimal equivalent is 1 kilometer per 0.62137119223733396961743418436331822158593 81 miles. Since that rounds to 0.62, we can use 0.62 as another approximation that is easily memorized. I am trying to give you a quick way, which is fairly accurate, to change miles and miles per hour to kilometers and kilometers per hour, and although 50 mi is actually a little bit more than 80 km, I think using that as our start point makes it easier if you can't find the actual ratio but can see a speedometer.

The following examples can give you an idea how convenient this estimation methods is. As you will see, there is a trade-off between speed and accuracy that applies whenever you use approximate ratios to do a conversion, and the size of the error increases when we are dealing with larger numbers.

Example 4

Use the approximate ratio of $\frac{50 \, mi}{80 \, km}$ to convert 100 kilometers per hour to miles per hour.

$$\frac{100 \, km}{1 \, hr} \times \frac{50 \, mi}{80 \, km} = \frac{62.5 \, mi}{1 \, hr}$$

Now use the approximate ratio of $\frac{0.62 \, mi}{1 \, km}$ to convert 100 kilometers per hour to miles per hour.

$$\frac{100 \, km}{1 \, hr} \times \frac{0.62 \, mi}{1 \, km} = \frac{62 \, mi}{1 \, hr}$$

Now use the approximate ratio of $\frac{1 \, mi}{1.61 \, km}$ to convert 100 kilometers per hour to mile per hour.

$$\frac{100 \, km}{1 \, hr} \times \frac{1 \, mi}{1.61 \, km} = \frac{62.1 \, mi}{1 \, hr}$$

These same approximate ratios can be used for distances on road signs as well. If the town you are heading for is 200 kilometers away, then multiplying it by 0.62 lets you recognize you are about 124 miles away. Using the ratio of 50 miles to 80 kilometers gives you a similar rough estimate of 125 miles. See example 5. The accurate answer is that you are about 124.27 miles from your destination. Depending on the situation, the convenience of a quick conversion may be more useful than getting the more precise result.

Example 5

$$\frac{200 \text{ km}}{1 \text{ hr}} \times \frac{50 \text{ mi}}{80 \text{ km}} = \frac{125 \text{ mi}}{1 \text{ hr}}$$

$$\frac{200 \text{ km}}{1 \text{ hr}} \times \frac{0.62 \text{ mi}}{1 \text{ km}} = \frac{124 \text{ mi}}{1 \text{ hr}}$$

$$\frac{200 \text{ km}}{1 \text{ hr}} \times \frac{1 \text{ mi}}{1.61 \text{ km}} = \frac{124.2 \text{ mi}}{1 \text{ hr}}$$

Example 6

Convert 60 miles per hour to kilometers per hour.

$$\frac{60 \text{ mi}}{1 \text{ hr}} \times \frac{80 \text{ km}}{50 \text{ mi}} = \frac{96 \text{ km}}{1 \text{ hr}}$$

$$\frac{60 \text{ mi}}{1 \text{ hr}} \times \frac{1 \text{ km}}{0.62 \text{ mi}} = \frac{96.8 \text{ km}}{1 \text{ hr}}$$

$$\frac{60 \text{ mi}}{1 \text{ hr}} \times \frac{1.61 \text{ km}}{1 \text{ mi}} = \frac{96.6 \text{ km}}{1 \text{ hr}}$$

I like to hold to a few pieces of essential information in my mind rather than being dependent on an electronic device or having to memorize multiple conversion formulas. Knowing the 5 to 8 ratio has helped me on numerous occasions. When I forget the decimal equivalents to this ratio, I can quickly figure them out, since I know that $\frac{5}{8}$ is 0.625 and $\frac{8}{5}$ is 1.6. I hope you find this information useful as well.

Eating and Drinking

"Whether you eat or drink, or whatever you do, do all to the glory of God." (1 Corinthians 10:31)

Diets

Nine years ago, a salesman visited me at work, and I hardly recognized him. I asked what he had done and he told me he lost fifty pounds under the guidance of a diet doctor. I went to the same doctor and also lost a bunch of weight, but all the weight I lost came back in a matter of months. I learned a few things in the process but was unable to continue with this program. For the next few years I continued to try and eat better in hopes of shedding some pounds, but I was not successful. I knew I needed to trim down but didn't know how. I thought I was pretty good about avoiding refined sugars and refined grains. I went to the gym a few times per week but wasn't losing any weight. I was listless and tired during the day and not sleeping well at night.

Then two years ago I made some drastic changes to the way I eat. I was convinced that if I did not lose weight, I would be in danger of becoming a diabetic. I also was concerned that I would not be healthy enough to care for my special needs son as I got older. I wish I could say my motivation to eat healthy was simply to glorify God in my body, but it was a combination of factors. Most of the information in this section is known and understood, but until we receive a wakeup call or reach critical mass, we rarely make lasting changes. I had my wakeup call in 2016 and was ready to hear about a solution that fall.

I was visiting one of my relatives, and I learned about a program which had helped them immensely. After researching (it wasn't cheap), I decided to sign up. I was mentally committed and just needed someone to show me what to do. Over the next few months I followed the protocol exactly as it was outlined and lost about 15% of my body weight. I am not going to mention the program I joined, but it was similar to plans which recommend you eat clean while avoiding foods which trigger inflammation. Under their guidance I eliminated refined sugars, refined grains, and dairy. I ate only protein, vegetables, and fruit. Since it worked so well for me, I decided to stick to this regimen even after the diet period was over. I have since added a homemade granola that I make with nuts and oats. I have maintained the weight loss for almost two years. I feel better, sleep better, my BMI numbers dropped five points, and now I am able to exercise at a local gym. When people notice my new look, they often ask what plan I am on, to which I respond, "The John the Baptist plan. He must increase, and I must decrease." :-)

Everyone of is unique. There is not one plan or one approach that fits everyone. And I do not pretend to be an expert on how to glorify God in our bodies by what we eat and drink, but I have learned a few general principles that I hope will encourage us and assist us in our individual journey.

Counting Calories

Our body needs energy to function. The amount of energy we consume in our food is measured in calories. The heat energy required to increase the temperature of one kilogram of water by one degree Celsius is called a food calorie. An average man needs about 2,500 calories per day and an average woman requires about 2,000 calories.

As we function throughout the day, we burn calories. As long as we are absorbing the same number of calories as we are burning, we will maintain our weight. That seems simple enough, but we regularly hear that the number of overweight adults in the U.S. is increasing. One way to determine who is overweight, and who is in the normal range, is by computing the BMI.

BMI

BMI stands for body-mass-index. BMI is a ratio that indicates how much fat is in adults over twenty years old. To compute your BMI, find your weight in kilograms and divide this number by your height in meters squared. I converted my 240 pounds to 109 kilograms and divided it by my height squared, which is 1.95 meters squared, or 3.8025. My BMI is 28.6. Two years ago, it was 33.7. I am now classified as overweight instead of obese according to the charts I consulted. These charts have four classifications: less than 18.5 is underweight, 18.5 - 25 is normal weight, 25 - 30 is overweight, and over 30 is obese. As of 2013 almost 3/4 of adult men in the US and 3/5 of adult women in the US were considered overweight.

You Are What You Eat

If you want to lose weight, many people simply say to lower your caloric intake. There is a common theory that goes like this: Since 3,500 calories equals about one pound of fat, if our goal is to lose a pound in seven days, then we need to consume 500 fewer calories per day than we are currently ingesting. I think this is oversimplified, since we are fearfully and wonderfully made. When we begin to eat less, our body takes note and releases less energy to compensate for the loss of calories coming in. Weight loss is a combination of diet and exercise. If you have seen any of the many weight loss products being advertised, they tout their product or service and then at the end say that this product must be accompanied by a healthy diet and regular exercise. You always need both components. In this lesson the goal is to learn to count calories and learn about eating. In a subsequent lesson we will consider exercise options.

Before we dive into the math, it needs to be restated that we are each different. There are many factors that contribute to weight loss and weight gain. One factor is the metabolism we have each inherited from our parents. Metabolism is the process by which your body transforms and converts food into energy. It also affects how quickly you burn fat. People with a high or fast metabolism can eat large amounts of calories and not gain weight, while those with a slow metabolism can look at a banana split and gain a pound! I am continually learning about food and calories, but I am also more cognizant of what my body needs and doesn't need. We each need to adapt this information and trust God to help us as we move forward.

Another helpful piece of information I learned is that inflammation can be a source of weight gain that has nothing to do with calories. When I was monitoring my weight closely by weighing myself each morning, I discovered that certain foods would trigger a one- or two-pound weight gain overnight. I had not eaten 7,000 calories the previous day, but the scale revealed this huge gain. If I eliminated the triggering food, in a day or two I was back to normal body weight. This is an example of one area that contributes to our body mass. Stress is another significant factor, as is the amount of water we drink each day.

A Typical American Diet

I did a little research and found a list of the most common foods consumed in the United States. I simplified the list and placed them in categories. Using this list, I can keep track of how many calories I consume in a day. There are some wonderful apps available to make this process easier. After a while you will know the numbers for the foods you eat on a regular basis. Most of us do not know how many calories we consume each day. If you are serious about your caloric count, keep a journal for a week or more of how often you eat, when you eat, what you eat, and how many calories you ingest each day.

Example of Counting Calories

Breakfast
Two scrambled eggs, three pieces of bacon, toast and butter, with a glass of orange juice.
2 Eggs: 180
Pork bacon: 150
Bread, 1 slice: 66
Butter, 1 tablespoon: 102
Orange juice, 8 ounces: 112
For breakfast: $180 + 150 + 66 + 102 + 112 = 610$ calories.

Lunch
Two hot dogs with ketchup and mustard, plus a cola and two ounces of potato chips.
Two hot dogs, $247 \times 2 = 494$
Cola, 12 ounces: 136
Ketchup, 1 tablespoon: 15
Mustard, yellow 1 tablespoon: 9
Potato chips, 1 ounces: $155 \times 2 = 310$
For lunch: $494 + 136 + 15 + 9 + 310 = 964$ calories.

Snack
An apple with peanut butter in the afternoon.
Apple: 72
Peanut butter, 1 tablespoon: 90
For the snack: $72 + 90 = 162$ calories.

Dinner
Two chicken breasts, carrots, corn, a cup of rice, a glass of milk, and ice

cream for dessert.

Chicken breasts: $142 \times 2 = 284$

Carrots: 52

Corn: 180

Rice, 1 cup: 205

Milk, 8 ounces: 122

Ice cream, 4 ounces: 145

For dinner: $284 + 52 + 180 + 205 + 122 + 145 = 988$ calories.

The number of calories for the day: $610 + 964 + 162 + 988 = 2,724$

Fruit (medium size)

Apple: 72

Banana: 105

Grains

Bread, 1 slice: 66

Oatmeal, 1 cup: 147

Spaghetti, 1 cup: 221

Rice, 1 cup: 205

Dairy

Butter, 1 tablespoon: 102

Cheddar cheese, 1 slice: 113

Milk, 8 ounces: 122

Parmesan cheese, 1 tablespoon 22

Vegetables (1 cup)

Carrots: 52

Corn: 180

Green beans: 40

Protein (3 ounce portions)

Chicken breast: 142

Two Eggs: 180

Ground beef patty: 145

Hot dog: 247

Pork bacon: 150

Pork chop: 221

Dessert

Chocolate chip cookie: 59

Ice cream 4 ounces: 145

Jelly doughnut: 289

Cake with frosting, 1 piece: 243

Drinks
Cola, 12 ounces: 136
Orange juice, 8 ounces: 112

Condiments
Ketchup, 1 tablespoon: 15
Mustard, yellow 1 tablespoon: 9

Snacks
Peanut butter, 1 tablespoon: 90
Pizza one slice, pepperoni: 298
Potato chips, 1 ounce: 155

Sauce (4 oz.)
Salsa: 35
Spaghetti sauce: 92
https://recipes.howstuffworks.com/45-common-foods-and-the-number-of-calories-they-contain.htm

Fast Food

You can receive calorie information for any fast food chain online. I chose some popular places like Chipotle, McDonald's, and Chick-fil-A to give us a "taste" of the number of calories in the drive-through world. According to one source, the Chipotle average order (burrito or salad) is over 1,000 calories and closer to 1,200 calories. A McDonald's large order of fries, has 510 calories, and a McDonald's quarter pounder with cheese 530 calories. The Burger King Whopper is 677.

A standard Chick-fil-A Chicken sandwich has 440 calories. Their Cobb Salad is 430 calories and my favorite is their Grilled Nuggets, which have 140 calories for eight pieces. Finding healthy fast food is not easy, but thankfully there are new healthy alternatives popping up around the country.

Reading Labels

Our family went through a season when we tried not to eat any refined sugar, since a few of our members had a yeast infection called candida. Since sugar fuels this infection we did our best to eliminate it from our food and in the process learned how to read labels.

When you read through the list of ingredients on a food package, the first one mentioned is present in the largest amount, followed by the second largest amount, etc. I was surprised to find out how many food items contained sugar or a similar substitute such has "high fructose corn syrup," which has essentially the same nutritional value and risks. When foods like ketchup have these added sweeteners which produce large amounts of fructose, they overload the liver. This additional fructose is turned into fat. Fructose is harmful when ingested quickly and in large amounts.

Fruit is intended to be eaten as God made it. When you eat the complete apple, you ingest a large amount of fructose, but you are also chewing and consuming water, fiber, minerals, antioxidants, and vitamins. The amount of time needed to digest this delicious fruit keeps it from being dumped too quickly into the liver. In addition, you feel full after eating a large apple. There is a fancy word for feeling fuller more quickly. It is called satiety. Because fruits fill you up, you will eat less in the long run.

Ketchup and Cheerios

The label on one ketchup bottle has the following ingredients in order of amounts: tomato concentrate, distilled vinegar, high fructose corn syrup, corn syrup, salt, spice, onion powder, natural flavoring.

The label also lists the serving size as one Tbsp or 17 grams. Under carbohydrates, sugars are listed as four grams. That means that almost 1/4 of the ketchup is sugar (a combination of high fructose corn syrup and corn syrup). It is no wonder that children like ketchup on their burgers AND their fries.

Interestingly in 3/4 of a cup of Honey Nut Cheerios (28 grams) there are 9 grams of sugar. That means that almost 1/4 of a cup, or 1/3 of a serving, of this cereal is sugar. Original Cheerios have one gram of sugar. That is quite a disparity, yet the marketing would have you believe that Honey Nut Cheerios, with honey and nuts, are healthy. Not so. Eating clean without additional sugar being added requires close examination of the labels and some understanding of how to read the ingredients.

Nutrition in Scripture

Daniel had some strong convictions about what he ate. He put his convictions to the test, and he and his three friends seemed to thrive on vegetables and water. "Daniel resolved that he would not defile himself with the king's food, or with the wine that he drank. Therefore he asked the chief of the eunuchs to allow him not to defile himself. And God gave Daniel favor and compassion in the sight of the chief of the eunuchs, and the chief of the eunuchs said to Daniel, 'I fear my lord the king, who assigned your food and your drink; for why should he see that you were in worse condition than the youths who are of your own age? So you would endanger my head with the king.' Then Daniel said to the steward whom the chief of the eunuchs had assigned over Daniel, Hananiah, Mishael, and Azariah, 'Test your servants for ten days; let us be given vegetables to eat and water to drink. Then let our appearance and the appearance of the youths who eat the king's food be observed by you, and deal with your servants according to what you see.' So he listened to them in this matter, and tested them for ten days. At the end of ten days it was seen that they were better in appearance and fatter in flesh than all the youths who ate the king's food. So the steward took away their food and the wine they were to drink, and gave them vegetables." (Daniel 1:8-16)

Regardless of your convictions about what to eat and what not to eat, it is wise to consider Paul's counsel to the Romans. "One person believes it's all right to eat anything. But another believer with a sensitive conscience will eat only vegetables. Those who feel free to eat anything must not look down on those who don't. And those who don't eat certain foods must not condemn those who do, for God has accepted them." (Romans 14:2-3)

Our culture seems to revolve around food. It is especially tricky to maintain unity in the local church when you have some folks who bring extra sweet food to church gatherings and are offended if you do not sample it. It is then that I think of Romans 14 and remember that I am not to condemn or look down on anyone because of their food choices. At the same time that I am pursuing peace in the body of Christ, I also need to recall that the inspired word of God also tells each of us to "be fully convinced in his own mind." (Romans 14:5) So be convinced in your own mind and give grace to others who have different convictions. "For the kingdom of God is not a matter of eating and drinking but of righteousness and peace and joy in the Holy Spirit." (Romans 14:17)

Is This Good for My Body?

When we were being very careful about our eating choices, while battling yeast infections, one of my sons came to the Post Office with me. The nice lady behind the counter asked him if he would like a lollipop as she handed him one. He looked up at me and said, "Papa, is this good for my body?" I shook my head side to side and I watched in admiration as he handed it back and said "No thank you." Wow! May I learn from his example. Instead of asking myself does this food taste good, I should be asking if it is good for me, like Daniel and my son Joseph. Amen.

The Missing Ingredient, Fellowship

"Two people are better off than one, for they can help each other succeed. If one person falls, the other can reach out and help. But someone who falls alone is in real trouble. .... A person standing alone can be attacked and defeated, but two can stand back-to-back and conquer. Three are even better, for a triple-braided cord is not easily broken." (Ecclesiastes 4:9-10, 12 NLT)

If you believe God is leading you to adopt more healthy lifestyle choices, including what you eat, pray and look for someone to walk with you on your journey. When I was on my weight-loss program, I was in touch electronically daily and face-to-face weekly. I was also a part of a social media group. Old habits die hard, but new habits are possible with God and at least two or more other people. The disciples went out two by two and so must we. Many people begin to make changes with good intentions, but those who succeed usually have someone at their side.

Always Remember

Regardless of our weight, our looks, or how smart we are, God loves us to pieces. This heavenly affection never changes. There is nothing we can do to make God love us more than He already does, and there is nothing we can do to make God love us any less. God is love. Nothing can separate us from His affection and care.

The first and last verses of Romans chapter 8 remind us that there is NO condemnation to those who belong to Jesus and NOTHING can separate us from His love.

"There is no condemnation for those who belong to Christ Jesus." (Romans 8:1 NLT)

"I am convinced that nothing can ever separate us from God's love. Neither death nor life, neither angels nor demons, neither our fears for today nor our worries about tomorrow—not even the powers of hell can separate us from God's love. No power in the sky above or in the earth below—indeed, nothing in all creation will ever be able to separate us from the love of God that is revealed in Christ Jesus our Lord." (Romans 8:38-39 NLT)

Temple Maintenance

I have a good friend who was out jogging one day. One of the pastors of our church spotted Phil as he was driving by and slowed down to talk with him. He asked him what he was doing, and Phil responded, "temple maintenance." I have never forgotten that picture or that expression. Phil is in his 50s and still in good shape. He recognizes, as did Paul, that his body is a temple of the Holy Spirit. "Don't you realize that your body is the temple of the Holy Spirit, who lives in you and was given to you by God?" (1 Corinthians 6:19 NLT)

I have had success in changing the way I eat and am now seeking to improve the way I exercise. The one constant I have is daily walking, which I normally do for a half-hour each morning. I make a loop in our neighborhood that is between a mile and a mile and a half depending on which roads I take. I enjoy the rhythm of walking early, but I also recognize this is not enough physical activity for me, so I am seeking ways to have a more intense workout three times per week in addition to my daily walking.

Groups

I enjoy walking by myself, for it is my special time of communing with God, but when it comes to working out, I do better with people. I like people and enjoy the camaraderie. The most consistent I have been this year is when I paid to join a fitness group. Since I am paying, I make sure I am there a few times each week, since I don't receive any benefit for my monthly fee if I skip workouts. The workouts are an hour long and led by a coach. Each workout is different with new techniques, and I enjoy the diversity. When I am by myself, I do not have the desire nor the discipline to get on a treadmill or stationary bicycle for an hour at a time. I sometimes refer to the treadmill as the dread-mill. But when I am in a class running, biking, stretching, and lifting weights, the times goes by quickly, and I don't mind the treadmill. I also have a competitive gene in my makeup. Having fellow athletes to my right and left spurs me on to do better than I would by myself. The fastest I ever ran on a treadmill happended because the guy to my left was nicely prodding me to do better! To me, the best part of the class is still when the session is over, and I read my printout to see how many calories I have burned.

Benefits

"Physical training is good, but training for godliness is much better, promising benefits in this life and in the life to come." (1 Timothy 4:8)

Some of the benefits of regular exercise are lowering blood pressure, strengthening the heart, increasing the metabolism which contributes to weight loss, slowing the development of type 2 diabetes, lowering stress, and burning unhealthy fat. Other benefits are the following: making us happier, improving muscles and bones, increasing energy levels, improving brain activity, and deeper sleep. Are you convinced? The more research I do for this lesson, the more I am ready to go to the gym!!

Some is Better Than None

Any physical activity is better than no activity. I have read articles where people did simple things like park far away from a store so they would walk further to shop. Others take the stairs instead of the elevator. I remove the snow from my driveway and rake the leaves in our yard. If you are wanting to begin, jump right in, the water is fine!

My grandfather used to meet people who said they were waiting to get around to it. He creatively began cutting out round pieces of wood and putting the letters T-O-I-T on each circle. When he handed it to them he would say, "Now you have a round TO-IT!" Here is one for you :-)

Some people do not do anything without a plan. If that is the case, make one. There are plenty of suggestions online. My advice is to find something you enjoy doing and do it with a friend. Do you enjoy swimming? Biking? Walking? Running? Rowing? Playing basketball? Playing volleyball? The best exercise is the one you do.

Balance between Eating and Exercise

The National Institute of Diabetes and Digestive and Kidney Diseases has designed a helpful resource called the "Body Weight Planner." This is for adults over 18 years of age and allows users to make a personalized calorie and physical activity plan to reach a goal weight within a specific time period and maintain it afterwards. https://www.niddk.nih.gov/bwp

Which Exercise?

There are multiple ways to workout. Here is a sampling of common exercises: aerobic, strength, calisthenics, HIIT (High-intensity interval training), boot camps (high-intensity circuits that combine aerobic and resistance exercises within a specific time frame), flexibility, and stability. I think I have done most of these at one time or another. Find out which one works for you. Most gyms I have frequented have an open house, where they let you sample the different classes, experience the exercise, and meet the instructors.

Exercise for Weight Loss

I am interested in almost all of the benefits listed, but especially losing weight and increasing my metabolism. I am not a fast walker when I am sauntering around my neighborhood in the morning, but even so, I burn 180 calories per 30 minutes. That is about six calories per minute. If I ran for 30 minutes, I would burn about 450 calories or 15 per minute.

We used to go to the gym for indoor rowing classes. I liked these classes since the instructor would break up the routine with sprints, races, relays, and other group activities.

Plus rowing is a complete body workout using the your legs, core, and upper body, while being gentle with your joints. Rowers can expect to burn 300 calories in 30 minutes or 10 calories per minute. If you want a more vigorous activity, consider jumping rope as you can burn between 200 and 300 calories in 15 minutes. That is an average of 16.7 calories per minute.

I am not a swimmer, but I have friends who are. They enjoy swimming laps and the research recommends this as a wonderful exercise. The number of calories you burn depends on your weight and your speed. A 160-pound person, swimming fast for 30 minutes, can burn over 700 calories, or 23 per minute. If the swimmer moves slower, they can still burn 550 calories or 18 per minute.

Heart Rate

According to the American Heart Association, follow these three steps to manually find your heart rate.

1. Take your pulse on the inside of your wrist, on the thumb side, or using the cartoid artery under the chin on the neck.
2. Use the tips of your first two fingers (not your thumb) and press lightly over the artery.
3. Count your pulse for 30 seconds and multiply by two to find your beats per minute.

With all the apps and electronics simply measure your heart rate at rest, as in the first thing in the morning. The gym I attended required me to buy a heart rate monitor, and I learned to keep track of my own heart rate throughout the workout.

The recommended maximum heart rate is about 220 minus your age. If you are 60, then your maximum rate is $220 - 60 = 160$. When I am at the gym, I spend most of the hour staying between 70% and 85% of my maximum heart rate. This is my target zone. Seventy percent of 160 beats per minute (bpm) is 112 bpm. Eighty-five percent of 160 bpm is 136 bpm. A sixty-year-old should aim to stay between 112 and 136 bpm for about 85% of the workout or for about 48 minutes out of an hour. If they want to take their exercise up a notch into the high intensity zone of 85-95% of their maximum heart rate, they would be between 136 and 152 bpm. This should only be for about 12 minutes or 20% of the one-hour session.

If you are 17, then your recommended maximum rate is $220 - 17 = 203$. For a 17-year-old, the target zone for 80% of the workout is between 70% of 203 which is 142 bpm, and 85% of 203 bpm which is 173 bpm. If you want to move into the high intensity zone of 85-95% of your maximum heart rate, you would be between 173 and 193 bpm. This should be for about 12 minutes or 20% of the one-hour session.

Metabolism

We know that we are all born with a certain metabolism. We can't change that. We are not able to ask for a do-over or a different body type. We are who we are. However we can improve and increase our metabolism by regular exercise. Muscle cells use energy, which means they burn a bunch of calories. Muscle cells burn more calories than fat cells, even when resting. Every pound of muscle uses about six calories a day just to maintain itself, while each pound of fat only burns two calories daily. Muscles should be increasing so fat will be decreasing! The average muscle mass of a healthy woman between 18 and 40 years old is about 27% of her body weight. The average percentage for a healthy man between 18 and 40 years old is about 36% of his body weight

H₂O

Your body needs fuel in the form of food, and it needs to be hydrated or have plenty of water. If you are dehydrated your metabolism may slow down. Warming up ice water can also burn some very small amounts of energy. According to one study, some adults who drank eight or more glasses of ice-cold water a day burned 8 more calories than those who drank four glasses of ice-cold water (which is about as much as 2 minutes of walking would burn). Regularly drinking water also helps your kidneys flush out waste. In this way water helps to move toxins from your body.

How Much Water?

We used to hear that everyone needs to drink 8 glasses of water a day. This may not be accurate. I have read a few articles on this topic and the consensus seems to be that each of us should strive to drink one-half an ounce of water for every pound of body weight. A 180-pound man should aim to drink 180×0.5 or 90 ounces of water each day. A pint is 16 ounces or 90 ounces is about six pints. I try to drink 120 ounces per day, which is almost a gallon (128 ounces). It is beneficial to drink a glass of water as soon as you wake up and before you eat.

I have measured my glass, and it holds 12 ounces of water. Just drinking as soon as I arise in the morning and before each of the three meals throughout the day comes to 48 ounces. I only need to drink another six glasses by the end of the day to fulfill my quota. This amount may increase if it is a hot humid summer or if I am working out more than normal. I have had jobs where I was sweating all day and I drank a lot more than 10 glasses over the course of the day. In any event, one-half ounce per pound is a good place to start.

I also keep a case of 16.9 ounce water bottles in my car. These are 500 ml (one-half liter) containers. When I am on a trip or just driving around town on errands I drink water. When I fly into a town to speak at a conference, I make it a practice to stop and buy a case of water, a bag of apples, and a jar of almonds. Then I have healthy snack foods and plenty of water, plus I save a bunch of money. I have seen individual bottles of water, which are normally $1.79, in hotel rooms for $4.00 or $5.00. When I buy a case of 24 bottles of purified water for $4.00 the cost is 17¢ each!

Hungry or Thirsty?

Another tip is to learn to listen to your body. My dad used to tell me to drink water when I felt hungry. Sometimes when we feel the desire to eat, we are really thirsty. One study said that adults who drank a glass of water before a meal ate an average of 75 fewer calories per meal. Every little bit helps. Water also aids in digesting the food we eat. If you do need to eat some food for an afternoon or midmorning snack, choose fruit which contains water. Approximately 80 percent of apples, grapes, pears, and bananas are water. Watermelon is 92% water and is a wonderful snack alternative.

Don't Wait Until You Are Thirsty

"The rule of thumb is, if you're thirsty, you're already dehydrated. Keep well hydrated by drinking plenty of water, even before you begin your outdoor activity," said Dr. Irvin Sulapas, a primary care sports medicine physician and assistant professor of family and community medicine at Baylor. Keep water nearby and drink it throughout the day. I like to keep water bottles in my car. I also take periodic breaks from working to drink water. Drinking several glasses one after another is counterproductive. Drink in small amounts throughout the day.

Just Find an Activity and Begin

You may not find the perfect exercise right away, but remember that any exercise is better than no exercise.

INSURANCE AND ASSURANCE

Insurance

Insurance is associated with protecting yourself against a loss of home, auto, income, health, or life. Assurance is the conviction that we serve a living God who has promised to be with us, now and forever. I have to consciously and regularly choose to trust in God and not live in fear of misfortune. On the other hand, walking by faith doesn't preclude being savvy and diligent.

Assurance

When considering insurance, whether for health, home, or car, be led by a sound mind that considers the facts rather than by a spirit of fear. I have noticed, when speaking with members of the insurance sales force, that they like to share stories of woe and despair. This "fear" of potential catastrophe is fostered to get you and me to buy more "insurance." God knows the past, present, and future. He doesn't want us to be fearful or unbelieving, but neither does He want us to be imprudent.

Provident

We have discussed setting aside money for future expenses. Sometimes we are faced with expenses that have not been planned for. We have been saving money for the next car, but a tree falls on our car during a severe wind storm. How will we cover that? Or, lightning strikes our home and it catches fire, and all we have owned is now gone. These situations are not expected, but they are catastrophic. That it is why we have auto insurance and home insurance. Owning a home and a reliable vehicle are two of a family's largest investments and need to be protected.

History of Insurance

Over 700 years ago, businessmen who were conducting commerce on the oceans began the concept of insurance to cover their loss if a trading vessel was sunk or the cargo was stolen by pirates. In the 1600s, fire insurance was available as a convenience to homeowners, but after the Great London Fire, fire insurance became necessary.

In 1666, 70,000 of the 80,000 people in the city of London had nowhere to lay their head after 13,000 houses were destroyed in the five-day conflagration. Businesses sprang up to offer fire insurance. Some of these early companies created their own fire departments to protect the homes of their clients. The homes that they insured had a mark affixed on the front of their home designating which company provided coverage to them.

Insurance in the Americas

In 1732, one of the first fire insurance companies in the American colonies began in Charleston, South Carolina. Twenty years later, in 1752, Benjamin Franklin began his own firm in Philadelphia called "The Philadelphia Contributionship for the Insuring of Houses from Loss by Fire." This followed a disastrous fire in 1730 on the wharf in Philadelphia. Franklin reported the fire in his newspaper and began promoting and educating the public about fire hazards and concerns. In 1736 the first volunteer fire department was formed with Franklin's help.

Many of the ideas and principles that were developed then are still prevalent in our modern agencies. Inspecting properties before selling the owner a policy, and safety measures like not storing combustible materials in a wooden structure became accepted procedure. His company also worked to develop a cash reserve for future claims. If a home was deemed unsafe, the occupant's rates could be raised. Franklin's fire insurance company raised awareness of fire hazards and contributed to fire prevention efforts. The Contributionship declined coverage to houses made of wood, since they presented too great a risk.

Modern Insurance

The current world of insurance has come a long way since those humble beginnings. There are a variety of different kinds of insurance, such as auto insurance, home insurance, renter's insurance, life insurance, disability insurance, health insurance, pet insurance, dental insurance, vision insurance, and many more. Before we look at a few types of insurance lets think through a few basic principles of coverage.

Smartphone Owners

You and your friends decide to pool your resources in case one of your screens needs to be replaced or on of your phones is stolen. According to research, one in four smartphone users will crack their screen (average cost to replace: $125.00) and one in ten owners will have their smartphone stolen. If the average price of a phone is $350.00, the owners need to determine the monthly premium for members of your group.

After a few meetings where these statistics were deliberated and digested, the 32 members of your group decide that $3.25 per month should cover the expenses and still enable them to set aside some money towards developing a cash reserve. They live in a rural area and thought that the one in ten rate for stolen phones was a little high. Several members of the group had cracked their screens and affirmed this statistic. They also decide that whoever loses their phone or needs a new screen would pay the first $50.00 out of their own pocket. This amount is called a deductible.

Their data looked like this: instead of setting aside $3 \times \$350.00$ for three potential thefts, they cut this in half to make $3 \times \$175.00 = \$525.00$. If eight members need to repair a screen, and they pay the $50.00 deductible, the Smartphone Owners' responsibility will be $8 - \$75.00(\$125.00 - \$50.00) = \$600.00$.

The total projected expenditures for claims which are presented should be about be $\$600.00 + \$525.00 = \$1,125.00$. Dividing this number among the 32 members works out to $35.16 apiece ($\$1,125.00 \div 32 = \$35.16$). The total premiums, were set at $3.25 per month. These fees are called premiums. When each person pays their premium, the amount collected each year will be $3.25 × 12 months × 32 members = $1,248.00. If they are careful and have a normal number of claims each year, the group will be able to save $123.00 annually.

The members also determined to encourage each other to purchase cases for their phones which would protect their screens and cut down on repair expenses. They also encouraged one another to explore ways to track a stolen phone. These ideas were written down and agreed to by each of the original thirty-two smartphone owners.

Home Owners Group

A group of individuals without insurance congregate to decide how best to protect themselves from unforeseen expenses or emergencies. They discuss ways to protect their homes from fire and damage. They contact friends and neighbors and discuss a plan to pool their joint resources together to provide a kind of safety net for their homes. Soon after their meeting to talk about this idea, a fire burns a local home to the ground. This catastrophic event galvanizes the community, and there is an increased interest in forming this group. In a short time, a thousand people apply to be members of the proposed association.

The new members decide to enlist the help of someone accomplished in math named Matthew. Matthew does his homework with the best data that is available, and discovers the average cost of a house in this area is $100,000.00. In the past 25 years, only 1 in 1,000 houses have burned down. He also learns that 50 out of 1,000 homes did report some kind of damage due to downed trees, hail storms, or lightning. The expenses for each repair averaged $700.00. Since the group has 1,000 members, the data suggests that one of the group will experience a serious fire and 50 will have some storm damage. Matthew pulled out his calculator and added the $100,000.00 plus 50 × $700.00 for a total of $135,000.00.

If he simply divided that sum by 1,000, then each member would contribute $135.00 annually into a common fund. However the organization wanted to charge a little more to build a cash reserve, plus they need to pay Matthew for his ongoing research. Someone would also be needed to be a part-time administrator to collect fees, write checks for repairs, and monitor the records for the group. Based on this data, they all voted to make the annual contribution per family an average of $200.00.

After more discussion the association proposed three levels of premiums based on the amount of deductible. This is the money a member will deduct from the amount of their need and pay out of their own pocket before reporting their need, or claim, to the whole group.

The annual premium for those in tier 000, who chose a $0.00 deductible is $225.00. The members of tier 250 have a deductible of $250.00 and are responsible to pay an annual premium of $200.00. Those who select the highest deductible of $500.00 will pay $175.00 annually and are in tier 500.

Tier 000	$0 deductible	$225.00 annual premium
Tier 250	$250 deductible	$200.00 annual premium
Tier 500	$500 deductible	$175.00 annual premium

If there are homes damaged by wind, that can be repaired for $185.00, only the people with $0.00 deductible will report their claims to the group. The other members will make their own arrangements to repair their homes. The Walker family has storm damage which removed shingles from their roof. They receive an estimate for $425.00 to repair it. They have chosen to be in the second category with a $250.00 deductible. The Walkers submit the estimate to the association, who pays them $175.00 ($425.00 - $250.00). They pay their deductible of $250.00, and the association pays the remainder of the bill, or $175.00.

The first year Sarah was hired as a part time administrator. She is to be paid $13,000.00 for her work. Matthew is paid $4,500.00 annually as a consultant, to continue to monitor the data needed for the group. The association received $200,000.00 in premiums from all the members, paid $17,500.00 for the employees, and had claims presented for $126,000.00, for a total of $143,500.00. They were able to set aside $56,500.00 for their cash reserve.

Definitions

Insurance is a practice or arrangement by which a company or government agency provides a guarantee of compensation for specified loss, damage, illness, or death in return for payment of a premium.

Insurance is something people buy to protect themselves from losing money. People who buy insurance pay a "premium" (often paid every month) and promise to be careful (a "duty of care").

Insurance is a contract that transfers the risk of financial loss from an individual or business to an insurance company. The company collects small amounts of money from its clients and pools that money together to pay for losses. These contributions are called premiums.

The premium is the monthly, or annual amount of money, each member pays into the pool to cover the needs of their group.

An actuary is the person who does the math, examines the statistics, and looks at the data to determine how much the premium should be. In the Home Owners Group, Matthew is the actuary.

The pool is the group of people being covered. It is a noun and a verb. To pool resources is to draw from all the members of the group to insure their emergency needs are met.

A claim is the amount of your expense. When you have received an estimate of how much it will cost to repair your home, car, or body, you write up and submit a claim to the group.

Deductible is the amount a member must pay before submitting his needs to the group. This is called out-of-pocket expense.

Catastrophic expense is sometimes referred to as an "act of God." This could include a flood, tornado, or hurricane. This can be a very large expense and, without group insurance to help, may mean the loss of a significant part of your possessions.

An insurance policy is a contract between you and an agency. You are required to pay a fee, called a premium, to the agency. They in turn insure that your expenses or losses are reimbursed.

Agent

When choosing an insurance agent and/or agency, there are more factors to consider than just the price, but price is important. It is advisable to get several quotes from different agencies before making a final decision. A big factor in deciding which agent is a good fit for you is the agent's customer service, or how well the agent works with you and returns your calls. When a need arises, you want to be able to contact and work with your agent. Another factor is the agency's track record and financial solvency, both of which can be researched through your state insurance department or insurance commissioner. I have found it is beneficial to network with, i.e. talk to friends and relatives to see whom they use for their insurance needs and why they have chosen those companies.

Auto

Let's begin with auto insurance. All states have different laws governing their policies, but all of them have some form of requirement placed upon drivers to make sure they can cover costs if they are in an accident. The minimum insurance required by law is liability insurance. This is the bottom line and covers a person's basic responsibilities or liabilities in case of an accident. The numbers associated with liability are the limits an insurance company is required to pay in the event of a loss. When I was younger and had older cars, I carried only liability insurance, because the clunkers I drove wouldn't be worth fixing in the event of a collision. When I was able to afford a nicer vehicle, I made sure it was appropriately covered. Now I carry collision and comprehensive as well.

Comprehensive insurance coverage will pay to cover everything other than collision or the car rolling down a bank. This can be hail damage, flood, fire, vandalism, a branch landing on the car in the driveway, or hitting a deer. We live in a litigation-happy world with many uninsured drivers on the highways. Now that I can afford more than the minimum, I consider it a good investment to have collision and comprehensive as well. Liability insurance is 55% of the premium.

Home

Even though your home is worth more than the cost of replacing a car, it is not driving around at 60 mph. The value of your home is higher than the value of your car, but the premiums are proportionately much less. The deductible plays a role in the amount of the premium. The higher the deductible, the lower the premium. When I checked prices for home owner's insurance for a $100,000-dollar house with several different deductible amounts, here is the result.

$0 deductible	$516.00 annual premium
$100 deductible	$436.00 annual premium
$250 deductible	$372.00 annual premium
$500 deductible	$342.00 annual premium
$1,000 deductible	$312.00 annual premium

You can often receive additional savings on your insurance premiums by bundling them. If you have your auto and home insurance with the same company, you can often take an additional 15% off of your premium when they are bundled.

Life

Life insurance is like car insurance. You don't need car insurance unless you are in a wreck. Similarly, you won't need to cash in on your life insurance until you lose your life! Life insurance is marketed as a way to help family members upon your demise. It can pay funeral costs, probate expenses, and other significant outstanding debts, like college loans or mortgages. When you fill out the application for insurance, you choose who will receive the benefits from your policy. This person or persons are called the beneficiaries.

There are several types of life insurance. The two main categories are permanent and term. Permanent, or whole life insurance, requires you to pay a premium for a death benefit, as well as for a savings account. As long as you pay your premium, your survivors will receive compensation (death benefit) when you pass away. The compensation is the face value of the policy, say $50,000.00. This policy is also a savings account, in that you are building equity by paying into your account. This is called the cash value. Traditional life insurance doesn't pay the highest returns on your money, but you do have a growing nest egg to tap into if emergencies arise. You will have to reimburse the fund, but it is a type of reserve for you.

Term life is cheaper because you are renting a policy instead of owning one. If you purchase a term policy for 15 years and continue to pay your premiums, your beneficiaries will receive the face value of the policy when you die, but if after 15 years you are still alive, there is no cash available. Your rental agreement has run out. Term life is likened to renting a home, while permanent life is compared to owning a home. Whole life lasts for your lifetime and is both an insurance policy with a benefit, as well as an investment tool.

Remember "God has not given us a spirit of fear and timidity, but of power, love, and self-discipline." (2 Timothy 1:7, NLT)

Medical Insurance and Bearing One Another's Burdens

Common Health Insurance

Now that we are more familiar with the concept of insurance, let's look into personal medical insurance. While it is possible to have medical coverage if you are self-employed, most people participate in health insurance offered by their employer. In this scenario, the company offers a program, and you and your employer both make contributions towards your personal insurance. Before we delve into the plan, we need to learn some new vocabulary.

Heath Plans

One fourth of health plans are Health Maintenance Organizations (HMO). An HMO is a medical group plan that provides physician, hospital, and clinical services to participating members in exchange for a periodic flat fee. In an HMO, you will most likely need to pick a primary care physician, or PCP. That person will serve as a "gatekeeper" or a "quarterback." Before you see a specialist, you will first consult with your PCP, or physician, who will provide a referral before you can see a specialist. In exchange for less flexibility, HMO coverage is typically less expensive.

One half of health plans are called Preferred Provider Organizations (PPO). This type of health plan comes with a list of preferred providers. The policy holders receive substantial discounts by choosing from the health care providers who are partnered with their particular PPO. A PPO plan gives you flexibility to see any doctor in a large network without a referral, while an HMO plan usually has a much smaller network and may require a referral to see a doctor outside of the network. Either way, if you choose a physician outside of your network of providers, you will typically pay more for the medical care either in the form of a copay or in some cases coinsurance. For example, if you work with a provider within the preferred network, the copay might be $0 or $25 depending on your insurance pland and the coinsurance payment would probably be 0%. If you chose a specialist "out of network," your copay might be $25 or $50 and the coinsurance could be 40% or 50%. PPOs usually have higher premiums than an HMO to make up for the benefits of the larger network.

Definitions

A copay, or copayment, is a fixed amount rather than a percentage. It is paid for receiving a particular health care service, such as a visit to your doctor or a prescription. The remaining balance is covered by your insurance company.

A deductible is a fixed amount the policy holder must pay during a given time period, usually a year, before his health insurance benefits cover the remaining costs for the year.

Some insurance plans also have coinsurance costs which are like copays except that they are a percentage of costs rather than a flat amount (usually coinsurance costs only apply outside the network).

Insurance is a contract that moves the risk of financial loss from an individual or business to an insurance company. The company then charges amounts of money, called premiums, to its clients and pools that money together to pay for losses.

A network is the group of health care providers who are working together with your particular insurance plan. When you choose doctors and specialists within this network you receive discounted services. In a PPO you can use providers outside the network, but you will pay a little more. For example, in one company plan, the copay is $25.00 for in network and $45.00 for out of network. HMOs restrict you to their providers; otherwise you pay for the services yourself.

Out of pocket describes the maximum amount of cash you could possibly have to pay from your own resources in a given year. This works like a deductible except that it includes any extra coinsurance or copays that you might be charged for using services out of network. When your maximum is reached, the insurance company pays 100% of all the rest of your bills.

Your PCP, or primary care provider, is probably your family physician. They know most of your overall health care concerns and can recommend specialists for your continued care. I am presently seeing a dermatologist. My physician thought he would be a good choice and referred me to his office.

A policy is the document between you and the insurance provider specifying the arrangements you have agreed to. You agree to make your payments and they agree to pay their percentage of the claims.

Demme Learning Health Plan

Our company used a PPO plan in 2018. There were a few different options for the employees to choose from. For this lesson, I chose to look at PPO 2000. The number in the name of plan was the amount of the deductible. The PPO 2000 plan at our company that year had a deductible of $2,000.00. After the deductible had been reached, all in-network costs were covered and 50% of out-of-network costs were covered.

Here are what the payroll expenses and annual costs for an individual employee were in the PPO 2000 plan. Employees are paid bi-weekly, and the premium is deducted from each paycheck. The company also pays a portion, so the actual cost of the plan is $6,834.88 for the year but for the employee the cost is $88.88 per paycheck or $2,310.88 per year.

	Biweekly Premium	Annual Premium	
Cost to the employee	$88.88	$2,310.88	(26 × $88.88)
Cost to the company	$174.00	$4,524.00	(26 × $174.00)
Total cost	$262.88	$6,834.88	(26 × $262.88)

The Episode

This year I awoke in the middle of the night with intense pain in my abdomen in the area of the appendix. My oldest son once had a ruptured appendix, and I knew this could be serious. Sandi drove me to the emergency room at the hospital at 2:00 AM. When I checked in, I informed the front desk that I was self-pay, meaning I did not have insurance and would be responsible to pay the bills. I was wheeled down the hall in a wheelchair and taken to the ER, where they inserted IV tubes. After I was stable, I was carted off to receive an MRI. The doctor looked over the results, saw what appeared to be a small kidney stone, and, since I was feeling better, I went home. I was in the hospital for about two and a half hours.

Here is the bill I received.

	Bill
Hospital	$8,998.56
Radiology Tests	$367.00
Emergency MD	$1,750.00
Total	$11,115.56

If I had had the PP0 2000 plan and this was my first medical expense of the year I would have only paid $2,000. If I had already reached the deductible earlier in the year my cost would have been $0 as long the hospital was part of of the Blue Cross network (if it was outside the network I would have had to pay half the additional costs as coinsurance). Those costs also would have been adjusted to be much lower because the insurance company would negotiate with the hospital to get lower costs (you can see an example of this in Part 2).

Christian Sharing Programs

There are alternatives to the kinds of insurance I have been describing up to this point. These are often referred to as sharing plans. Sharing plans are not insurance, but they do provide a different option than traditional medical insurance. Members pay, or share, each other's expenses. We have been a part of one for several years, and our bills have been covered when they have arisen.

A common thread in each of these programs is the Biblical principle to encourage each member of our pool to love each other, pray for each other, and bear each other's burdens.

"Love one another with genuine affection." (Romans 12:10 NLT)

"Share each other's burdens, and in this way obey the law of Christ." (Galatians 6:2 NLT)

"Confess your sins to one another and pray for one another, that you may be healed." (James 5:16)

This practice of sharing each other's burdens will not only contribute to increased health physically and spiritually, it is also a sign to the unbelieving world that we are disciples of Jesus.

"Your love for one another will prove to the world that you are my disciples." (John 13:35 NLT)

Admission Requirements

Christian sharing plans have requirements for their membership. They are related to a person's faith and lifestyle. When I joined Samaritan Ministries, I had to fill out an application where I affirmed their statement of faith and lifestyle requirements. I also had to have a letter sent in from my pastor affirming I was an active participant in the life of the church and attended services regularly.

As I have studied the five sharing programs listed below, I noticed they each have similar statements of faith about the Trinity, the inspired Word of God, and faith in Jesus as the only way to be forgiven of sin and inherit eternal life. Their lifestyle requirements are also similar, with a few modifications. Members are to abstain from excessive alcohol, be committed to bearing one another's burdens, avoid drugs and tobacco, abstain from sexual activity outside of marriage, and pursue a healthy lifestyle.

The Episode, Part 2

When I checked in to the hospital, I informed the front desk that I was self-pay, meaning I did not have insurance and would be responsible to pay the bills myself. I was wheeled down the hall in a wheelchair, and was taken to the ER, where they inserted IV tubes. After I was stable and feeling much less pain, I was carted off to receive an MRI. A few hours later the doctor looked over the results and saw what appeared to be a small kidney stone. Since I was feeling better, I went home. I was in the hospital for about two and a half hours.

I am a member of a Christian Sharing Plan called Samaritan's Ministries. My monthly share is $220.00 per month or $2,640.00 per year. I also pay an additional $133.00 per year for the catastrophic aid program, which is for expenses that I may incur over $250,000.00. My annual contributions are $2,640.00 + $133.00 = $2,773.00.

During the next month, as I began receiving bills from the hospital, the doctor, and the radiology department, I submitted them to Samaritan, and they approved the charges. Then my need was assigned to nine members, who sent me checks which paid for the three bills.

Often a sharing program will look at the bills and coach me in how to negotiate a lower charge. In this case, I did not have to do this. Since all three providers knew I was self-pay, they automatically marked down their bills. I have the amount of the markdowns under the column adjustments. The original charges added up to $11,115.56, but after the $8,658.92 of adjustments, my responsibility was $2,456.64.

Samaritan	Bill	Adjustments
Hospital	$8,998.56	<$6,832.89>
Radiology Tests	$367.00	<$266.74>
Emergency MD	$1,750.00	<$1,559.29>
Total	$11,115.56	<$8,658.92>
Submitted Claim	$2,456.64	

For more information on these plans:

www.samaritanministries.org (Samaritan Ministries)

www.chministries.org (Christian Healthcare Ministries)

www.libertyhealthshare.org (Liberty HealthShare)

www.mychristiancare.org (The Christian Care Ministry or Medi-Share)

www.altruahealthshare.org (Altrua HealthShare)

Runners

Many life insurance companies will give you discounts if you are a runner. These companies have observed that runners are more health conscious, take better care of their bodies, avoid smoking, and live longer as a result. Because of their lifestyle choices, their monthly premiums are lower, for the data suggests they will live longer.

Steve's Sharing Guidelines

In the spirit of the runners and their healthy lifestyles, I would add a few questions to the insurance applications about whether the applicants and their families keep one day a week for rest and how many hours they sleep. I have found that one day of rest each week contributes to my overall health as much as eating well and exercising. Stress and a lack of ease, or dis-ease, are huge contributors to sickness. We have a tendency to look at physical symptoms for sickness, but there is a spiritual/emotional component that is often the root of the physical malady.

> "Observe the Sabbath day by keeping it holy, as the LORD your God has commanded you. You have six days each week for your ordinary work, but the seventh day is a Sabbath day of rest dedicated to the LORD your God. On that day no one in your household may do any work." (Deuteronomy 5:12-14 NLT)

Sleep habits also contribute to overall health. Believing that God does not sleep or slumber as He cares for me 24/7, enables me to turn off my worry engine and rest better in the evening.

> "I lift up my eyes to the hills. From where does my help come? My help comes from the LORD, who made heaven and earth. He will not let your foot be moved; he who keeps you will not slumber." (Psalm 121:1-3)

> "It is useless for you to work so hard from early morning until late at night, anxiously working for food to eat; for God gives rest to his loved ones." (Psalms 127:2 NLT)

Catastrophic Loss Coverage

When it comes to personal medical insurance, it seems like just about everyone needs some kind of policy. Even if you don't plan on using insurance to cover regular doctor bills, an unexpected emergency may arise that could cost tens of thousands of dollars. It seems wise to carry coverage for costly catastrophic needs. While my faith is in God, I still think it is prudent to have coverage for at least these unforeseen emergency medical expenses. Today's health care costs are very high, and we are being told that, without adequate coverage, we could lose all we possess paying for just one serious injury.

Several years ago a statistic was repeatedly fed to us through the mainstream media about how many families were going bankrupt because of a medical emergency. When I heard this misinformation I visualized a family losing their home to pay catastrophic bills as a result of an accident or serious illness. In my research I have discovered that the purveyors of this untruth did not do their homework well. It is only a small percentage of Americans who lose all their assets paying huge medical bills. What is more prevalent is people going bankrupt and being unable to pay for their mortgage or car payments because they have not been wise in living within their means and because of how much personal debt they are carrying. When these people are unable to work because of a medical condition, they do not have the funds to make car payments and end up losing it as the car is repossessed.

This research tells me that Americans need to plan for potential illnesses by rethinking their debt load. We'd all be much less vulnerable if we kept our debt payments down to a level that would be manageable on a reduced income, instead of buying as much car and home as we can afford. Some of the savings from lower payments could be used to buy short-term and long-term disability insurance, either through our employers or a private broker. Then we could contribute to an emergency fund that would carry us through, say, a three- or six-month illness.

The Business of Insurance

If an insurance company receives $2,000,000 in premiums for policies in one year but they only receive claims for $1,750,000, they've made a profit of $250,000. Insurance is big business. Blue Cross Blue Shield Association (BCBSA) is a federation of 36 separate United States health insurance organizations and companies, providing health insurance in the United States to more than 106 million people.

Our Confidence

Regardless of what kind of plan we carry, we each need to have our hope fixed on God. We have incredible resources, for which we are thankful, but ultimately it is our incredible God that we look to, call on, and depend on to heal and care for us. May God help us to count on Him instead of insurance policies.

> "This is what the LORD says: 'Cursed are those who put their trust in mere humans, who rely on human strength and turn their hearts away from the LORD.'"

> "Blessed are those who trust in the LORD and have made the LORD their hope and confidence." (Jeremiah 17:5, 7)

THE COST OF POST SECONDARY EDUCATION

Counting the Cost

"Which of you, desiring to build a tower, does not first sit down and count the cost, whether he has enough to complete it?" (Luke 14:28)

Perhaps this verse could be rephrased to say: "Which of you, desiring to go to college, does not first sit down and count the cost, whether he has enough to complete it?" This lesson is to help you get a grasp of the cost of post high school education options. The cost of college continues to escalate. Before beginning this part of your journey, the more information you have, the better you will be able to make informed decisions.

The Old Days

I did a little digging and discovered that the cost for me to attend Grove City College in the 1970s was $1,900 per year. The median income for men during the same time frame was around $10,000, so the cost of my schooling was 19% of our family's total income. In 2016, the average annual expense for college grew to $21,000, and the average income was $40,500. The percentage of a family's income paying for college is now over 51%!

Local Schools

The rising costs of education have families rethinking how they are going to afford it. Since I live in Lancaster, Pennsylvania I chose to find out how much it costs to attend five local institutions: Millersville University (a state school), Lancaster Bible College (a private Christian school), Franklin Marshall College (a private liberal arts college), Thaddeus Stevens, a College of Technology, and Harrisburg Area Community College (a two-year school for commuters).

Tuition is the cost of the classes, while room and board covers the expense of housing and food. These expenses are for one school year from September to May, or two semesters. Since Millersville University and Harrisburg Area Community College are state sponsored institutions, there are higher costs for out of state students.

	Tuition/Fees	Room & Board	Total
Four Year Degree Programs			
Millersville University			
Instate PA resident	$12,200	$13,800	$26,000
Out of state student	$22,200	$13,800	$36,000
Lancaster Bible College	$25,000	$8,750	$33,750
Franklin & Marshall	$56,500	$14,000	$70,500
Two Year Technology Degre			
Thaddeus Stevens College of Technology	$8,000	$8,330	$16,330
Two Year Commuter School, with no campus housing or meal plan.			
Harrisburg Area Community College			
Instate PA resident	$3,341		
Out of state student	$3,774		

AP Exams

I took an Advanced Placement test for Calculus when I was in high school. I had completed the course work during the spring and fall semesters, and then took the test. I received a score of 3 out of 5. At many institutions I would have received college credit for this score. The college I attended did not honor this exam, and I had to take it again my freshman year. Some of my high school classmates went to institutions that did honor this test and received credit for several classes. They saved the time and effort of taking these courses, plus the money in tuition expense.

Save Time with CLEP Exams

Similar to an AP exam is a service called CLEP which stands for College-Level Examination Program. This program is becoming so popular the word CLEP is now a verb as well as the name of a program. I did not know about "clepping" courses when I was attending college. To "clep" means to take a test demonstrating proficiency in a certain subject, and then receiving credit for your knowledge. These exams are available for 33 subjects as of 2018 and cost less than $100.00 per exam.

In lieu of taking a class in College Algebra, you can take the CLEP exam for College Algebra. If you pass the exam, and if the college where you are attending honors the results, you can get full credit for this course just by getting a passing grade on the exam. This saves you the time and money of investing in textbooks, sitting in class for hours, and doing course assignments.

Often the first few years of school have several required courses. These are general classes covering information you may already know. By passing CLEP exams, you don't have to enroll in these classes, but can focus on courses that are more interesting and applicable towards your degree.

Save Money with CLEP Exams

A typical schedule for an academic year would be five three-credit classes in the Fall semester and five three-credit classes in the Spring semester. If you were attending Lancaster Bible College, where tuition is approximately $25,000 per year, that would be $2,500 per class, per semester. If the cost of one CLEP exam is $100 then you saved $2,400 per class, plus the hours in class, the time doing assignments, and the late hours studying for exams.

There are pros and cons to this approach. Independently studying for, and passing these kinds of exams, takes a good bit of self-discipline. Not being in the classroom and interacting with the professor and other students is also a drawback. I am not sure I would have the discipline to do this by myself, but if I was a part of a group seeking to save two years of college, along with a bunch of money, I might be motivated to try this approach.

Aid

After researching this subject, I came to the conclusion that although post high school education can be expensive, there are a lot of people and organizations lined up to help you attend the school of your choice. Take heart. If God is leading you to an institution that has high prices, there are many resources to help bear the burden of the expenses.

Types of Aid

There is a huge difference between a grant or scholarship, and a loan. You don't have to pay back a grant or scholarship. You are responsible to pay back a loan, with interest.

Grants or Scholarships

These types of gift aid, are divided into two types: merit-based and need-based. A merit-based scholarship is given to reward an individual who excels at academics, sports, art, or some other endeavor. Students compete with other students to receive a particular scholarship. Often there is a requirement that the scholarship recipient maintain a certain GPA (Grade Point Average). Typically, 20% of students receive some form of scholarship aid.

A need-based grant is based on your financial circumstances and/or the financial wherewithal of your family. Most of these types of aid come from federal and state governments. To receive financial aid, complete the FAFSA form (Free Application for Federal Student Aid) which is a part of the U.S. Department of Education. fafsa.ed.gov

The information which you provide the government is used to calculate your EFC, or Expected Family Contribution. When you have competed these two forms, you will have a number which is used by the college of your choice to determine your level of need. On the Lancaster Bible College page which lists fees, I read this sentence: "97% of all undergraduate students receive financial aid." So apply!

Private Organizations

There are many groups and organizations that offer scholarships and grants. This is where it is important to network with your friends and family. The company your parents work for may have a scholarship. Your church may know of grants available to members of your fellowship. Perhaps you work at Chick-fil-A! This is from their website, "Since 1973, Chick-fil-A has helped nearly 46,700 Team Members achieve their remarkable futures through a total investment of $61 million in scholarships. This year alone, we awarded $14.65 million in scholarships to more than 5,700 incredible Team Members." As the black and white cows say, "Eat more chikin!"

Loans

There are two kinds of loans, government issued fixed interest and private loans. Currently the price of a fixed loan from Uncle Sam is about 6%. Private loans can have fixed or variable rates. These rates vary from 5% to 12%, depending on the lender. The lender may be a bank or credit union. Just as we have discussed before, a loan from one of these financial institutions is affected by your credit score. How low of a rate you receive will depend on your credit score, or the credit score of your co-signer, who will most likely be one of your parents or close relatives. If one of your parents or grandparents co-signs your loan, they will have to pay it back if you are unable to pay it back. This is important to remember.

Establishing Credit for a Private Loan

If you are nearing the end of high school, and think it is beneficial to begin establishing a positive credit history, consider applying for a department store or gasoline station charge card. Use this to buy clothes or gas and then diligently pay off the complete balance when the bill arrives each month, so you will not accrue additional interest charges.

Another option may be to ask your bank if they have credit cards that would be available to you. If you already have a checking account with them and have established a relationship with them, this will help.

All of your purchase history is being recorded every time you make a purchase, receive a bill, and pay off your balance. After you have had time to establish yourself as a diligent customer who pays their bills in a timely fashion, eventually you should be able to qualify for a Visa or MasterCard. Do remember to pay off the bill when it is due, so you don't incur late fees and interest expense.

Fiscal Discipline

Another bonus of having your first credit card is developing the discipline of living within your means and paying off the balance due each month. A credit card is not free money. Before you borrow tens of thousands of dollars for college, you might even consider purchasing a car on credit and seeing how long it takes you to pay it off. Some people have the discipline to pay off their loans and some don't. Start developing the fiscal discipline to pay back outstanding bills now before accruing a mountain of debt in college. Don't assume you are a good steward of money, but take steps to become one.

Paying off the Loan

Many students make the mistake of thinking they will have plenty of money when they land their first job and will have no problem paying off their student loans. According to an April 28, 2017 article in USA Today: "Student loan debt surpassed credit card debt and then later exceeded $1 trillion for the first time. That shocking statistic keeps climbing, with no sign of slowing down: Americans now have more than $1.4 trillion in unpaid education debt, according to the Federal Reserve." https://www.usatoday.com/story/money/personalfinance/2017/04/28/average-student-loan-debt-every-state/100893668/

Let's imagine you live in Pennsylvania and attend four years at Millersville University. You have worked hard in the summer, your parents have helped out as much as they could, you received some financial aid, and one scholarship. Upon your graduation you have a $30,000 debt in the form of student loans.

The Loan

With your $30,000 debt, you are not alone. According to studies, 68% of college graduates in 2017 have an average debt of $30,000 when they receive their diploma. The average salary for a student who graduates with a Bachelor's degree is around $50,000. Let's look at how your personal budget may look after you secure an apartment in town for $1,036 per month in rent. In this example, I chose to use the budget categories which Dave Ramsey recommends.

Since you graduated from a school where you were able to attend without having a car, you now need a reliable vehicle and begin searching for a Honda Civic. After praying and researching, you find a used 2013 Honda Civic. You have a good credit score, and the bank loans you money to buy the car. You agree to make payments of $302 per month for three years. The good news is that in three years you will own the car and be saving $302 per month on your budget.

The transportation figure is computed by adding the expense for gas and regular maintenance. If you drive 1,250 miles per month, and the car averages 26 miles per gallon of gas, you will spend $125 for fuel, and $32 for ongoing monthly maintenance, for a total of $157.

The government loan for the $30,000 you were able to secure, has a 6% interest rate and is to be paid back in 10 years, or 120 months. Using a loan calculator, your monthly payment will be $333.06 for 120 months. That $30,000 which has been borrowed, will end up being $39,967.38 after you pay back the principal plus the $9,967.38 in interest.

All of the budget categories are listed, but focus on housing, transportation, and debt percentages, which are in italics.

Category	Percentage of Overall Spending
Utilities	5–10%
Food	5–15%
Healthcare	5–10%
Charitable Giving	5–15%
Investments/Savings	5–10%
Entertainment/Recreation	5–9%
Misc. Personal	2–7%
Housing	25–35%
Transportation	10–15%
Debt Payments	5–10%
Housing, debt, and transportation total	**40–60%**

If your annual salary is $50,390 gross, this works out to a $40,018 net income. This figure is divided into 12 months, to find the monthly net income of $3,335.

Housing	$1,036.00	31%
Transportation	$157.00	4.7%
Car Payment	$302.00	9%
College Loan Payment	$333.00	10%
Total		**54.7%**

Additional Payment on the College Loan

If you choose to pay $400 per month instead of $333.06 (an additional $66.94 per month), you can pay off the loan in seven years and 11 months instead of 10 years. Now the total interest expense is $7,694.35 for the life of the loan, and you save $2,273.03 in interest, plus you will have paid it off two years and one month earlier than expected.

Ask for Help

Most of the colleges I researched had very helpful information on scholarships, financial aid, and the costs you will need to be aware of as a student. Here are some additional sites I consulted when compiling and computing these costs:

Information about financial aid: studentaid.ed.gov

Information about student loans: studentloanhero.com

Actual take home pay: https://smartasset.com/taxes/income-taxes#PDFndzrC1t

Loan calculator: https://mathusee.com/e-learning/stewardship-calculators/

Closing Thoughts

Once you have talked with God and your family and friends and made a decision, go for it. Wherever God is leading you, know that He has gone before you and is with you on this phase of your journey. You are an adult. You have made an informed decision and now it is time to press on with confidence and not fear.

Post High School Alternatives

Steve's Post High School Experience

When I was in my senior year of high school, all of my friends and classmates were planning on attending a four-year college. The question was not if we were going to a college or university, but which one. I went along with the flow, spoke with my guidance counselor, applied to several institutions, and made one campus visit. I wasn't sure about what my major was going to me, but since I was strong in math, I began my freshman year as an engineering major. I completed that year with a decent grade point average, but decided I did not like being in labs during the afternoons, and thought about switching my major from engineering to some kind of business major. The second year, or sophomore year, I changed my major to business administration and math.

I didn't learn much during my first two years in college. I did learn how to do my own laundry, albeit with some pink undergarments. I finally figured out how to balance a check book, after several hard lessons about overdraft fees.

During the summer between my junior and senior year, God began moving in my heart as I prepared to spend the summer at a camp for troubled teens. As I was reading "The Cross and the Switchblade" I put the book down and said, "Okay God, here we go." When I returned to complete my senior year, I knew I wanted to make some changes in my course work to prepare for Christian ministry of some sort. I decided to finish the business degree, but I replaced the math classes I had intended to take with religion courses. I signed up for Introduction to Greek, Letters of Paul, American Religious Traditions, and a wonderful class on the writings of C. S. Lewis.

I was determined to seek first His kingdom. After graduating with a Bachelor of Arts in Business Administration, it seemed I had two options: either join a campus ministry or receive more training. Upon graduation I decided to pursue more education and headed for seminary, where I began studying for a Master of Divinity degree.

Hindsight

There is a saying that hindsight is 20-20. That means that looking back, I may have made different decisions based on what I know now. Nevertheless, our God is a wonderful Redeemer and works all things together for our good. Even though I may have made different choices, I was doing the best I could with the information I had, and I have no regrets. In researching and thinking about the material in this book, I think I would have benefited from pursuing a gap year program to add a year of maturity and have more experience understanding how God had designed me. However, I am getting ahead of myself, so let's explore a few alternatives after high school.

College Can Wait

All four of our sons were homeschooled. When it came time for them to make a decision where to go, and what to do when they graduated, the three oldest chose to attend a small inexpensive Bible School. There they studied Scripture and Bible related subjects in the mornings, worked on the premises in the afternoons, and lived in a small dormitory. Sandi and I felt this program would give them a chance to be on their own, become more grounded in the Word, learn how to interact in a dormitory setting, acquire some practical work skills, and grow up a little more. Eventually all three sons enrolled in college and received Bachelor's degrees. When they stepped on campus as freshmen, they were each at least twenty years old. I believe they benefited by going to college a little later than "normal." They were more focused on what they wanted to study, more mature, and had a better sense of who they were.

God Knows Best

If you are studying this curriculum you probably are a follower of Jesus and seeking to glorify God in your life (If not, I pray you will be). The first thing to do, when considering where God would lead you following your high school graduation, is to pray and seek God for His will. The question is not "What do you think is best?" but "What does God know is best?" God loves you to pieces and has only your good in mind. He also knows you better than you know yourself. Ask Him. Seek Him. You will find Him. "Commit everything you do to the LORD. Trust him, and he will help you." (Psalm 37:5, NLT)

Ask Him how you can best use your skills, talents, gifts, and experience to extend and contribute to the kingdom, while providing for your needs and the future needs of your family. Then ask your parents, trusted friends, relatives, and people in the body of Christ. "Where there is no guidance, a people falls, but in an abundance of counselors there is safety." (Proverbs 11:14)

If God is leading you to attend college, the first question you may want to think about is not which one is closest, or cheapest, but whether you should attend a Christian institution or a secular one. As in many topics we have covered, I think there are pros and cons for both options.

Christian - Pro

The fellowship is special. You will be living, learning, and studying with other believers. You will make lifelong friends among these brothers and sisters in Christ.

The chapel speakers are remarkable. Often you will have the opportunity to hear gifted Christian leaders from around the world who will come to visit your campus and lead seminars. I met outstanding men and women of God during my time in college and seminary.

If you are fortunate to attend a school that emphasizes a Biblical worldview in every discipline, count yourself blessed. Hearing about how God designed and created each of us as the basis for psychology, instead of evolution, is refreshing.

You will meet Christian professors that care about your faith as much as your academic pursuits. The president of my college and I were friends until he passed into heaven a few years ago. The last time we spoke, we prayed together over the phone while I was driving.

Christian - Con

Cynicism can creep in. When I attended seminary, which is a masters level program after completing college, many of the students who came from leading Christian colleges seemed to have lost their first love (Revelation 2). I could relate to these folks, because even though I was studying Christian disciplines in class, my faith became dry and academic. I learned that even in this godly environment, I had to fight to keep my relationship with God fresh and real. My personal devotions became very important to me. I couldn't neglect my personal prayer life, just because we prayed in chapel and in many of the classes.

The most insidious threat to a person's faith is attending a Christian institution, admiring the faith and testimony of one of your professors, and then discovering they do not embrace your views of scripture, or creation, or marriage, or gender, or the Lord's return. It is hard to stand up to someone with a PHD and try to defend your position. Many students are led astray by well-meaning but misguided professors. Make your expectations realistic so you are not caught off guard when a well-meaning professor teaches something different than what you believe. Keep your armor on and your defenses strong, while maintaining a vital relationship with Jesus yourself.

Secular - Pro

Even though you will be in enemy territory, there are usually wonderful vibrant Christian fellowships such as Cru with 5,300 campuses worldwide (www.cru.org), InterVarsity which is present on over 650 campuses (www.intervarsity.org), Navigators with a presence on 160 campuses (www.navigators.org), CCO which is on 140 campuses (ccojubilee.org), and other ministries, to join for fellowship and encouragement.

Being in a secular environment, learning to be strong in the Lord, and sharing your faith with your classmates is excellent training for the rest of your life when you will be in similar situations. Knowing that unbelievers are watching your life, keeps you growing and on the alert. You are salt and light. Don't lose your saltiness!

Secular - Con

Sin is rampant. Alternative lifestyles (unbiblical) are the norm. Free speech is a myth, and your faith will be under attack on all fronts. Unless you commit to be connected with a strong Christian fellowship, you will not make it on your own. "Do not be deceived: 'Bad company ruins good morals.'" (1 Corinthians 15:33)

"Though a man might prevail against one who is alone, two will withstand him—a threefold cord is not quickly broken." (Ecclesiastes 4:12)

College or Work

When I was graduating from high school, I only remember two choices, either go to college or get a job. It was assumed a college graduate would invest four to six years on his education and in return make a higher income than if he only had a high school diploma. The statistics supported this idea, and college was much more affordable when I was a high school graduate.

Two factors have changed the way we are thinking about preparing for an occupation. The first is the increasing costs of a four-year college or university education. According to my research, the typical student is graduating today with a with a debt of over $30,000 dollars. If this graduate marries someone they met at college, they will have a combined debt of $60,000 dollars.

The second factor is the need for skilled craftsmen such as plumbers, electricians, mechanics, HVAC technicians (the acronym for Heating, Ventilation, and Air Conditioning) and health care workers. Check out this website for more information along this line: https://www.mikeroweworks.org

On "All Things Considered" aired April 25, 2018, by National Public Radio, Ashley Gross and Jon Marcus had some interesting statistics in their broadcast entitled "High-Paying Trade Jobs Sit Empty, While High School Grads Line Up For University."

"Seventy-percent of construction companies nationwide are having trouble finding qualified workers, according to the Associated General Contractors of America; in Washington, the proportion is 80 percent. There are already more trade jobs like carpentry, electrical, plumbing, sheet-metal work and pipe-fitting than Washingtonians to fill them, the state auditor reports. Many pay more than the state's average annual wage of $54,000. Construction, along with health care and personal care, will account for one-third of all new jobs through 2022." [1]

Apprentice

An apprentice is someone who works with a skilled professional to learn their trade. For centuries this was how tradesmen passed on their knowledge to the next generation. Abraham taught Isaac, who taught Jacob, who taught his sons, how to care for cattle. Moses taught Joshua how to lead the children of Israel. Jesus learned his trade from his father Joseph. College and schools are a recent invention. Learn all you can from your parents, aunts, and uncles, and grandparents.

One family I know has a son who aspires to being a building contractor. He decided the best way to learn all of the trades would be by practical work experience. He offered his services at a discounted hourly wage so that while he was learning he would not have to be paid as much as someone who was already experienced. I like this approach. He earns while he learns. The tradesmen acquire the services of a teachable, willing worker at a discounted rate. It is win-win situation for the employer and the employee.

This ambitious young man spent time on a carpenter framing crew, learned how to install insulation, acquired skills in a cabinet shop, and learned the basics of being an electrician. He worked as a roofer, a plumber, a finish carpenter, installed flooring, hung sheetrock, and painted it. After a few months in each trade he had a wonderful hands-on education that gave him a unique perspective into his chosen occupation of being a general contractor. Even if he does not become a contractor, these skills will be invaluable as a homeowner.

Some of these trades require years of training to become proficient. My brother has acquired certification in HVAC, in plumbing, and as an electrician. He has a natural bent to working with his hands and understanding these fields, and it still took him years of study and application to become a skilled worker. Our young apprentice did not become an expert, but he acquired skills that no book or youtube video could teach.

If you have a pretty good idea of what field you would like to go into, consider being an

---

1 https://www.npr.org/sections/ed/2018/04/25/605092520/high-paying-trade-jobs-sit-empty-while-high-school-grads-line-up-for-university

apprentice. Ask people in that field if you could come alongside of them and learn more about their job. Try to offer something in return for the time they will be investing in you. Perhaps you could offer to improve their presence on social media, an area where companies always need help from young people who are tech savvy.

If you are involved in a short apprentice relationship, you will have a first-hand opportunity to get a taste for this occupation. You may discover this job is not your cup of tea. That is also a benefit. Now you don't have to spend thousands of dollars preparing for a job you don't like!

Gap Year

In our local church a friend of ours works as the site director for OneLife. I asked Zac Northern to tell me more about the program over a lunch. I was intrigued by the possibilities and wished I could have participated as a student when I was contemplating my options after high school.

For those of you who are leaning towards college, but are not quite sure if this is the best fit for you, read on. Would you like to taste several different options before committing to a four-year brick and mortar college? Consider participating in a gap year. The cost is comparable to a year of college, but with a wide array of classes and experiences.

You can enroll in a gap year before college, or while you are in college. The credits are often transferrable, and the cost for a year is $22,900, which covers tuition, room and board, books, and travel expenses. In this program, 91% of the students receive some form of financial aid and/or scholarships. Some of the courses include: Introduction to the Bible, Speech, Personal Finance, and Archaeology and Land of the Bible.

"ONELIFE is a nine month Christian gap year program for students who want to grow in their faith, experience genuine community, serve others, and travel while earning credits for college." Learn more here: https://www.onelifepath.org

Assessment for a Career

I never took a complete assessment questionnaire, but I do think it could be beneficial as any insights we can each receive into how God has wired us can only be helpful. I have long followed Larry Burkett and respected his work and ministry. When I took orders to the post office at 3:30 PM in the afternoon I had the opportunity to listen to his radio broadcast. I always benefited from listening to him teach and from the wise counsel he gave to people who called him for financial advice. He is now in heaven, but the ministry he founded, Crown, is still operating and has a plethora of wonderful resources on how to be a faithful stewards of God's resources. They have an assessment tool for a very affordable fee here: https://www.crown.org/career/#my-investment

HSLDA

In 2005, the Demme family became the second lifetime member of HSLDA. We had been paying annual dues for several years, but at a homeschool convention in Massachusetts, Chris Klicka encouraged me to "upgrade" our membership classification. I have long been a fan of Home School Legal Defense Association and am grateful for the work of this organization, which began as a group of lawyers defending our right to home educate our children. Since those early days, they have grown and expanded to offer other services for home educators. I was researching many of the subjects in this lesson and found excellent resources right here: https://hslda.org/content/highschool/college.asp and https://hslda.org/content/highschool/testing.asp

An Alternative Online Degree Program

If you do believe God is leading you to receive a college degree, Lumerit Education provides an alternative to the traditional approach of living in a dormitory for four years and accumulating debt. Their website declares, "Join the community of students who say 'no' to college debt and make the world their campus."

I have been acquainted with the leadership of Lumerit (Woody Robertson and Jonathan Brush) for many years and admire their heart and integrity. When I first became acquainted with this approach to obtaining a degree, they were known as College Plus.

According to Jonathan, home educated students who have studied math with MathUSee, have done well in their program. Learn more about them here https://lumerit.com.

Instead of leaving college and entering the workplace with a huge mountain of student loan debt, they offer college credits taken online from accredited colleges and universities for $5,400 per year. I am grateful for God giving vision and creative options to men like Woody and Jonathan.

Unique

When you do apply to a college or other entity, don't sell yourself short. If you have been educated at home, you have received a unique and special education. Many colleges and other institutions value diversity in their student body. International students, as well as homeschool graduates, provide value to the school as a whole.

When you fill out the application, make sure you list all the educational experiences you have had, including field trips and travel. Keep a record of all the books you have read. You may be surprised to learn that many school students have figured out how to pass exams, without reading the text. Good friends of ours met students attending prestigious universities who cannot recall reading a complete book since Curious George. These individuals consulted Cliff Notes and other shortcuts, instead of thoroughly reading and digesting the contents of a good book. Don't assume that everyone has had the same advantages as you have had by being taught at home, with time to read and explore your own interests.

In Pennsylvania we have several hoops to jump through to receive permission to home educate our children. Many years ago, I had to meet with our local public school principal to show the accomplishments and progress of one of my sons. As I showed him a paper my son had written and the list of books he had read, the principal commented that this was exceptional and above most of the students' accomplishments in his school. You have a received a wonderful gift by being taught at home.

"With their unique schooling, homeschool students may be eligible for scholarships based on their non-traditional education." unigo.com

APPLYING FOR WORK AND UNDERSTANDING YOURSELF

This curriculum has been a trip down memory lane for me as I have thought about all of the jobs and occupations I have had over the course of my life. As I look back, I can see how each of the work experiences I had prepared me for other tasks later in life. Compared to me, you are each just beginning to develop employment experience, job skills, and work habits. With God by your side, it will be an interesting journey.

Assemble Your Resume

When you apply for a job, your potential employer will want to know what kind of person you are, what experience you have, and what skills you possess. Start keeping a record of what you have done to show to potential employers when you apply for work in the future. This is called making a resume. The word is derived from the French word *resumer* meaning, to sum up.

Hard and Soft Skills

On your resume, the skills that you possess, can be broken into two main categories; hard skills and soft skills. Hard skills are very specific and easy to measure. They are your education and work experience. Hard skills can be a four-year college diploma, a two-year certificate, great grades while in school, or a high IQ. When I applied to colleges and workplaces, the application process was all about my education, my work experience, and what activities I participated in outside of the classroom. Everything I listed was about what I had done.

Soft skills are harder to measure and quantify, but they are just as valuable. Employers now recognize that someone may sound qualified on paper with wonderful hard skills, but be unable to work or play well with others. Employers want to know if potential employees are diligent. They are trying to determine if they are teachable and if they will show up to work on time each day. These are soft skills, and are not about what people have done, but about who they are. Soft skills are internal and describe character and personality. I think it is understandable that a potential employer will want to know something about a person's character and personality before offering them a position in their company.

Here some of the top soft skills which employers are seeking when hiring new employees: Leadership, Teamwork, Written Communication, Problem Solving Ability, Strong Work Ethic, Verbal Communication, Flexibility, Adaptability, Time Management, Conflict Resolution, Positive Attitude, Self-Confidence, Ability to Accept, Learn From Criticism, and Willingness to Learn.

Soft skills are people skills. They are about relating to others. They are often classified as interpersonal skills.

Interpersonal or Interfamily Abilities

Since home school students are being educated with the other members of their family, they have unique skills and experiences. They interact with siblings of different ages, different genders, differing learning abilities or disabilities, and with adults, 24/7/365. There may be days that these students long to be with a room full of just their peers who are the same age and have similar abilities, but this environment will not prepare them for the real world as much as their home does. Once a student leaves a brick and mortar school, they will never again spend all day with a homogenous group of peers.

The lessons a person learns at home, by living with the diverse components of a family, are assets. This interaction with multiple ages and personalities is priceless preparation for real life. I have often thought of writing a book called "Everything I Need to Know, I Learned at Home." Treasure the soft interpersonal skills that can be acquired as you grow and learn together as a family. Use your time at home to develop your character qualities such as patience, tolerance, compassion, integrity, and a diligent work ethic while you are young. These habits will provide a solid foundation for the rest of your life.

Example of Hard Skills

Matthew Calvin, 18 years old

Education
Home Educated from 2006 until 2018.
Completed six credit hours at Community College in Mathematics.

Work Experience:
May-October, 2017   Lawn care for seven clients
July, 2018   Junior Counselor at Community Church summer camp
July, 2019   Senior Counselor at Community Church summer camp
June-August, 2019   Worked in shipping department at MathUSee

Extra Curricular Activities
December 2016, 2017   Volunteer at Good Samaritan Nursing Home
September, 2019   Volunteer at Historical Society

Example of Soft Skills

I have an outgoing personality and like people. I like working in groups and collaborating on projects. I enjoy learning and acquiring new skills. I learned the importance of being diligent when I was responsible for keeping the lawns of seven neighbors well-manicured each spring and summer. I take joy in serving and visiting the elderly.

References

When you apply for a position, you may be asked to provide references. These are people who know you and people you have worked for. In our example above, consider asking some of the folks whose lawn you cared for in 2017, or perhaps the director of the summer camp, or maybe your supervisor at MathUSee. If some of them agree to provide a reference, ask them whether the best way to contact them is via email or by phone, and then ask for their contact information. Sometimes you will be asked for a character reference from someone who has known you well, such as your pastor or a close friend of the family. I have been asked several times to give references as a friend, a pastor, and as an employer.

Interview

When I was 26, I interviewed for a position in a cabinet shop. At the time I had just graduated from seminary, was newly married, and we were expecting our first child. I was serving as an assistant at a small church. During the interview I was asked three questions: What is your experience? Are you planning on working for a year or more? Can you begin next Monday? I responded that my only experience in woodworking was working one summer as a carpenter's helper and a class in woodworking I had taken in eighth grade. Then I answered the second question by stating that my first responsibility was to the church, and this was to be a temporary job. As for beginning right away, I responded that I would like to talk to my wife and pastor before making a decision about starting next week. At the time, I felt like I was striking out with my responses and would never be hired. Surprisingly, I was hired and worked there for about six months. I learned a lot about wood working and made a lifelong friend of the foreman, who decided to follow Jesus more fully and became an elder in our fellowship.

Sometimes your honesty and uprightness does not produce what looks like good fruit. In Genesis, Joseph ends up being a servant in the house of Potiphar. He works so diligently, and God is so evidently blessing his labors, that Potiphar makes him the overseer of his property and possessions. Potiphar's wife "cast her eyes on Joseph" but he remained pure and did not give in to this temptation. Because of his integrity, Potiphar cast him into prison. Joseph may have been tempted to think that it was not a good business decision to be honest, but we have the advantage of knowing the rest of the story. Prison led to Jospeh becoming Prime Minister of Egypt. His becoming Prime Minister led to the preservation of the nation of Israel. God works all things together for our good. Walk in integrity even when it doesn't seem to make sense.

Reference

I was asked for references when I applied to be a teacher at the local high school. I gave the contact information for this cabinet shop. The manager of the shop gave me a wonderful recommendation because of my honesty in our first interview. My recommendation is be open and honest about your plans. I believe this kind of integrity is a way to apply Proverbs 3:6. "In all your ways, acknowledge Him, and He will make straight your paths."

Prepare

Here are some questions you may be asked. Think about them before you go to the interview.

1. Why are you applying for this job opening?
2. Did you like your last job?
3. Tell me what kind of things you did at your last job.

4. Of all your previous work experiences, which one was your favorite?
5. Why should we consider you for this job?

My cousin is an honest and diligent employee. He once applied to work in the sales department for a company that sold candy. Before he went to the interview, he went to the store and bought samples of all their products and tasted them. He then researched more about the company (this was before the internet) to familiarize himself with its operation. His interviewer was very impressed with how much he knew about their company and its products.

Follow Up

After the interview is over, it is a good idea to follow up with an email or hand-written note. Express your appreciation for the opportunity to meet with them and to apply for the position at their company. Be polite, grateful, and respectful. If they are interviewing several candidates for the open position, your note may be the deciding factor in their hiring you. Thankfulness and respect are becoming rare in the world today.

My Personality

I believe God designed all of His children with unique strengths and gifts, and it is important to discover how we have each been created. Then we can serve God more effectively based on how we have been designed. I made a list of all the jobs I could remember having, and for most of them, I would be classified as self-employed. I have always had a lot of initiative and liked being in charge. One of the reasons I have started multiple businesses is my strong "D" personality. If you do not know what I mean by a "D" personality type, sit back and keep reading.

DISC

I first learned this terminology while studying personalities using the DISC model. Here is a brief summary. This model has four quadrants, D-I-S-C, where D is Dominant, I is Inspirational, S is Steady, and C is Careful. Gary Smalley, and John Trent characterized these four types by using animals: D-lion, I-otter, S-golden retriever, and C-beaver.

The dominant lion is outgoing and task oriented. The playful otter is outgoing and people oriented. The steady golden retriever is reserved and people oriented. The careful beaver is reserved and task oriented. No personality is better than another. We are all a unique blend of these four types. Some adjectives for each personality are:

D-Dominant, Determined, Doer, Direct, Dogmatic, Demanding, Decisive
I-Inspirational, Influential, Interested in People, Interactive, Impressive
S-Steady, Supportive, Stable, Sensitive, Sweet
C-Careful, Cautious, Competent, Contemplative, Conservative

Quadrants

If you have never worked through a personality assessment, here is your chance! Ask yourself if you are outgoing or reserved. Generally outgoing people, the extroverts, know who they are. Reserved folks, who are introverted, will reflect and think about how they respond before making a decision. This is one example of how we are each wired. When you have decided which best describes you, think about whether you are a people person or more task oriented. This is a little tougher for some folks to determine, but it may help to think about how you recharge your batteries. If you have some free time and want to recharge, do you lean towards doing something with people, or putting on the headphones and cleaning up your desk or some other task. I like people. I get energized at a conference. My wife needs space to herself, and while she likes people, she frequently gets headaches at conferences. We are all different.

If you put your answers from these two questions together, you can now pull them together and form four quadrants. The two upper quadrants represent the extroverts and the lower ones the introverts. When these are put together with the task and people responses, you have four areas. The upper left is outgoing and task oriented. The lower left is reserved and task oriented. The upper right is outgoing and people oriented, while the lower right section is reserved and people oriented.

DISC Personality Profiles

In the upper left quadrant are the outgoing, task-oriented group. This is the smallest percentage on the grid. Words that describe these lions are dominant, determined, doer, direct, dogmatic, demanding, decisive, and driven. They make excellent dictators. They're charismatic, and use their charm to accomplish a task. Rule the world! Be the number one football team!

The fun otters are in the upper right quadrant. These people are outgoing and they like people. They're inspirational, influential, interested in people, and impressive. Where these likable influential people are, there's a party. If you attend a workshop led by an otter, you will have a ball. You might not learn anything, but you will have fun.

In the bottom right quadrant, you have someone that's reserved, and enjoys being with people. These are the golden retrievers, or the S type. They are steady, supportive, stable, sensitive, and sweet. Fortunately for the world, this is a large percentage of people. They are nice to be around. Whether they are following lions, or laughing at otters, they are pleasant.

The lower left quadrant describes people who are reserved and task oriented. Careful, cautious, competent, contemplative, conservative, are words which typify the C personality. They need quality answers. Their animal type is the industrious beaver.

Most of us are a blend of a few personality types. To make this clearer, let's assume you are teaching a group of four students, and each of them represents one personality type. The teacher asks a simple question, "Who discovered America?"

The high D personality, our dominant direct lion, would not even raise his hand. He blurts out the answer, "Columbus. Now what?" He wants to keep moving.

The I type, the impressive influential otter raises his handed and looks around the room to ensure that all are watching him. He laughs and says "Columbus?" The teacher acknowledges his correct response and gives him a sticker. The class is smiling and he is beaming. The lion is rolling his eyes. He doesn't need a sticker, but is pretty confident that he could teach the class better than the present instructor.

The sweet steady S won't even raise their hand lest it attracts attention. Finally the golden retriever softly says, "Columbus?" This student is just happy to be there and hopes the teacher will move on to someone else.

The conservative contemplative beaver is cogitating. He is thinking. He is pretty sure that he read about the possibility of the Vikings coming to the Americas around 980 AD. As he mulls over other possible solutions, the teacher finally says, "I think the correct answer is Columbus." The beaver responds, "Actually, Columbus didn't discover America. He discovered San Salvador." He's usually right.

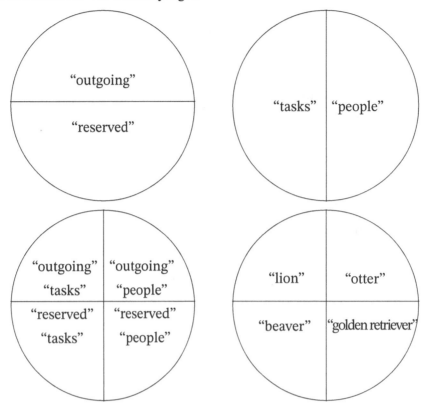

Pluses and Minuses

Every type has a weakness and a strength. The lions get things done. They are movers and shakers, but they have the potential to run over people in the process and could use a little dose of golden retriever. The otter is entertaining, but needs to do his homework with a beaver before leading a workshop. Golden retrievers are nice, but they may have to learn a few tips from a lion before they are prepared to be in charge of a group of students. The beaver will have a well-researched presentation, but he would benefit from having the otter give a few tips on how to make his speech more entertaining. I have included a five minute personality test on the "Resources by Lesson" page at stewardshipmath.com that I hope will give you a little more insight into how you are wired and some of your potential strengths and weaknesses.

Blends

Most of us are a blend of several types of these personalities. I am a blend of a "D" and an "I." When I took a personality assessment, I was mostly a lion and an otter, with a small amount of beaver and golden retriever. One study said that 80% of people are a blend while 20% are primary in one category. If you are one of the 20% you may be a "high C" meaning that you fit the beaver mold almost exclusively.

Jesus is the Perfect Blend

Even though we are each wired a certain way, we are also being transformed into the image of Jesus, who is the perfect amalgam of all four types. As a lion, He can cleanse a temple by himself. He was approachable and children were attracted to Him, like a golden retriever. He was likable and enjoyed being around people, as does every otter. Like a conscientious beaver, He fulfilled every jot and tittle of the law.

For Your Occupation

I was on a plane flying from Canada to the United State when I found myself sitting next to a lady who teaches DISC training to corporations. I asked her how she presented these concepts. She said that she first explains the four personality types and then has each employee choose the personality that best describes them and move to a corner with others with the same type. All the beavers are in one corner, the golden retrievers in another, etc. Then she gives each group a task to complete in a certain amount of time.

Here is what typically happens. The D-lions don't interact with each other. They all work by themselves to see who will complete the assignment first. The otters continually requested more time because they were networking and telling stories. The sweet retrievers complete the assignment quickly and efficiently, but no one person would report their findings to the larger group unless someone else would go with them. All the members of the beaver group used a mechanical pencil to work on the problem.

When I hire customer service people or a receptionist to be the first one to greet people as they enter our workplace, I look for golden retrievers. When I interview people for a sales position, I am looking for otters. If I want to find someone to proofread a book or do accurate research, I seek out beavers. If I need someone to be in charge of shipping, or to manage a team, I lean towards the lions. Understanding that we each have strong points and weak areas helps me in assembling a team of co-workers.

One in a Billion

When you factor in a person's birth order, their genealogy, their personality type, their spiritual gifts, where they are born, who their siblings are, and their educational opportunities, it is easy to see how we are all different. Personality tests and other assessment tools can help us understand how we are wired, but they are not definitive. The only thing we know for sure is that God made us all unique. In the next section there is a sampling of unique people in the Scripture and their occupations.

Occupations in the Bible

One job is not more spiritual or more godly than another. Since we are created and designed by our Maker, we all have special callings. I hope you are encouraged by the plethora of occupations in Scripture. If I had lived at the time of David, I would have wanted to be a warrior and a worshiper. It would fulfill my heart's desire to be a member of the family of Asaph, who was charged with giving thanks. What a great job: getting up each morning and thinking of how God has provided, and who He is, so that I could give Him thanks.

As you read through this list, notice the variety of professions. God uses people of all personalities and callings to accomplish His purposes. As Psalm 23 declares, He leads us in paths of righteousness, for His name's sake. Amen.

> Jabal and Jubal were brothers. Jabal was the father of those who dwell in tents and have livestock, and Jubal was the father of all those who play the lyre and pipe.
>
> Their cousin Tubal-cain, was the forger of all instruments of bronze and

iron.

Noah, a preacher of righteousness, built an ark and escaped the worldwide flood with his family.

Abraham was a shepherd, successful businessman, pioneer, warrior, and the Father of all who believe.

Job, a successful businessman and a peerless man, was tested by God.

Joseph began his work life as an administrator of Potiphar's household and of the prison. He was appointed Prime Minister of Egypt, and preserved the children of Israel.

Moses was a warrior, shepherd, prophet, and friend of God.

Bezalel and Oholiab were anointed, skillful, master craftsmen who created all the components in the tabernacle.

Miriam, the sister of Moses, led the people in worshiping and giving thanks.

Deborah was a judge and a prophetess.

Gideon began his career as a farmer, and then became a mighty warrior and a judge of Israel.

Hannah was the earnest, godly mother of Samuel. Her son anointed Saul and David as the first kings of Israel.

Ruth, the devoted, godly, loyal Moabitess, became the grandmother to David, and was in the lineage of Jesus.

David was a shepherd, musician, soldier, priest, prophet, and eventually King.

Asaph, the thanks-giver, was appointed by David to minister before God at the ark.

Heman, Asaph, and Ethan were to sound bronze cymbals.

Jehoshaphat, son of Ahilud, was the royal historian.

Daniel was a conscientious student, an interpreter of dreams, and an effective politician.

Jeremiah was destined to be a prophet to the nations.

Nehemiah served as a trusted cupbearer to King Artaxerxes. He also became an administrator and rebuilder of the walls in Jerusalem.

Ezra was a scholar, teacher, and spiritual leader.

Esther was queen of a mighty empire and instrumental in averting a massacre of the Jewish people.

Amos, a keeper of trees, was called to be a prophet.

Mary was the mother of Jesus, the Savior of the World.

Elizabeth gave birth to John the Baptist, the forerunner of Jesus.

Jesus was a contractor or carpenter and worked in the family business with His father.

Mary, Joanna, and Susanna were part of a group of loyal wealthy women who financially supported Jesus. (Luke 8:1–3)

Joseph of Arimithea, was a wealthy member of the religious council and a follower of Jesus.

Simon Peter, the fisherman, became a leader among the apostles.

Andrew the evangelist is seen introducing people to Jesus.

John, a fisherman, and a "son of thunder," became an apostle and was loved by Jesus.

Paul was a redeemed Pharisee and a tentmaker, who became a gifted scholar, teacher, preacher, and church planter.

Lydia, a worker in purple, had a gift for hospitality. (Acts 16:14–16)

Luke was a physician, an historian, a contributor to scripture, and a member of Paul's ministry team.

Lois and Eunice, mother and grandmother, led Timothy to Christ. (2 Timothy 1:5 and 3:15)

Barnabas was as an encourager and co-worker of Paul who labored in planting churches and preaching the gospel.

Aquila and Priscilla were tentmakers with Paul and served as mentors to Apollos.

Work to Bring Glory to God

"Whether you eat or drink, or whatever you do, do all to the glory of God." (1 Corinthians 10:31)

Work for the Lord

"Whatever you do, work heartily, as for the Lord and not for men, knowing that from the Lord you will receive the inheritance as your reward. You are serving the Lord Christ." (Colossians 3:23–24)

Work to Share With Others

"Let the thief no longer steal, but rather let him labor, doing honest work with his own hands, so that he may have something to share with anyone in need." (Ephesians 4:28)

Work to Provide for Your Family

"If anyone does not provide for his relatives, and especially for members of his household, he has denied the faith and is worse than an unbeliever." (1 Timothy 5:8)

Work to Preach the Gospel for Free

"Don't you remember, dear brothers and sisters, how hard we worked among you? Night and day we toiled to earn a living so that we would not be a burden to any of you as we preached God's Good News to you." (1 Thessalonians 2:9, NLT)

Work because God Designed Us to Work

"The LORD God took the man and put him in the garden of Eden to work it and keep it." (Genesis 2:15)

Entrepreneur

Entrepreneur

I have been called an entrepreneur, although I just learned how to spell this word! Dictionary.com defines an "entrepreneur" as a person who organizes and manages any enterprise, especially a business, usually with considerable initiative and risk. When I think of this term, I think of people who are creative, inventive, and who think outside the box. They have imaginative ideas, possess a good deal of self-confidence, believe in their product or service, and are willing to take risks to get their business off the ground. I recommend talking to people that you trust about your ideas and dreams, but while they give wise advice, they do not make the final decision—you do. I did not know if any of my business ventures would be successful when I began them, but I made the decision to try.

I have observed that many entrepreneurs are first born children, with a strong "D" personality. D-personalities believe they know the best way to accomplish things. They are born leaders. They love expressions like, "When confronted with an obstacle, some will find an excuse, while others will find a way." They relate to the story of the two shoe salesmen who were sent to a new market only to find all the people were barefoot. The first salesman called the home office and sadly told them there was no opportunity for a shoe store, since no one wore shoes. The second salesman enthusiastically reported that no one wore shoes!! What an opportunity!

Questions for Reflection

If you have an idea for a new business, think through some basic questions to evaluate your plan. Will your business be profitable? Do you have a competitive edge? What is in your hand? What experience do you have in this line of work? What need are you meeting?

A Competitive Edge

When I was in college I studied for a B.A. in Business Administration. The best business advice I received came as a result of a paper I was writing. My assignment was to interview an entrepreneur and ask him his advice on knowing how to begin a business. I had a good friend who worked for the local chamber of commerce, and she connected me with a local real estate developer. I made an appointment with the developer and met him at his office in downtown Pittsburgh, Pennsylvania. In the course of our conversation he said, "Only begin a business if you have an unfair advantage." I have also heard this same sentiment expressed by saying a startup business should have a "competitive advantage or competitive edge." In his situation, he was going to develop a large outlet mall (which he successfully did) on the intersection of an interstate highway. Before he embarked on this investment, he wanted to ensure that he owned the property on all four corners, which he was able to acquire. That was his edge, or advantage, over future competition.

My first legitimate enterprise was as a painting contractor. I started this business when I was 18. My competitive advantages were: I didn't mind climbing ladders, I had a long wingspan (long arms), my dad was a paint salesman, and I knew several reliable guys whom I could hire to work for me. Since my Dad worked for a paint company, I was able to buy paint and supplies at wholesale prices. Painters always seem to be in demand, since most people do not like to scrape and paint on a ladder. My biggest advantage was that I was significantly cheaper than professional painters. The outside of a house needs to be painted every few years, and periodic painting is necessary inside the house as well. If you are willing to be taught and work carefully, painting does not require extensive training, as does an electrician or a plumber.

What is in Your Hand?

"The LORD said to him, 'What is that in your hand?' He said, 'A staff.'" (Exodus 4:2) When Moses stood before God on the mountain, he had nothing but a staff. Yet with that staff, plus God, Moses successfully led the children of Israel out of Egypt. We each have some gift, skill, or talent. What is in your hand? What skills do you possess? What gifts has God given you? What talents do you bring to the table?

God gave me a gift of explaining information to students. I also like math. When I began teaching math in a classroom to high school students, I discovered that I enjoyed teaching and explaining math to students. The best part was seeing the light of understanding come to them while I taught. This gift or talent, is what was in my hand.

Identify a Need

What need are you meeting? Or, what service are you providing? I think all businesses should strive to serve the customer and meet a felt need that they have. Working just to make money for the sake of earning an income is not satisfying for the servant-hearted follower of Christ. Jesus came not to be served, but to serve.

In America, many people suffer from a fear of math, which some refer to as innumeracy. Because of difficult experiences parents had when they were in school, many of them are fearful of teaching their own children this important topic. This need to understand math as parent-teachers, and then to have a curriculum to use so their children can understand math, are some of the reasons MathUSee was created.

Experience

Sometimes we have specific work experience and other times all we have is a willingness to work diligently, and learn on the job. Both are legitimate. Everyone starts somewhere. When I began cutting grass and shoveling snow, my only experience was doing this at our house. When I began painting, I figured I could learn on the job. The more I did it, the better I became. I can now paint well with either hand while standing on a ladder. I had led youth groups for several years before I became a school teacher, but I still have never had a college class on how to manage a classroom, nor have I ever been a student teacher. Nevertheless, after two weeks as a substitute teacher I was offered a position as a full-time teacher. Within a few years I had lots of experience. :-)

Profitable

Ultimately the reason I worked was to earn money. I had many little jobs before I was 17: cutting grass, shoveling snow, working in a dairy mart, serving as a stock boy, etc. When I was about 14, I heard of an opportunity to sell sno-cones at our county fair. My mom drove me to the fairgrounds, where I learned I would purchase a tray with 20 of these cold fruity treats to sell for 15¢ each and I would make 10% or 1.5¢ per sno-cone. When I had sold them all, I would come back and buy another rack of 20 for $2.70. My net profit for selling 20 sno-cones was 30¢.

I loved working the crowd, walking up and down the grandstands, hollering "Sno-cones here! Get 'em while they're hot!" At the end of the evening I had worked four hours, sold 200 sno-cones and had a profit of three hard-earned sticky dollars. I did not do it the next day, because after I got home, I began doing the math and figured out I was working for 75¢ an hour. Even though it was a fun and interesting experience, the work was not profitable. It was a great deal for the folks who had the sno-cone stand. They were selling frozen water with a squirt of flavoring and they had a score of teenagers selling thousands of them for 15¢ apiece. For each tray that I made 30 cents they made $2.70!! Use your math skills to evaluate your profit and make sure you are earning a fair wage for your labor.

Steve's Jobs

Here are some examples of jobs I had, followed by the five criteria: Competitive Advantage (CA), Hand, Need, Experience (EXP), and Profitability. Remember, what one can do, another can do as well. One of my first jobs was shoveling snow and cutting grass for people in our neighborhood. The need was that people had snow on their driveways and grass that grew each spring and summer. What I had in my hand was a willingness to do the work. My competitive advantage was that I was the first one to knock on their door and I lived on the same street. I also had access to a free shovel and lawn mower, courtesy of my dad. My experience came from shoveling the snow in my own driveway and cutting the grass on our lawn.

CA	Cheap and a neighbor
Hand	Willing and nearby
Need	Snow and high grass
EXP	Working at our home
Profitable	I made a few dollars I would not have made watching TV.

House Painter

CA	Sherwin Williams, cost, long arms, I knew good guys who needed a summer job. I was confident.
Hand	Willing to work and climb ladders
Need	Peeling paint, high work especially in demand
EXP	Very little but I learned on the job.
Profitable	I made at least 2-3 times minimum wage. Yes.

MathUSee

Hand	I had a gift for teaching and I liked math.
Need	Math is a hard subject for many Americans. There wasn't a good curriculum for homeschoolers, who are tutors, that was hands-on, had cumulative review, and progressed at the child's pace.
CA and EXP	My work experience prepared me for each venue, as I had taught in homeschool co-ops, public schools, private schools, at a college, and in special needs classrooms. I had experience selling curriculum and educational resources to homeschoolers and school teachers.
Profitable	In the early years we barely had enough, but as it grew it became more profitable.

Getting Started

If you are interested in starting your own business, but don't know where to begin, here are a few principles which have worked for me:

1. Take an inventory of what you possess and what is in your hand. What are your gifts? What are some of your talents? What do you enjoy doing?
2. Pray and ask God to reveal a need which you can meet. Working for a living is not only about making money, it is also about serving others and being rewarded for your labor.
3. Use your own powers of observation to determine services and products which are needed.
4. Identify your competitive advantage and experience. What are your strengths? What gives you an edge over your competition?
5. Decide if this potential endeavor is profitable.

Consider interviewing people that you or your parents know by inviting them to lunch (you will have to pay) or meet with them at their place of business. Here are a few questions which may be helpful in getting the ball rolling:

1. Why did you start your own business?
2. Can you tell me how you got into this line of work?
3. What skills had you acquired which prepared you for having your own business?
4. What is the most rewarding aspect of owning your own business or ministry?
5. What is the most challenging part of running your own operation?
6. Do you believe you have a competitive advantage that contributes to your success?
7. What role does your faith play in your business ?
8. What advice would you give to someone who is just starting out, based on what you know now?
9. Do you have any other thoughts you would like to share with me/us?

Brainstorm with Buddies

One of those friends was acquainted with a relative of the founders of Outback Steakhouse. He told me how a few guys with restaurant experience, were trying to find a novel concept to begin a new brand of restaurant. In 1986 Crocodile Dundee was a very popular film and as the men tossed ideas back and forth, they decided to create an eating experience that would have American food, while the atmosphere would be fun, or Australian, like Paul Hogan, who played Mick in Crocodile Dundee. They opened their first location in 1998, and although they had a slow start, they have become extremely successful. For many years this was our favorite place to eat as a family.

Southwest Airlines is my favorite airline. They are fun, efficient, have reasonable fares, an incredible rewards program, and outstanding customer service. I have read their book called "Nuts" by Kevin Freiberg, which is the story of how this airline began. A few fellows were sitting around a table wishing there was an airline in Texas to fly between three cities. They drew a triangle on a napkin connecting Dallas, Houston and San Antonio. That was the beginning of what is now the largest and most popular domestic airline in the US. You never know what will come from thinking out loud with friends.

I enjoy learning about other successful companies such as Chick-Fil-A. This is a great story about a wonderful family and a superior product. I rarely eat at Chick-Fil-A anymore, because the lines are so long :-)

Necessity is the Mother of Invention

In the appendix are two accounts, one about the invention of the Wiffle ball and the other about the invention of the Braille alphabet, which arose because people were trying to meet a need. I describe these on the teaching video.

Business Arising out of a Passion

I have been blessed with good friends. One of my favorite families is the Farewells. Bob and Tina love God, their family, and great books. They turned these passions into a business called Lifetime Books and Gifts. With their five children, and a large bus converted into a motorhome, these seven intrepid travelers, spent six months on the road and six months at their home base in Florida. Their annual circuit took them to all parts of the United States and Canada. They sold books and resources at weekend homeschool conventions and visited parent support groups during the week. In every venue they led workshops, counseled parents, and spread their love for God, family, and great literature. They had the privilege of engaging thousands of families over their eighteen, yes eighteen, years on the road. And, they were able to make a good living in the process. I interviewed Bob Farewell on two podcasts, #190 and #191, about his story. You can listen to them here: http://www.buildingfaithfamilies. org/podcasts/ Or you subscribe on iTunes.

Demme Businesses

Similar to the Farewells, we initially created a business called "Our Family Resources" to share curriculum and learning aids which had helped us. These products had benefited our family, and we believed they would help others as well. We designed a brochure, contacted educational suppliers, and began sharing these resources to other families interested in education.

Another home business we started began as a result of health concerns. From 1987 to 1990 several members of our family were afflicted with autoimmune diseases. We earnestly prayed and sought God, who led us to an herbal company where we found great benefit from using their products. Eventually we began selling these herbal supplements in our basement.

The common theme in these two accounts is that if something helps you, it will probably help others. When we began attending conferences for health and nutrition we heard lots of interesting stories about how people just like us had found help in natural health products. This led them to share their knowledge with others. Almost everyone I have met in the nutrition industry has a testimony of how traditional approaches to disease have not worked, while alternative therapies and products had made a significant difference. When you meet someone who has their own business, ask them to share their story; I think you will find it interesting and encouraging.

Developing Your Business Practices

For several years I was a sales rep for other companies. I learned first-hand what it was like to represent other people's products, and I remembered my experiences when I enlisted the help of families to represent MathUSee. I learned good business practices that I wanted to emulate. I also experienced harmful practices that I wanted to avoid. I also had meaningful conversations with people I worked alongside with at curriculum fairs and conventions about what makes a good business. Those experiences and discussions helped me develop MathUSee and influenced how I treated and interacted with my sales reps.

Win-Win-Win

Looking back at all these varied business experiences, I recognize how much I learned about managing others, setting an example, hiring and firing employees, talking to customers, paying taxes, keeping records, estimating jobs, and determining my profit margin. While I was not a huge fan of painting when I first began this job, I did learn to enjoy painting, and I especially liked the fact that I was serving people. I discovered there is a satisfaction in leaving a house looking much better than when you first arrived. I liked seeing happy customers. I also found satisfaction in knowing that my friends who worked with me had a job for the summer. Of course, the primary reason I chose to paint houses was to make money for my schooling. At the end of summer, I found I had made enough money to cover my living expenses for college and seminary. It was a win-win-win situation for me, the workers, and the customer. One unexpected result was that the skill I acquired while painting has often been put to use in church and other service projects which helps and blesses others.

Lessons Learned Over Five Decades

Principle 1

Treat our workers, our customers, and our sub-contractors as we would like to be treated. In other words, operate the business by the golden rule where Jesus says to treat others like you would like to be treated yourself. One example is that when a bill was presented from one of our printers, I would seek to pay it as soon as possible. Eventually I received several letters from businesses thanking us for our prompt payment. As a business owner, I am aware of the potential cash flow issues that small businesses face, and sought to help them out by paying sooner rather than later.

Principle 2

Continue to improve the product and the customer service.

We have always had excellent customer service, from our first sales representatives to our current staff, who answer phone calls and emails and are present at conferences. These big-hearted, informed people truly enjoy serving and encouraging customers.

Healthy competition makes better products for the consumer. Our MathUSee books were originally plastic comb-bound manuals. One of our competitors had spiral bound manuals. We improved by printing hardback and perfect bound books. Another business had answer keys for all the problems, while we only had the answers for the odd numbers. In response, we added answer keys, with all the problems worked out, for all the exercises. We have a better product today, because competition forced us to improve.

Principle 3

Respond to the needs of the customer.

The primary reason we have a Stewardship Course is because I was asked many times for a consumer math course. I was happy to comply, and this was the first math course written from a Christian perspective, and the first books printed with perfect binding and hard covers.

Principle 4

Don't borrow money or go into debt.

In order to produce plastic manipulative blocks, I needed money to pay for the cost of the injection molds. My father offered to loan me the money to do so, and he was repaid within twelve months. I never applied for a line of credit, choosing to operate in the black (as opposed to the red).

Confidence and Self Esteem

You need a measure of confidence to begin your own business. I have observed that self-esteem is who you think you are, and it is shaped and formed by people who play a significant role in your upbringing. This begins with your parents and family. People who inherit a low self-esteem from a troubled childhood will sometimes battle this malady for years and years.

Self-confidence on the other hand can be acquired. It increases when you achieve significant accomplishments and overcome obstacles. Having my own businesses as a youth, and during my college years, gave me confidence. If I had not overcome the small challenges when I was young, I would not have had the courage to take on larger challenges as an adult.

Self-esteem is who you think you are, and it takes time and energy, with God's help, to change. Self-confidence can be nurtured by what you accomplish and achieve.

Take Initiative and Start Small

When I was a young teen, I remember going door to door selling household goods to support the Boy Scouts. When I was 13 or 14, I walked around the neighborhood where we lived knocking on doors to find work cutting grass and shoveling snow.

When I turned 16 I thought it was time to get a "real job" and set out one day to find one. There was a busy road near our home with businesses lining both sides of the street. I walked into the first business and asked if they had any job openings. I continued to do this for several hours and many miles. I did receive some part-time yard work from one fellow. After many doors and 3.4 miles of walking (I just mapped the route online to find the exact distance), I landed a job working at a CoGo's, which is like a Seven-Eleven, but found in western Pennsylvania.

If you have an idea, pray and do your homework, then go for it. Jump in the pool and figure out how to swim as you go. Everyone is nervous when they begin. Walt Disney said, "The way to get started is to quit talking and begin doing." Even if you don't make a ton of money, every business experience will become a learning experience. Even if it is not a smooth ride, each lesson learned will prepare you for the next opportunity. Peter could have continued to walk on the water, if he had kept his eyes on Jesus. Hop in, the water is fine! Start small, keep your eyes on Jesus, and start!

Running a Business

Knowing what I now know about personalities and jobs they are particularly suited for, if I was a high "I" personality (otter), I would be the face of the company and interact with people, for this would be my strength. To complement myself and my weaknesses in other areas, I would hire an accountant (beaver), someone to help manage the details of the business (lion), and a golden retriever to interact with customers.

If I was a strong "S" personality, I would find a partner. Golden retrievers do better working with someone else. "C" personalities need some "I" and "S" people to work with their customers, and a "D" to make decisions and manage, while the beaver continues to develop the product. I am over-simplifying in hopes that you will recognize your strengths and your weaknesses and plan accordingly.

I am also the first-born son of a family of three boys. I think first born children have a tendency to be self-employed. I learned this when I began choosing regional sales representatives for MathUSee. At our second annual conference, I asked who was a first born. Of the twenty people present, eighteen raised their hands. The only two who weren't first born children sat quietly side by side in the last row.

Self-Employed

Since I am a D, when I think something is a good idea, my nature is to jump in and do it. I have always had difficulty with the passage about stopping and counting the cost before beginning. "Which of you, desiring to build a tower, does not first sit down and count the cost, whether he has enough to complete it?" (Luke 14:28) I generally have confidence that I can figure out and overcome obstacles as I encounter them. I reason to myself that, "What one person can do, another can do."

I once read there were three kinds of people, those who when presented with an opportunity say "Why not" those who say "Not now" and the third group who says "Maybe later." My parents and my maternal grandparents, were "Why not" folks, and I inherited their genes, for which I am grateful.

Employer or Employee

Self-Employed

The idea of working for yourself, or having your own business, is different than working for someone else. As I studied my past occupations and work experiences, I discovered that I have engaged in many kinds of employment. I have worked for others as an employee and I have operated my own business where I was the employer. The I.R.S. calls people engaged in owning their own enterprise "self-employed."

I think it is interesting how people often dream of working for "themselves." In my experience, everybody has a boss. Employees have one boss, while folks who are self-employed work for many bosses. Their bosses are called customers. We all work for somebody!

Team

Everyone is a part of a team. When we hear the word self-employed, we assume that one person runs their own business. When I began MathUSee, yes, I took the plunge and assumed the risk, but I was not alone. My wife and children supported and helped me. I remember my sons helping me collate pages of material and binding them with plastic comb binding equipment. I also have a vivid memory of my wife and I packaging orders and then driving them to the post office in time for the afternoon pickup.

My parents loaned me money to purchase the steel injection molds to make the plastic manipulative blocks. My pastor prayed for me and the business daily for many years. God brought devoted and servant-hearted sales representatives who helped shape the company and its culture. Was I self-employed? On paper, yes. In reality, I was privileged to be a part of a great team.

Employees

As you will see, I had many jobs where I was paid to do a task by my boss or employer. I was the employee. My employer paid my wages, took out taxes, and sent them to the state, local, and federal governments. He found the jobs, talked to the customers, paid insurance to cover the employees, and was ultimately responsible for the work being done well. My job was to do the task assigned me by my boss. I was to show up on time and work diligently while I was on the job. My responsibility was to do what I was told to do, to the best of my ability. As long as I fulfilled my part of the contract, then I received a paycheck and employee benefits.

Here are some pluses and minuses of being employed by someone else.

+ Less responsibility	− Not much input for decisions
+ Leave work at work	− Punch the clock for 40 hours/week
+ Steady income you can depend on	− Little potential for large rewards
+ Benefits like health care	− Not responsible to find work for the company
+ Taxes are deducted for you	− Can lose your job with 2 weeks notice

Employers

When I was the boss of a painting crew, it was my responsibility to talk to customers, procure the paint beforehand, and hire an accountant to compute the taxes. I was also the one who made sure we had adequate equipment like ladders, brushes, scrapers and drop clothes. In the evenings, I often visited prospective customers, and provided them with a free estimate of how much it would cost to have their house painted.

My workers, or employees, showed up at a specific time, and I assigned them their task for the day. At the end of the day they went home. Once a week, I would pay them their wages for their time on the job. If I estimated the final cost of the project correctly, I made a nice profit. If I did not estimate well, and the project took more time and required more supplies, I barely broke even. "Breaking even" means that after paying my employees, taking out the taxes, and buying the paint and materials, I did not have any money left for my time. I paid all my bills, but essentially worked for nothing, as I did not make any profit on that particular job.

There are rewards and risks involved when you are self-employed and make the final decisions. Here are some of the pluses and minuses of having your own business. Harry Truman had a plaque on his desk that read: "The buck stops here."

+ You make the final decision	− Have to live by your decisions
+ Greater potential for reward	− Greater potential for risk
+ Freedom to choose your work hours	− Long hours, work never really over
+ Feast when business prospering	− Famine in dry times
+ Do things your own way	− Lonely at the top
+ Ability to make changes quickly	

Long Hours

Let me explain what I mean when I say work is never over. When I say long hours, I mean that you never seem to leave work. When I was a painting contractor, I left work, ate dinner and cleaned up, and then often spent evenings giving estimates to customers for jobs in the future. I sometimes bought materials in the evenings and on weekends. I never kept track of my hours, but I know they were more than forty. My workers, on the other hand, left work, and played softball, or went home and watched TV. When they completed their eight hours on the job, their responsibility ended.

Passion

There are folks who encourage you to identify your passion and then choose a vocation that fits your desire. Confucius is reputed to have said, "Choose a job you love and you will never have to work a day in your life." I understand this sentiment now, because I awake in the morning with joy and gratefulness for the opportunity to serve and do the work He has given me to do. I love what I do. I love the God that I serve. If you have the opportunity to have a job that you thoroughly enjoy and which fits how you were designed, rejoice and enjoy the ride!

Preparation: Give Thanks in All Things and for All Work Experiences

Sadly, for many people, work can be tedious and toilsome. I don't think that every job has to be wonderful. For many years and through differing job experiences, I dreaded hearing the alarm going off in the morning. Now that I am older, I can look back and see how the varied business experiences I had shaped me. Some of the jobs I enjoyed, and some I didn't, but they all were used of God to prepare me for what I am doing now. Even Jesus had to learn life lessons the hard way. "Though Jesus was God's Son, he learned obedience from the things he suffered." (Hebrews 5:8, NLT)

> "I have not failed. I've just found 10,000 ways that won't work." Thomas A. Edison

> "Many of life's failures are people who did not realize how close they were to success when they gave up." Thomas A. Edison

Moses, David, Joseph

I am pretty sure Moses did not enjoy the forty years he spent in the wilderness caring for Jethro's flocks. However, these years prepared him to lead the children of Israel through this same wilderness for forty years.

David spent years herding sheep, developing his skill with a sling to defend them against bears and lions, finding water and grass, and locating caves for shelter. He had time to deepen his relationship with God, worship on the lyre, and write songs of praise and worship in the quiet evenings. All of these skills prepared him for defending Israel against Goliath, writing the Psalms, and caring for hundreds of families in the wilderness.

Joseph was torn from his home to find himself managing the household affairs of a leading citizen of Pharaoh's court. Then after being falsely accused by Potiphar's wife, he spent years in a prison. In this unique training ground, he learned how to speak the language and how business was conducted in Egypt. He rubbed shoulders with some of the leading citizens of Pharoah's court. God made him know that He was working all things for good, even if his brothers meant to harm him.

Eventually Moses, David, and Joseph each find their role in the redemptive story of Israel. God will help us each find our place in His kingdom in our day. When I did find my niche, I recognized how God had been preparing me for what I am doing today. Without those difficult times, I would not be prepared or equipped for the tasks He has called me to do. God was orchestrating all things to work together for my good. He was discipling and training me. Here are some of the lessons I learned while earning money.

> "Failure is not the opposite of success; it is a stepping stone to success." Arianna Huffington's mother, Elli

An Employee receives a Promotion and the Employer Acts Quickly

As I reread Genesis this January, I observed an illustration of the flexibility and the ability to make quick decisions in the actions of Pharaoh, and the faithful Joseph. If you have read Genesis, you know the account of the life of Joseph as he went from beloved son, to slave, to the house of Potiphar, then into prison, and finally to the court of Pharaoh. In this drama, think of Pharaoh as the employer and owner of his own firm, the Egyptian Empire. Joseph is a diligent employee who has served well in Potiphar's home and in the prison. We'll break into the story as the chief cupbearer explains why he thinks Joseph can be a help to Pharaoh.

"The chief cupbearer said to Pharaoh, 'I remember my offenses today. When Pharaoh was angry with his servants and put me and the chief baker in custody in the house of the captain of the guard, we dreamed on the same night, he and I, each having a dream with its own interpretation. A young Hebrew was there with us, a servant of the captain of the guard. When we told him, he interpreted our dreams to us, giving an interpretation to each man according to his dream. And as he interpreted to us, so it came about. I was restored to my office, and the baker was hanged.' Then Pharaoh sent and called Joseph, and they quickly brought him out of the pit. And when he had shaved himself and changed his clothes, he came in before Pharaoh." (Genesis 41:9–14)

"Pharaoh said to his servants, 'Can we find a man like this, in whom is the Spirit of God?' Then Pharaoh said to Joseph, 'Since God has shown you all this, there is none so discerning and wise as you are. You shall be over my house, and all my people shall order themselves as you command. Only as regards the throne will I be greater than you.' And Pharaoh said to Joseph, 'See, I have set you over all the land of Egypt.'" (Genesis 41:38–41)

Faithful, diligent, Joseph received a quick promotion without going through the interview process with Human Resources. He did not have to find references or negotiate his salary and benefits. His employer, Pharaoh, did a quick consultation with his advisers, and Joseph went from being in charge of the prison, to becoming the virtual prime minster of Egypt, second only to Pharaoh.

When I read this inspired look at the life of Joseph and his rapid promotion, the words of Jesus come to mind: "The master said, 'Well done, my good and faithful servant. You have been faithful in handling this small amount, so now I will give you many more responsibilities.'" (Matthew 25:23, NLT)

The Boss Sets the Tone

When I was a painting contractor, all of the employees would meet at my home, and then we would drive in my car to the job site. Sadly, there were many mornings when my guys woke me up in the morning. Some days our paint crew was not on the job until 10:00 AM. When I slept in, we started late, having wasted time in the morning. The boss sets the tone for how hard to work and when to begin. The owner leads by example, not by words. If you are beginning a small enterprise and have the opportunity to work side by side with your employees, work diligently. You "catch a fire from someone who has a fire." If you enjoy what you are doing and work hard at your craft, your love and diligence may be caught by those around you.

Be Consistent

Jesus is described in John as the word made flesh. His disciples lived with Him and had the opportunity to see that His walk and His talk were absolutely consistent. He never asked His followers to do something He was not already doing.

Never ask an employee to do a task you are not doing yourself. I learned this lesson when I was in college. As a member of the Inter-Fraternity Council, I came up with the idea to have "Help Week" as an alternative to "Hell Week." The idea was that the young men who were seeking to join a fraternity, could perform a helpful task in the community instead of enduring hazing at the hands of the upperclassmen. I organized the event, contacted local organizations, and matched up their needs with willing members of the college frats.

Our fraternity was assigned to move furniture into an attic of a local church. Bill and Jeff showed up and spent several hot, sweaty hours moving chairs and desks. I was not there—after all, I was the organizer. At our next fraternity meeting, I heard about it, in angry tones. I was reprimanded for talking but not doing. I never forgot that lesson. Set an example, and not just an agenda.

Lowly Carpenter's Helper

Say please and thank you to everyone, even the people who are lowest on the totem pole. My first full time summer job had a crew of about six men. The owner was brusque and business-like. John was the best carpenter. He had a ponytail, rode a motorcycle, and only worked long enough to make sufficient money to return to Mexico to party. However, to his credit, John treated the two high school guys with respect. He always said "please" and "thank you" when asking for our help. I never forgot that lesson.

Look for Teachable, Diligent Employees

If people are willing to learn and be taught, they can do almost anything. One of my best employees was a man named Eugene. He was a hard worker and teachable. He graduated from college, eventually joined the U. S. Marine Corps, and became a Colonel. During the summers while we were in college, he joined our painting crew. When he started to work he did not have any experience. I showed him how to hold a brush, how much paint to put on it, etc. By the end of the summer, I trusted his newly developed skills, and even had him paint the front door on a customer's home.

Another fellow I hired was the son of a painter, had his own ladders and brushes, came to work with special painting clothes, but sadly, only lasted a week. On the first job, I assigned him the task of painting white window trim on the second floor of the back of a house. After a few hours, I climbed the ladder to examine his work. The windows sashes were pink, not white. His brushes had not been cleaned well from a previous job, and there was red paint at the bottom of his brush. I pointed out the pink paint, and he did not take it well. In his mind, he knew how to paint. He was not teachable. I had to let him go. Firing young men when they were 18 and I was 19 was not easy, but it had to be done.

MathUSee

School Teacher

I learned so much in this, my first full time place of employment. Since I was a math teacher during the day and an assistant to the pastor in the evenings and on weekends, I had very little time to take work home. I diligently used my planning period and after school time to record homework assignments, test grades, and daily paper work. I rarely wasted a minute at work, and developed a disciplined work ethic. The teacher I was replacing had only covered a few chapters of the textbook the previous year. I determined to complete all twelve chapters in the book I was assigned. I mapped out lesson plans to finish the book by the end of the year, which we did. By sticking to my plan, I did not slow down or lallygag through the material I had to teach. With God's help, I was disciplined and stayed on track.

Standing up before a room full of teenagers all day taught me how to think on my feet and communicate to an audience. I observed how to read their facial expressions and body language. I learned how to present material clearly and how to keep them engaged. This training was indispensable in my becoming a public speaker.

Tutor

As a teacher with thirty students in a class and a commitment to complete the book in one year, I did not waste time. Surprisingly, while I was motoring through the textbook, I discovered how efficient and superior a tutor was to even a disciplined, focused classroom teacher.

I had a student who was sick for three days, which was about 135 minutes of time in a classroom. When he returned to school, he came to my classroom at the end of the day so I could catch him up on what he had missed. I watched his eyes, moved at his pace, and taught him until he understood the material. In 15 minutes we were done. I was amazed.

Upon reflection, I realized that when I am teaching one on one, I don't have to take roll, pass out papers, make announcements, and answer a lot of questions, nor did I have to address issues of discipline. Much of a classroom teacher's time is taken up with managing the classroom dynamics of a large group of students. Experts have calculated that out of an hour of classroom interaction, there are only about ten minutes or less of effective teaching that occurs.

Concept Mastery

In all of my teaching assignments in various schools, I learned the importance of understanding the concepts of math and not just memorizing the facts and formulas. Knowing the essential facts and formulas and understanding the concepts of math, are equally important for a student to become a confident problem solver. If you have done other MathUSee courses you can see how and why I developed my curriculum as I did. The textbooks I used in the classroom often moved quickly from one topic to another without providing adequate time for the new topic to be mastered. These same books also lacked sufficient hands-on illustrations to help students "see" math and understand it. I wished there was a program to help students see and understand math, while providing them the time they need to master what they had been taught. I didn't know of one available, so I created one!

Communicating with Professional Educators

Teaching senior high, junior high, and elementary students at public, private, and Christian schools, helped me understand all three of these different school environments and the challenges at each level. Being a teacher at these private and public schools, as well as a little teaching at the college level, was instrumental in my ability to understand and connect with certified classroom instructors. It takes one to know one.

A Gift

When I started to receive awards for teaching math in a public high school, I began to recognize that perhaps God had given me a gift for teaching. This has since been confirmed many times, but this was my first inkling. I had never planned on being a teacher. My experience attending public school taught me that school was stressful, and even traumatic, at times. I would not have chosen to go back to this environment, but God knew what He was doing. I thoroughly enjoyed teaching young people, and to this day I miss being in the classroom. Every day was different and filled with new challenges. I like people. I also discovered I enjoyed seeing the light of understanding appear in the eyes of the students I was teaching. I was designed to teach.

Importance of Parents

I have worked for years teaching in Sunday schools, leading youth groups, overseeing and volunteering at summer camps, in addition to being a teacher of young adults. One of the main lessons I observed in all of these arenas was that you cannot replace parents. Involved, committed parents have the greatest impact on their children. Teachers, programs, churches, and ministries can support young people, but parents are the primary influencers of their progeny.

Providence of God

Having a special needs son opened up a whole new world to me. If I had not been a dad to a child with Down Syndrome, I would not be aware of the large population of children with Autism, Down Syndrome, and Cerebral Palsy. One of the organizations that has been a blessing to me and my family is Joni and Friends. We first met them at a summer Family Retreat. These weeklong events were created to minister to the whole family. This wonderful ministry was founded by Joni Eareckson Tada as a result of her diving accident in 1967. I am not sure how little colorful blocks and the curriculum I designed works so well with special leaners, but it does. We have received many letters and emails from grateful parents and students who are finally able to succeed in learning math. I didn't even know what dyscalculia and dysgraphia meant until these families let me know how MathUSee had helped them. Children with dyslexia have also been helped. I am sharing this to magnify God who graciously used a burned-out classroom teacher to provide for his family and help many others in the process.

Burn Out

When John was born, I was fragile. I had a tendency to work too hard and be involved in too many activities. I was teaching, the pastor of our church fellowship, and several other worthwhile activities. During the first year of his life, John almost died of a virus and had open heart surgery which was followed a few months later by intestinal surgery. Caring for our other three sons and making multiple trips to the hospital took a toll on my health and the health of our family. I was unable to continue serving in all of these capacities, so I resigned from each my responsibilities one after another and eventually the next summer, our family moved to Massachusetts to regroup and heal. I was burned out emotionally. I taught one year in a Christian School, then began tutoring individuals and small groups in math. One group asked me to develop materials for their children as I taught them week by week. The program I developed for these families, was the beginning of MathUSee.

Looking back I can see clearly that if John had not been born into our home, I would not have written MathUSee. Since that difficult time, thousands of kids with learning issues have now been helped by this multi-sensory math program. Men and women affected by disability, would not be working for MathUSee today. We would probably not have chosen to have a son affected with a disability, but we are very grateful God chose to give him to us.

Closing Reflections on Work and Employment

Work is Necessary

God designed us to work. He created us to work six days followed by resting one day each week. Having a job, and doing it well, provides dignity and purpose for people. As I am writing this section, it is now the first week of January. Christmas has been celebrated, followed by New Year's Eve and New Year's Day. Because of how the holidays landed, it was a long break. Most people are now back on the job. I was speaking to my graphic designer this morning, and she shared how she liked being back at her computer and feeling productive. The holidays were nice, but she missed the rhythm of her work schedule. God designed us to work. When we do what we were designed to do, we experience a special kind of satisfaction.

Work Provides Dignity

Work is especially meaningful for the "least of these;" those individuals who are affected by a disability. My son John loves to go to work. He does not enjoy holidays or snow days. He anticipates being a part of the shipping team at MathUSee. Work empowers him. He can sense that he is making a contribution to a company because of what he has accomplished. If you are working with some of these special folks, please don't patronize them. They sense your attitude. Rather, seek to treat them as you would want to be treated if you were in their shoes. Remember, they have value because of who they are, not what they do. They are our neighbors who were also created in the image and likeness of God.

You are Not What You Do

I am not the math guy. I am not the conference speaker. I am an adopted child of God. Don't let your business define you. Work hard, work smart, work with God, but remember that your identity is that you and I are adopted children of God by faith in Jesus. You may lose your business, and most of your money, but God is still your Dad, and He loves you for who you are, and not for what you do.

Since God is God, and He lovingly and wisely is guiding your life, consider these passages from His heart:

> "Whatever your hand finds to do, do it with your might." (Ecclesiastes 9:10)

> "Lazy people want much but get little, but those who work hard will prosper." (Prov. 13:4)

> "Work willingly at whatever you do, as though you were working for the Lord rather than for people." (Colossians 3:23, NLT)

COMPOUND INTEREST

Simple Interest

There are two kinds of interest: simple and compound. Simple interest is the amount a bank, or savings and loan, pays on the amount you are originally depositing or starting with. This amount of money is your principal. If you put $200.00 in a savings account that agrees to pay you 8% interest annually, you would receive $16.00 at the end of the year ($200.00 × 0.08 = $16.00). This is straightforward and simple. In order to receive the interest payment of $16.00, you will need to leave the principal, $200.00, in the bank for the entire year. In the second year, you would also receive 8% on the original principal and you would again receive ($200.00 × 0.08 = $16.00). The interest is paid only on the principal. Hence the name "simple interest."

If you leave your money in the bank for 10 years, your balance will be $360.00. This is the sum of the principal, $200.00, plus 10 years times $16.00, which is $160.00. $200.00 + (10 × $16.00) = $200.00 + $160.00 = $360.00

Compound Interest

What if another bank decides to compete and says they will pay the same interest rate, but they will compound your interest? Which is the better overall rate? When they use the term compound, they mean they will pay interest on the balance for each period, which includes both the original principal and any interest you have received up to that point. You are now receiving interest on your principal plus accumulating interest on your interest. If the interest were calculated annually, the difference would look like this:

	8% Simple Interest Added Annually			8% Interest Compounded Annually		
Year	Original principal	Interest on principal	Ending balance	Starting balance	Interest on balance	Ending balance
1	$200.00	$16.00	$216.00	$200.00	$16.00	$216.00
2	$200.00	$16.00	$232.00	$216.00	$17.28	$233.28
3	$200.00	$16.00	$248.00	$233.28	$18.66	$251.94
4	$200.00	$16.00	$264.00	$251.94	$20.16	$272.10

The difference after only a few years is rather small, but as you will see later it can add up to a lot over a longer period of time.

Compounded Quarterly

Interest can also be compounded more frequently than just once at the end of the year, which makes a smaller difference. Let's recalculate that first year but compound the interest quarterly instead of annually. Since there are four quarters in a year and the rate is 8% per year, we are going to receive 2% each quarter (8% ÷ 4 quarters = 2%). Let's do a quarter at a time.

Example 1

First Quarter

$200.00 × 0.02 = $4.00 interest

$200.00 (principal) + $4.00 (interest) = $204.00

Your investment has grown by $4.00 in three months.

Second Quarter

$204.00 × 0.02 = $4.08 interest

$204.00 (balance) + $4.08 (interest) = $208.08

Your investment has grown by $8.08 in six months.

Third Quarter

$208.08 × 0.02 = $4.162 interest

$208.08 (balance) + $4.162 (interest) = $212.24

Your investment has grown by $12.24 in nine months.

Fourth Quarter

$212.24 × 0.02 = $4.245 interest

$212.24 (balance) + $4.245 (interest) = $216.49

Your investment has grown by $16.49 in twelve months.

A simple interest of 8% gives you $216.00 at the end of the year. If we begin with the same principal, but compound it four times during the year instead of once at the end of the year, the new balance is $216.49. The extra 49 cents isn't much, but the difference continues to grow over time. This same interest rate compounded monthly would yield $216.60 and if it were compounded weekly would increase to $216.64. The best return on your investment is when it is compounded continuously. Look at each of the columns. The differences based on how often you are compounding aren't much, but the difference between simple interest and compound interest becomes very large over a longer period of time. Here's a comparison:

After	Simple Interest	Compounded Yearly	Compounded Quarterly	Compounded Monthly	Compounded Weekly	Compounded Continuously
1 year	$216.00	$216.00	$216.49	$216.60	$216.64	$216.66
2 years	$232.00	$233.28	$234.33	$234.58	$234.67	$234.70
5 years	$280.00	$293.87	$297.19	$297.97	$298.27	$298.36
10 years	$360.00	$431.78	$441.61	$443.93	$444.83	$445.11
50 years	$1,000.00	$9,380.32	$10,496.98	$10,775.64	$10,886.12	$10,919.63

The Compound Interest Formula

Now that you have seen how much work would be involved in computing compound interest at every step in the process, consider the following formula, which lets us calculate the end result for any period of time.

In its simpler form the equation for interest compounded over any unit of time is

$F_V = P(1 + r)^t$ where
F_V is the future value
P is the Principal
r is the rate of interest per unit of time
t is the number of units of time

In cases where interest is compounded more than once per year it can be difficult to remember that the rate per unit of time is not the same as the annual rate (for example if the unit of time was months, r would have to be the monthly interest rate with this formula). To help you remember this, we can rewrite the formula to look like this:

$$F_V = P\left(1 + \frac{r}{n}\right)^{y \cdot n}$$

F_V is the Future Value
P is the Principal
r is the annual rate of interest
n is the number of times the money is compounded in a year
y is the number of years

Here is the situation from Example 1 (8% annual interest compounded quarterly for 4 years):

$$F_V = P\left(1 + \frac{r}{n}\right)^{y \cdot n}$$
$$F_V = \$200\left(1 + \frac{0.08}{4}\right)^{1 \cdot 4}$$
$$F_V = \$200(1 + 0.02)^4$$
$$F_V = \$200(1.02)^4$$
$$F_V = \$200(1.08243216)$$
$$F_V = \$216.486432 \text{ which rounds to } \$216.49$$

You have several options for solving the problems in the student workbook which involve compound interest.

1. You can calculate it by hand for each step and record the answer to each step on paper.
2. Or you can use a spreadsheet program to repeat the same calculations for each step, which will be much faster than pencil and paper.
3. Or you can use the compound interest formula, either by hand or with a calculator.
4. Or you can use the Stewardship Investment Calculator on the MathUSee website at: www.mathusee.com/invest/

Equivalent Interest Rates

Figure 1

Year	Simple Interest			Compound interest		
	Starting balance	8% interest	Ending balance	Starting balance	8% interest	Ending balance
1	$200.00	$16.00	$216.00	$200.00	$16.00	$216.00
2	$216.00	$16.00	$232.00	$216.00	$17.28	$233.28
3	$232.00	$16.00	$248.00	$233.28	$18.66	$251.94
4	$248.00	$16.00	$264.00	$251.94	$20.16	$272.10
5	$264.00	$16.00	$280.00	$272.10	$21.77	$293.87
6	$280.00	$16.00	$296.00	$293.87	$23.50	$317.37
7	$296.00	$16.00	$312.00	$317.37	$25.39	$342.76
8	$312.00	$16.00	$328.00	$342.76	$27.43	$370.19
9	$328.00	$16.00	$344.00	$370.19	$29.61	$399.80
10	$344.00	$16.00	$360.00	$399.80	$31.98	$431.78

Here is a graph showing the comparison of simple interest and compound interest in our first example at the beginning of the lesson. The simple interest and compound interest lines, both begin with a balance of $200.00. The simple interest is shown by a straight line, while the compound interest is represented by an exponential curve.

Figure 2

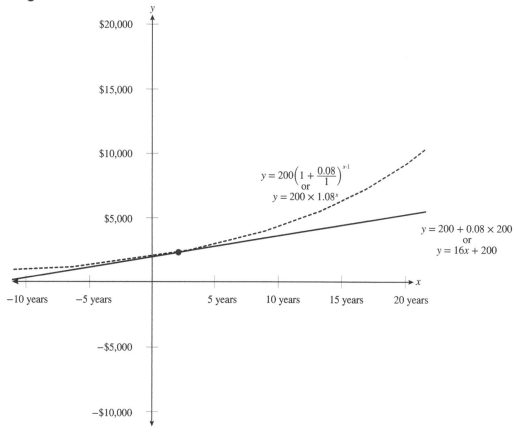

$$y = 200\left(1 + \frac{0.08}{1}\right)^{x \cdot 1}$$
or
$$y = 200 \times 1.08^x$$

$$y = 200 + 0.08 \times 200$$
or
$$y = 16x + 200$$

Working Backwards

One interesting question is, "What would the annual simple interest rate have to be to produce the same result as an 8% rate of interest compounded annually for 10 years?" We can find this by working backward. In the example in figure 1, we can see the result of our $200.00 investment in an 8% interest rate that is compounded annually. At the end of 10 years, the final balance is $431.78. If we subtract the original principal of $200.00, to discover how much of that was earned as interest. $431.78 - $200.00 = $231.78

Since we are looking for the simple interest rate, we can divide $231.78 by 10 to find out how much interest was earned for each of the ten years. $231.78 ÷ 10 = $23.18 when we round to cents. What percent of $200.00 is $23.18?

Solution 1

$$W_P \times \$200.00 = \$23.18$$
$$W_P = \frac{\$23.18}{\$200.00}$$
$$W_P = 0.1159$$
$$W_P = 11.59\%$$

Another way to think of this problem is to ask yourself what kind of simple interest rate of return would you need to yield $23.18 in one year on a principal of $200.00. Since our principal is $200.00, if we divide it by 2 then we would have a new principal of $100.00. But we can't divide the principal by 2 without dividing the interest return as well. When we divide $23.18 by 2, then the interest return is $11.59.

Solution 2

$$W_P \times \$200.00 = \$23.18$$
$$\frac{W_P \times \$200.00}{2} = \frac{\$23.18}{2}$$
$$W_P \times \$100.00 = \$11.59$$
$$W_P = \frac{\$11.59}{\$100.00}$$
$$W_P = 0.1159$$
$$W_P = 11.59\%$$

This is much simpler math, since to make $11.59 on a principal of $100.00 your interest rate would have to be $11.59%.

If you are computing the interest over several years, you would need to find the final value, then subtract the original principal, and divide the total interest by the number of years of the investment.

Example: Find the final value of a six-year investment with a principal of $7,000.00 at 4.25%, compounded continuously, by using the Stewardship Investment Calculator.

If you had your money in an account with simple interest, what would the interest rate have to be to give you the same return on your money?

Solution 3

$7,000.00 with an interest rate of 4.25% compounded continuously for six years is $9,033.23.

First subtract the principal from the final value to discover the interest which has been accumulated. $9,033.23 - $7,000.00 = $2,033.23

Then divide this amount of interest by how many years it has been accumulating.

$2,033.23 divided by 6 for the six years = $338.87

Now we can find what percent per year of simple interest.

$$W_P \times \$7,000.00 = \$338.87$$

$$W_P = \frac{\$338.87}{\$7,000.00}$$

$$W_P = 0.04841$$

$$W_P = 4.841\%$$

Solution 4

We could also divide both the principal and the interest rate by 70.

$$W_P \times \$7,000.00 = \$338.87$$

$$\frac{W_P \times \$7,000.00}{70} = \frac{\$338.87}{70}$$

$$W_P \times \$100.00 = \$4.841$$

$$W_P = \frac{\$4.841}{\$100.00}$$

$$W_P = 0.04841$$

$$W_P = 4.841\%$$

INVESTING

From Your Surplus

Let's fast forward a few years and assume you now have a regular source of income. You have finished your formal education, have a job, and perhaps you are newly married. When those paychecks begin coming, return your tithe, set aside amounts for each of your budgeted obligations, and hopefully you will still have a few dollars left over, which is your surplus.

I am assuming you have paid off any credit card debt, and are now looking towards the future to begin investing for your elderly years, prepare for emergencies, and want to develop a nest egg for your children. This next stage of life is when you begin making investment decisions to achieve these goals. You are wondering how to best invest your surplus to prepare for the future.

Avoid Rash Speculation

At some point in your life as a responsible wage earner, someone will approach you with an opportunity to invest money in a get rich quickly scheme. Phrases like "once in a lifetime opportunity" and "can't miss" and "limited offer to only a few people" will pop up in the sales pitch. Don't bite. These folks want you to speculate not invest. The difference between investing and speculating is significant.

When you speculate, you risk losing everything you put into the money-making scheme. One cardinal rule of thumb is the greater the risk, the greater the reward. You may hear of a few people who have "made a killing" on a speculation, but there are multitudes of people who have lost their money.

"The simple believes everything, but the prudent gives thought to his steps." (Proverbs 14:15)

Embrace Careful Investing

When we talk about investing in this course, we are referring to methodical and patient planning for our future. A good illustration may be the grocery store. If you visit a grocery store with a set budget and a shopping list (and having eaten before you go), you will not be tempted to buy what looks great or sale items that look attractive. You walk in with a plan, and make decisions based on your plan. If you head to the store with no list and without a set budget, and you are hungry, you can waste a bunch of money buying what looks good, but not what you need.

One investment advisor that I respect is Austin Pryor who founded Sound Mind Investing. He encourages folks to avoid rash speculation but aim for a modest return of 3%-5% above inflation.

"Wealth from get-rich-quick schemes quickly disappears; wealth from hard work grows over time." (Proverbs 13:11, NLT)

Inflation

Price inflation is when prices gradually rise and are higher. Or inflation may be defined as taking more money to buy the same item, like milk. I did a little research on the price of a gallon of milk in the past few decades as compared to the average salary of a person working in the United States. A gallon of milk sold for about $1.60 in 1980, $2.25 in 1990, $2.80 in 2000, and $3.80 in 2010.

The average salary in 1980 was $12,513, in 1990 it was $21,028, in 2000 it grew to $32,155, and in 2010 it was $41,674.

Dividing the salary in 2010 by the salary in 1980 $41,674 ÷ $12,513 = that is a ratio of 3.33 to 1. If this ratio is applied to the price of milk, then we multiply $1.60 by 3.33 and milk should now cost $5.33, if the inflation of milk was the same as the inflation of salary.

If the price of milk was the same today as it was 30 years ago, this would not be a big issue. But prices keep rising, and the percentage at which they rise each year is called the rate of inflation.

Since prices keep inflating or expanding, if your money isn't growing or increasing as the same rate of inflation, you are losing ground. For example, consider $100.00 put in a shoe box in 1980. That money would have bought 62.5 gallons of milk at $1.60 per gallon. In 2010, with the price at $3.80 per gallon, the $100.00 from 1980 now only buys 26.3 gallons of milk.

The price of milk increased or inflated, but your money did not. If you had placed that $100.00 in a simple savings account with a rate of return of 3% compounded monthly, it would have grown to $245.68. At $3.80 per gallon you could buy 64.7 gallons of milk. Since the price of most items increases from year to year your money needs to be growing as well.

Economists keep track of the cost of many items and come up with an annual percentage increase, which is the rate of inflation. Over the previous twenty years, inflation has averaged about 2% per year. I mention this to encourage you not to lose money. If you have your money in a savings account at your local bank with a rate of 1.5%, and inflation is over 2%, then you might want to consider other places to invest your money. Because of these numbers I have taken my emergency fund out of the local bank which is paying less than 1% and have it in an online bank receiving 2.75% interest.

Harness the Power of Compound Interest like the Determined Tortoise

I would like to encourage you to begin setting aside some of your paycheck on a regular basis to save for the future. As we saw in a previous lesson, the sooner you begin saving, the greater will be the impact of compound interest. The tortoise saves a little regularly over a long period of time, while the hare waits until the last minute then begins to save furiously. As in the fable, the tortoise is generally the winner.

Example 1, the 15 for 25 Scenario for the Determined Tortoise

When you are 15, you determine to invest $15.00 per month in a fund with an interest rate 5%, compounded monthly. You maintain this habit for 25 years and thanks to the exponential return of compound interest, your nest egg has a value of $8,932.65. The amount you have invested is $15.00 per month, for 25 years, or $4.500.00. The earned interest is $4,432.65

($8,932.65 - $4,500).

Example 2, the 25 for 15 Scenario for the Speedy Hare

When you are 25, you determine to invest $25.00 per month in a fund with an interest rate 5%, compounded monthly. You maintain this habit for 15 years and thanks to the exponential return of compound interest, your nest egg has a value of $6,682.22. The amount you have invested is $25.00 per month, for 15 years, or $4,500.00. The earned interest is $2,182.22 ($6,682.22 - $4,500).

Example 3, the 40 for 1 Scenario for the Procrastinating Woodchuck

When you are 40, you finally get around to investing $375.00 per month in a fund with an interest rate 5%, compounded monthly. You maintain this habit all year and thanks to the exponential return of compound interest, your last-minute investment has a value of $4,604.57. The amount you have invested is $375.00 per month, for 1 year, or $4,500.00. The earned interest is $104.57 ($4,604.57 - $4,500).

	Invested monthly	Length in years	Total invested	Value of investment	Interest accumulated
Tortoise	$15	25	$4,500	$8,932.65	$4,432.65
Hare	$25	15	$4,500	$6,682.22	$2,182.22
Woodchuck	$375	1	$4,500	$4,604.57	$104.57

The best exercise is the one you do.

The best investment is the one you begin.

APY and APR

When you enter this stage in your life, you will begin to see the initials pop up in credit card ads and loans for purchasing a new car. They are similar sounding, but they are two different ways of representing simple interest and compound interest.

The initials APR are for Annual Percentage Rate. Think annual interest. An advertisement will inform you that the APR to buy a new car is 18%. That is the interest rate. When the interest is compounded more than once per year the APR will be lower than the APY and looks better than the APY because it appears to be less, but this percent can be deceptive.

The APY stands for Annual Percentage Yield. When you calculate the APY you begin with the interest rate, or APR, then compound it for one year to find the APY. For example, an APR of 18% compounded yearly has an APY of 18%, but an APR of 18% compounded monthly has an APY of 19.56%. To change from an interest rate compounded yearly (or a simple interest rate) to an interest rate compounded more than once per year you can use the Compound Interest Formula and modify it to just show the interest for one year.

$$\text{APY} = \left(1 + \frac{r}{n}\right)^n - 1$$

As usual, r is the annual rate of interest (APR) and n is the number of times it is compounded in a year. We left out the y because we are looking at one year and 1 times n is n. We assumed a principal of 1 and then subtracted 1 so that we would just get the interest and not the ending balance.

The APY shows you exactly how much interest you're considering, whether in a loan or an investment. When you know the APY you can begin to compare apples to apples when looking at different borrowing offers and investment opportunities. Be careful when comparing an APR to an APY as they are sometimes different.

Example 4

Find the APY for a 18% APR compounded monthly

$$APY = \left(1 + \frac{0.18}{12}\right)^{12} - 1$$

$$APY = (1.015)^{12} - 1$$

$$APY = 0.19561817146 \text{ or approximately } 19.56\%$$

Example 5

Find the APY for a 12% APR compounded quarterly

$$APY = \left(1 + \frac{0.12}{4}\right)^{4} - 1$$

$$APY = (1.03)^{4} - 1$$

$$APY = 0.12550881 \text{ or approximately } 12.55\%$$

Credit Card Concerns

Compound interest can be a blessing when you are investing and seeing your money grow. Credit cards also use APR and APY and compound interest on your debt. It is helpful to me to think of credit card debt as reverse compound interest. The borrower pays interest on what they owe, in addition to the monthly charge, which is a transaction fee or late fee for not paying off your balance in full.

The average interest rate (APR) for credit cards in 2019 is 18%, but since credit card interest is compounded daily if you don't pay the balance each month, that works out to a little over 19.7% APY. It helps me to look at specific examples to understand how credit card debt works. Lets examine what transpires when I purchase a large ticket item for $5,000.00 on my credit card with an 18% APR.

When my statement comes it will show the balance of $5,000.00 and then have a minimum payment amount due. Here are two possible methods to determine the minimum payment: 2% of the balance; or the interest on the balance, plus 1% of the balance.

Minimum Payment option 1

2% of the balance of $5,000.00 is $100.00, so that would be the minimum balance for the first month.

Option 1 will take 472 months to be rid of your debt and the total paid during 39 years and 4 months is $13,396.53 in interest. As the balance decreases, your payment decreases, but it is still sad to even consider this. Don't forget that if you aren't making the minimum payments you will be charged an additional late payment fee which could increase the time and cost substantially.

Minimum Payment option 2

The monthly interest plus 1% of the balance.

The monthly interest rate is approximately equal to 18% divided by 12, or 1.5%. 1.5% of 5,000 is $75.00. 1% of $5,000.00 is $50.00, so adding them together the minimum balance for the first month

Option 2 will take 273 months to be rid of your debt and the total paid during 22 years and 9 months is $6,923.09 in interest. As the balance decreases, your payment decreases. The original 5,000 and we will have spent an additional $6,923 in interest. That $5,000 charge ended up costing almost $12,000. Ouch!

The Rule of 72

Try these next two problems and notice the relationship between the initial amount you invest and the final value of your investment.

Example 6

Find the final value of $820.00 invested for 12 years at an annual interest rate of 6% compounded continuously. Using the MathUSee investment calculator, the final value is $1,684.64.

Example 7

Find the final value of $820.00 invested for 6 years at an annual interest rate of 12% compounded continuously. Using the MathUSee investment calculator, the final value is $1,684.64.

Do you see the similarity between these two answers? In example 6, the final value is $1,684.64, and in example 7, the value is $1,684.64. Do you see any relationship between the number of years and the interest rate? The initial $820.00, when doubled, is $1,640.00. Both of the answers to these examples are $44.64 more than $1,640.00. Try two more problems to observe the pattern developing between the years and the interest rate.

Example 8

Find the final value of $820.00 invested for 8 years at an annual interest rate of 9% compounded continuously. Using the MathUSee investment calculator, the final value is $1,684.64.

Example 9

Find the final value of $820.00 invested for 9 years at an annual interest rate of 8% compounded continuously. Using the MathUSee investment calculator, the final value is $1,684.64.

In all of these examples, the interest rate times the number of years is 72. This is called the rule of 72. 6×12, 12×6, 8×9, and 9×8 all equal 72. The rule of 72 states that if the interest rate times the number of years is 72, then your investment will double in value. We have seen that it is close but not exact. Knowing this rule will help you get a fairly accurate approximation of the rate of return on your investments.

Diversification

> "Send your grain across the seas, and in time, profits will flow back to you. But divide your investments among many places, for you do not know what risks might lie ahead." (Ecclesiastes 11:1, NLT)

> "Cast your bread upon the waters, for you will find it after many days. Give a portion to seven, or even to eight, for you know not what disaster may happen on earth." (Ecclesiastes 11:1)

Scripture encourages us to not put all of our eggs in one basket, but to invest in many places. I have listened to financial advisors encourage me to invest your money in seven or eight different places. This is called diversifying your investing. Talk to your parents, investment counselors, and advisors at the bank. Read books, and generally educate yourself on the possibilities. This topic is outside the scope of this course, and many helpful books have been written on this subject. I am not an expert in investing, but here is one resource I have found helpful and reliable. Sound Mind Investing was founded by Austin Pryor after a conversation with Larry Burkett. I respect both of these men. https://soundmindinvesting.com/investing-basics/the-9-principles

Portfolio

All of your investments make up your portfolio. This can be a combination of real estate, stocks, collectibles, IRS and Savings Accounts.

Real Estate

Real estate means the portion of all the things you own (estate) that stay in one place and don't move when you do—in other words your land and any structures built on it. Buying a home will probably be your main investment for your retirement years. In most scenarios, if you own a home for many years and then sell it, it will be worth much more than when you bought it. Many people today are buying land as an investment, since, based on trends over the past several decades, it seems to be the most reliable place to put their money. Thank God that we own our own home. This is generally a family's most significant, and most reliable investment.

Collectibles

I am not a collector. But when my father passed away I inherited some gold and silver coins. Some people have significant collections of baseball cards, art, stamps, or comic books. These can be a neat part of your portfolio.

Savings Account

Probably the easiest way to get started saving and investing is to open a savings account at your local bank (or online) and make it a habit to contribute to it regularly when you get a paycheck. Generally, the rate of return is lower than with other options, but savings accounts are safe and convenient.

Certificate of Deposit

Another area to look at is buying a CD (certificate of deposit). With a CD you loan your money to a bank for a set time period. This will pay a little better, and you will see that the longer you leave your money with the bank, the higher the yield will be. These are advertised in the newspaper, at your bank, and on the Internet. Notice the language about the percentage yields. An APR may have a larger APY.

IRA

I just received an encouraging email from a young lady who completed the Stewardship Curriculum. She thanked me for the class and told me that because of this lesson, she had opened a Roth IRA.

IRA stands for Individual Retirement Account. If you put money into one, you are setting aside funds for retirement. There are two kinds of IRAs, a Standard or Traditional IRA and a Roth IRA. One difference between them is when you pay taxes on this investment.

If you open a standard IRA your taxes are deferred until you begin to withdraw them to use when you are older. If your income is $45,000 per year and you contribute $6,000 into your IRA, then you only pay taxes on $39,000. So you save money on taxes now. In 30 or 40 years, after this money has been growing, thanks to compound interest and wise investments, and you begin to withdraw from your nest egg, you will have to report how much you withdrew and pay taxes on this money. Paying taxes later is called deferring taxes.

One advantage of a Roth IRA is that you pay taxes on your income now, then put it into your account. When you take the money out years later, you don't have to pay taxes on it. If your income is $45,000 and you pay income taxes on this amount, then make a contribution of $6,000, and it grows and compounds, when you begin to make withdrawals, you don't owe any taxes. Many people assume they will be making more money after they retire and in that case it would be wise to pay taxes and open a Roth IRA when you are younger.

401(k)

The most popular retirement investment vehicle today is the 401(k). It is a strange name, but originates from the subsection in the Revenue Act of 1978. There are two kinds of 401(k) plans, one is like the standard IRA and the other is like the Roth IRA. Some advantages of a 401(k) are that there are higher limits on how much you can invest and your employer may match your contribution up to a certain amount or a specific percentage. These contributions vary from company to company but when you are hired ask them to explain their plan.

Some people refer to a matching contribution from your employer and as "free money." If I were working for ACME Lawnmowers and for every dollar I contributed to an IRA, ACME would match the same amount up to $2,500; what they contribute is "free money" to me. Since I am paid 26 times per year, or every two weeks, I decide to contribute $75 per paycheck. At the end of the year, I now have $3,900 in my IRA, $1,950 out of my pocket that I contributed, and $1,950 from ACME when they matched what I contributed. This second portion is a gift from the company and is often referred to as "free money."

One of the reasons Congress passed this law was to give employees incentives to save for retirement. When you move to another workplace, you will be able to move your 401(k) as well. As of Sept. 30, 2017, 401(k) plans accounted for almost 20% of the $27.2 trillion in total retirement-plan assets in the United States, according to the Investment Company Institute.

Advisor

When you follow these principles and begin to acquire a nice sized nest egg, consider hiring a financial advisor to manage your IRAs and other financial investments. I am frugal and tend to do my own taxes and make own investments. But years ago I hired an accountant to do my taxes, and even after paying his fees, he saved me money because of his knowledge of the tax code.

Because of this experience, I also have a financial adviser to oversee my investments and IRAs. He is paid a small percentage of my portfolio. He is good at what he does. I work at what I am good at, and pay him to do what he is good at.

Continue Your Education

I hope you are enjoying the Stewardship Curriculum. I also hope it is not the last class you take on being a good steward of your time, talents, and treasure. As an adult I have listened to Larry Burkett and Howard Dayton for many hours on the radio. I have also attended weekend seminars and participated in small group studies on financial topics. May I strongly encourage you to be a lifelong learner and continue to grow in your knowledge of being a good steward of the resources which God has given you? You have a good foundation and I hope that you continue to build on the concepts in this course and consider taking a class from one or all of these organizations:

Compass https://compass1.org
Crown https://www.crown.org
Financial Peace University, by Dave Ramsey https://www.daveramsey.com

Traditional Charity: Praying, Giving, Going

For decades, traditional giving focused on a willing heart and an open wallet. Needs for food, water, shelter, starving children, and spiritual darkness were presented, and you had a choice of three responses: pray, give, or go. I have always considered prayer to be a given, followed by giving money or resources, and as God leads, serving on a short-term summer missions trip or as a lifetime calling. I have participated in two short-term summer mission projects, and visited a children's home in India as a member of their board of directors. Before we delve into how to respond to the needs of the world, let's examine what we believe about praying, giving, going, and seeing the needs first hand.

Praying

There is a separate lesson on praying in the Scripture Studies. John Bunyan has succinctly summed up my sentiments. "You can do more than pray, after you have prayed, but you cannot do more than pray until you have prayed." Amen. John Bunyan is the author of Pilgrim's Progress which he wrote while serving a twelve-year sentence in prison because of his faith.

Giving

I don't remember thinking much about giving until I received Jesus as my Savior and was born from above. I was a new creature in Christ, and church was very different for me than when I had attended as a boy. I now relished hearing the word of God, singing worship songs, and praying. It was as if I had awoken from a spiritual slumber and was now fully engaged in the life of the church.

As a young earnest Christian, I loved to read biographies of committed Christians. Many of them were wonderful givers such as R. G. LeTourneau, who gave most of his income away instead of amassing a fortune for himself. This good man only completed seventh grade in school, yet made astounding contributions to the manufacturing and construction industry, and he gave large sums of money to support the work of Christ. His book, Mover of Men and Mountains certainly inspired me. LeTourneau worked hard and gave generously. I recall how he wanted to be able to give 90% to others and live on 10% of his income. I aspired to be like men and women of God who were willing, open-handed, generous, cheerful givers.

I have come to realize that giving is a Christian virtue which springs from God Himself. God loved us and saw our need, so He took the initiative and sent His Son to take away our sins: "God so loved the world that he gave." (John 3:16) Jesus also encourages us to give as we have received: "Freely ye have received, freely give." (Matthew 10:8 KJV)

In attending church over the years, I became aware of opportunities to give to mission, charities, and many other worthwhile activities. It is hard to recall exactly what I heard such a long time ago, but I do recollect examining and searching my own heart more than learning about the need itself.

Was I a cheerful giver? Was I generous? Was my heart open and pliable to the needs of others? Would I be willing to give to someone in need? Would I be a part of the solution? Often, I was confronted with staggering statistics of the number of people who had never had a chance to hear about Jesus dying for their sins. Someone would tell about the billions of individuals who did not have ready access to food, clothing, or clean drinking water. When I opened my heart and my wallet, I felt like I was making a difference in someone's life, and it felt good.

Statistics tell us that I am not the only one who gives to help others less fortunate than myself. Citizens of the United States of America are wonderful responders to the needs of others deemed less fortunate. We give billions to disasters and other charitable organizations. A poll showed 90% of Americans are involved in some form of charity or nonprofit organization. (Note: I live in the United States and am writing from this perspective. If you live in a different country, I encourage you to do some research and see how much your average countryman donates.)

Going to Help Others in the United States

During the summers when I was 16 and 17, I spent a few weeks at a service project in one of the poorest counties in Kentucky. Our church youth group raised money for the adventure by selling hoagies. Early one summer morning we packed a bunch of earnest teenagers and a few adult volunteers into a few vans and drove from Pittsburgh, Pennsylvania to Wilmore, Kentucky, where we stayed in dormitories at a local college. During the day we were each sent out to serve the poor and needy in different capacities.

On the first morning, my group went to assist a family that needed to have the outhouse moved over a new hole. They also needed to have a drainage ditch dug from the kitchen to the backyard, because they did not have indoor plumbing. After we finished these tasks, we were gratefully thanked for our labors. The best part of this story is that we went back the next summer to see this family, and noticed that they had made other improvements on their home by themselves. It seems that having us help with a few of the larger jobs inspired them to do other smaller tasks by themselves.

On my second assignment job that week, I was asked to work side-by-side with a coal miner who had lost his job when he developed epilepsy. Together, he and I hung sheet rock on a large room in his home. This was hard work, but after a day or two we completed the ceiling. When we were done and it was time to say our goodbyes, he gripped my hand and looked me in the eye. I was deeply moved by this simple man's earnest thanks simply expressed in the form of a firm handshake. We had become friends as we worked together on this project. I was so moved that I wept in the back of the car as we drove back to our dormitory.

For the next several years while I was in college, when people asked me what I planned on doing when I graduated, I told them I wanted to move to Appalachia and work with the poor.

Traveling Abroad

When a need arose, I did not think about the implications of my giving, or about the people who were receiving my donations, I simply wanted to be a cheerful giver and help.

While I was attending seminary, I met a man from South India who became a good friend. He and his wife had begun a children's home to care for poor children and orphans. I saw pictures of the kids and heard many stories of how much these children lacked in food, water, clothing, and shelter. I had an opportunity to make a difference in the lives of these children. A nonprofit entity was set up to channel money to the home, and to help raise funds for the children. Fund raising newsletters were sent out, and soon I was chairman of the board in the United States. I did not have much money, but I was willing to donate my time, energy, and prayers.

All seemed well until rumors began to surface about how the money was being used, and questions arose about whether the children were receiving a healthy diet. I began seeking counsel from Christian leaders who had ties with this part of the world and learned that most of the charitable work with children was a scam to support individuals. The funds which were being sent to them rarely made it to the children. I had no way of confirming the validity of the work, so I made a surprise visit and found, to my relief, the children were being cared for and my fears were temporarily assuaged.

However, within a few years other concerns and accusations came to light concerning the makeup of the staff, which was made up mostly of family members and relatives. Eventually we discovered that the land and buildings which had been constructed for the ministry were not owned by the nonprofit organization, as we assumed, but were titled in the name of the family.

I was disheartened and learned a big lesson. Many charities are not what they seem. It is not enough to be willing to give and be involved; careful thinking and discernment must accompany a willing heart and a desire to do good.

Treasure Follows the Heart

When I was attending seminary, I took a class on the "World Mission of the Church" and participated in lunchtime prayer meetings. I learned much about the spiritual needs of the world. I discovered that billions of people have never had the opportunity to read God's word or hear that Jesus has died for their sins and risen again to give them the hope of eternal life. When a compelling missionary would visit our campus, I was ready to sign up and become a foreign missionary to carry God's word to the lost. I never sensed God giving me the green light to go, but my heart has ever been with those who do go, and I have been supporting them financially and in prayer for many years. Since 2003, I have made one or two trips abroad each year to encourage and help missionaries with the educational needs of their family. God has granted my desire to serve Him on this field.

When I graduated from Gordon-Conwell Theological Seminary, Sandi and I were married, and we began serving at a small church. I was the youth pastor and assistant to the pastor. While serving this fellowship of believers my convictions began to grow about the importance of the family in the plan of God. I began speaking about family devotions and family dynamics decades ago and this grew into a ministry called Building Faith Families. Because of these convictions I have supported and prayed for other groups such as Focus on the Family, Family Life Today, and Pennsylvania Family Institute.

Another cause that is near to my heart is the pro-life movement that fights for the lives of the unborn children who are being murdered in their mother's womb. I have participated in the March for Life in Washington, DC, and support many like-minded organizations and ministries that stand for life.

I am telling you about the burdens on my heart for spreading the gospel and making disciples of the nations, supporting pro-life causes, and defending the unborn, because that is where my time, energy, prayers, and finances have been going for many years. Jesus says, "Where your treasure is, there will your heart be also." (Luke 12:34) The heart is passionate about we value and hold most dear. I think the converse is also true; what my heart holds most dear, my treasure will follow. My heart is committed to these groups and causes, and my giving has followed my heart.

One of the struggles I have is trying to discern if I am giving just so I will feel good or because my efforts will make a significant impact. I expect this will always be a struggle, since we don't know our own hearts and we need to continue to depend on God to give us the correct motives and attitudes.

Loving my Neighbor

Jesus was asked, "'Teacher, which is the great commandment in the Law?' And he said to him, 'You shall love the Lord your God with all your heart and with all your soul and with all your mind.' This is the great and first commandment. And a second is like it: 'You shall love your neighbor as yourself.' On these two commandments depend all the Law and the Prophets." (Matthew 22:36-40)

Uncertain Fruit of Charity

I used to think any giving is better than no giving; I don't believe this any more. I now believe unwise giving does more harm than good. In the past few years, I have learned a better way to make a difference in the lives of those living in a hopeless cycle of poverty and dependence.

In 2011, I had breakfast with Peter Greer, who is the president of Hope International. We shared books we each had authored and had a contest to see who could read each other's book first. I set myself to read *The Poor Will be Glad* (this book has been revised as *Created to Flourish*) which Peter had co-authored. I completed it in two days and won a free breakfast! I was intrigued by this book which was the beginning of my journey to become a better steward in the areas of giving to the poor and breaking the cycle of poverty.

I also read *Toxic Charity: How Churches and Charities Hurt Those They Help (and How to Reverse It)*, by Robert D. Lupton. I have read both of these books more than once. I also read several chapters in *When Helping Hurts: How to Alleviate Poverty Without Hurting the Poor... and Yourself*, by Brain Fikkert and Steve Corbett.

Pray-Give-Go has been a part of our Christian culture for decades. It took me years of study, attending lectures, reading books, and interacting with organizations for God to transform my thinking about the physically and spiritually poor. Buckle your seatbelt and be prepared to be stretched in your thinking about a more effective way to help the needy of the world. It has taken me time to understand how giving can do more harm than good.

Who is Poor?

In the next few lessons we will examine some of the unfortunate results of applying well-meaning but outdated and ineffectual strategies for helping the poor. Before we can serve well, the first question we might consider is "What is poverty?" We usually begin by measuring their income, their lack of food, clothing, clean water, medical supplies, and shelter. I generally view poverty in physical, measurable, material terms. Those who have been immersed in a lifetime of service to the poor have found the issue is more complicated than the data found on a spreadsheet.

Poverty involves the whole man, his spirit as well as his body. In the 1990s, a study was done by the World Bank. They did something revolutionary by going directly to the poor and asking them what it means to be poor. They interviewed 60,000 people living in 60 countries who were living in poverty. Here are some of the individual responses from this three-volume publication called *Voices of the Poor*[1]

> "For a poor person everything is terrible-illness, humiliation, shame. We are cripples; we are afraid of everything: we depend on everyone. No one needs us. We are like garbage that everyone wants to get rid of." (Moldova)

> "When I don't have any [food to bring my family], I borrow, mainly from neighbors and friends. I feel ashamed standing before my children when I have nothing to feed the family. I'm not well when I am unemployed. It's terrible." (Guinea-Bissau)

> "During the past two years we have not celebrated any holidays with others. We cannot afford to invite anyone to our house and we feel uncomfortable visiting others without a present. The lack of contact leaves one depressed, creates a constant feeling of unhappiness, and a sense of low esteem." (Latvia)

> "When one is poor, she has no say in public, she feels inferior. She has no food so there is famine in her house; no clothing, and no progress in her family." (Uganda)

Notice the words used to describe what is it like to be poor. Even though the lack of material needs is mentioned, the sociological, emotional, and psychological needs are even greater. The poor experience shame and a sense of being inferior, powerless, helpless, and depressed. Some have called this state of mind a "poverty of being." This poverty is not a lack of money or food, but a description of how they feel and view themselves. They exist with a sense of shame and low self esteem for their plight while feeling isolated, hopeless, humiliated, and without a voice.

Pride

The poor have emotional and mental needs which are just as viable as physical needs. What has been a revelation to me is that I am also poor. My poverty is not a lack of physical necessities; it is internal, invisible, and hard to acknowledge. It has been called the most insidious sin, the hardest to identify, and the most dangerous. It is pride.

C.S. Lewis, one of the great Christian apologists of the 20th century, writes of pride in *Mere Christianity* which I think should be required reading for every believer. He writes:

---

1   "Voices of the Poor was an effort in the 1990s through 2000 by the World Bank to collect the experiences of the poor across the world." https://en.wikipedia.org/wiki/Voices_of_the_Poor

"Today I come to that part of Christian morals where they differ most
sharply from all other morals. There is one vice of which no man in the
world is free; which everyone loathes when he sees it in someone else;
and of which hardly any people, except Christians, ever imagine that
they are guilty themselves. I have heard people admit that they are
bad-tempered, or that they cannot keep their heads about girls or drink,
or even that they are cowards. I do not think I have ever heard anyone
who was not a Christian accuse himself of this vice. And at the same
time I have very seldom met anyone, who was not a Christian, who
showed the slightest mercy to it in others. There is no fault that makes
a man more unpopular, and no fault which we are more unconscious of
in ourselves. And the more we have it ourselves, the more we dislike
it in others. The vice I am talking of is Pride or Self-Conceit: and the
virtue opposite to it, in Christian morals, is called Humility."

Blind Spot

We mean well, but our pride reinforces our sense of superiority and the poor person's
sense of inferiority. We have a blind spot since we think that we are self-sufficient and don't
need help. We look upon the needy as less fortunate than ourselves and give out of a sense
of obligation. When we give with this mindset, both parties suffer, the giver and the person
receiving our assistance. This traditional approach to charity "affirms the superiority of the
giver, who thus gains a point on the recipient, binds him, demands gratitude, humiliates him,
and reduces him to a lower state than he had before" states Jacques Ellul, in his book Money
and Power. The writer of Proverbs puts it this way, "The rich rules over the poor, and the
borrower is the slave of the lender." (Proverbs 22:7)

The unspoken assumption in everything I have written on this topic to this point is that
we in the affluent West have an abundance of wealth both spiritual and physical. It is our
responsibility to share what we have been given to help those less fortunate. I have suggested
ways to give from our plenty to alleviate the needs of the poor while being mindful to pray
for them and share the good news of Jesus. Most of those reading this book have been blessed
financially (in relation to the poorest of the poor who live on less than $1.25 a day) and are
rich spiritually. If you are like me, your heart is moved when you see needs and it is within
your power to help.

The feelings described above are foreign to those of us who grew up with an abundance
of spiritual opportunities and physical plenty. I have never gone hungry. I have always had
a roof over my head. I have always had a full closet and access to medical care. I have over
twenty Bibles, live in a county with over 700 churches, and can hear Bible teaching on my
computer or Christian radio station 24 hours of every day. I am rich by every metric.

When prosperous, well-meaning Christians seek to help the downtrodden, we can be
blind to our pride. We unknowingly embrace the posture that we can supply what others
need and swoop in with our superman capes to engage in rescue missions by delivering food
baskets, gifts, presents, and second-hand clothes.

As we acknowledge we are not superior, embrace an attitude of genuine humility, and
come alongside those created in the image and likeness of God, and for whom Christ
died, we can do some lasting good. Until we come along side in humility with a sense of

brokenness, we are in a position to give a hand out, but we will not be qualified to provide a hand up.

Acknowledge our own Poverty of Spirit

Before we delve deeper into the best way to meet this complex issue of poverty with an approach that addresses the whole man, we need to address our own blind spot which many of us in affluent countries possess. In their book, When Helping Hurts, the authors state, "one of the major premises of this book is that until we embrace our mutual brokenness, our work with low-income people is likely to do far more harm than good." (Page 61)

Humble Jesus

As I have pondered this American blind spot which we all share to some degree, I thought of how Jesus entered into our world to serve us when we were poor and needy. He could have come like the King He is, swooped in and come to our rescue. Instead He came without fanfare, as a baby, born in a humble manger. He entered our world with humility.

Servant Jesus

> "Jesus called them (His disciples) to him and said, "You know that the rulers of the Gentiles lord it over them, and their great ones exercise authority over them. It shall not be so among you. But whoever would be great among you must be your servant, and whoever would be first among you must be your slave, even as the Son of Man came not to be served but to serve, and to give his life as a ransom for many." (Matthew 20:25-28)

Like Jesus

Paul exhorts the Philippians to adopt the posture of Jesus when seeking to serve and help others.

> "Do nothing from selfish ambition or conceit, but in humility count others more significant than yourselves. Let each of you look not only to his own interests, but also to the interests of others. Have this mind among yourselves, which is yours in Christ Jesus, who, though he was in the form of God, did not count equality with God a thing to be grasped, but emptied himself, by taking the form of a servant, being born in the likeness of men." (Philippians 2:3-7)

Then in a letter to the Colossians he encourages them to

> "put on then, as God's chosen ones, holy and beloved, compassionate hearts, kindness, humility, meekness, and patience," (Colossians 3:12)

> "And above all these put on love" (Colossians 3:14).

The Inner-City Christmas, Part 1

(The following story has been adapted from an actual event in Robert Lupton's *Toxic Charity*)

An inner-city ministry, seeking ways to connect the needy with the affluent families of the suburbs, came up with a plan. Each suburban family would adopt a family from the city and during the Christmas season, bring presents for their needy neighbors in the city. Here is a glimpse into what actually transpired in one home several years ago.

On Christmas Eve, a family living in poverty, whom I will call the Kingstons, anxiously anticipated a visit from an affluent family, the Millers, from the suburbs. When the big moment arrived, the Millers were welcomed into the home and after exchanging pleasantries, distributed gifts to each of the children. Mrs. Kingston smiled and thanked the Millers for making the trip to their home and for their generosity.

While the gifts were happily and noisily being distributed Mrs. Kingston noticed that Mr. Kingston had left the room and was no longer a part of the celebration. The Millers were beaming as the children excitedly opened the presents which they had brought. Mrs. Kingston continued to be gracious and maintain a fixed smile. She was the only one to note his absence.

Inner City Christmas, Part 2

After witnessing the impact on Mr. Kingston, the inner-city ministry leaders came up with an alternative plan. They approached the church in the suburbs and requested their continued support, but in a different way. Would they ask their suburban families to donate unwrapped toys and gifts to the local Family Store instead of giving them directly to the homes on Christmas Eve? These items would then be placed on the shelves and sold at bargain prices to needy families in the community.

Those parents who were not able to afford to buy, even at the discounted prices, were offered jobs at the store to earn enough money to buy what they needed. Fathers and mothers were able to purchase these items and have the joy of giving them to their children on Christmas morning.

A Better Response to Traditional Forms of Charitable Giving

You have had one lesson to process what it has taken me several years to begin to comprehend. Since we are followers of Jesus and lovers of God, we want to also love our neighbor as ourselves. The reason we are searching God's Word to discover wisdom about how best to love our neighbor, is because of the work of God in our hearts. We have been born from above and now are beginning to understand His kingdom on this earth. We have become co-laborers with Him.

Jesus said that if we love God, we ought to obey Him. "If you keep my commandments, you will abide in my love, just as I have kept my Father's commandments and abide in his love." (John 15:10)

To love our neighbor as ourselves, we need to do the work of putting ourselves in their shoes and discerning how our best efforts come across. We tried to do this as we read of the inner city Christmas. We sought to understand how each of the characters in this story felt within a traditional charitable encounter.

Physical Poverty and Poverty of Being

There is no doubt that the lack of clean water, food, clothes, shelter, sanitation, and medicine abound. There is plenty we don't know about how we can respond to someone's physical needs in a way that also encourages the spirit of the receiver while recognizing their poverty of being. How can we supply their felt needs while also addressing their dignity, self worth, hopelessness, shame, and sense of inferiority? This is where we need to work to develop a better model of serving and giving.

As we work through new models and better ways of responding to the serious and important needs all around the world, let's be mindful of the impact of giving on the giver of the charity as well as on the receiver. Let us also remember the impact of giving on whole family including the children of the receiver and the giver.

Poverty

Globally, 1.2 billion people live on less than $1.25 a day. Increasing the income poverty line to $2.50 a day raises the global income poverty rate to 2.7 billion people.[1] 70% of these needy people are women and children.

Approximately 783 million people do not have access to clean water and almost 2.5 billion do not have access to adequate sanitation. Six to eight million people die annually

---

1. From the United Nations Development Program. Human Development Report 2014. Sustaining Human Progress: Reducing Vulnerabilities and Building Resilience. http://www.compassion.com/multimedia/human-development-report-2014-undp.pdf

from the consequences of disasters and water-related diseases.[2]

Bob Pierce

The needs are great, but so is our God. The scope of what we just read drives us to our knees, for only God can move these mountains. One of the prayers that touches me was prayed by Bob Pierce. He asked God, "Let my heart be broken by the things that break the heart of God." Bob became the founder of two international charity organizations: World Vision International in 1950 and Samaritan's Purse in 1970.

Our Response

When we read these statistics and recognize that they are not numbers, but real people, we feel a need to do something. We don't want to close our eyes and walk on the other side of the road as in the case of the Good Samaritan. Do we give? To whom do we give and how much? Do we go and serve them ourselves? We recognize that there are basic physical needs as well as needs of the spirit. Now that we are beginning to recognize that unwise giving can harm the recipients, we want our giving to be thoughtful and beneficial to giver and receiver alike.

One of the reasons that traditional strategies have produced such harmful fruit is that we use short term strategies to address long standing problems. When an earthquake devastates a city, a tsunami ravages towns and villages, a tornado levels a town, or a hurricane sweep through an area, there are immediate needs of clean water, housing, food, and clothes. Relief agencies are geared to respond to disasters quickly and efficiently. Our quick response may mean the difference between life and death. As critical as these needs are, they are temporary. These scenarios normally last for a short time, and then the long-term work of rebuilding the infrastructure of a community begins, which demands a different giving strategy.

When we continue to provide temporary or a short time solution over a long period of time, our quick response, which was appropriate and necessary at the time of the incident, can become harmful. The recipients of the first rush of support begin to make a habit of looking for more "free aid" and do not address the work of rebuilding their homes, their families, and their communities. Our giving turns sour and engenders dependence and entitlement.

- Give once and you elicit appreciation;
- Give twice and you create anticipation;
- Give three times and you create expectation;
- Give four times and it becomes entitlement;
- Give five times and you establish dependency.[3]

Birthday party

The best way I have of trying to understand the transition from appreciation to entitlement is by thinking through gift giving to children on their birthdays and special holidays.

---

2. www.unwater.org/water-cooperation-2013/water-cooperation/facts-and-figures/en/
3. Robert Lupton in *Toxic Charity*, p. 130

The joy to the giver at a birthday celebration is seeing the wonder in a child's eyes when he realizes these gifts are for him. He is excited and grateful. When that same child is a few years older, he has begun to anticipate and expect gifts. Within another year or so, their expectation has grown into entitlement. He knows he will be having a party with special food, and several gifts. It is not "if" he will be receiving gifts, but "when and how many?"

Impact

When our continued unwise giving in response to a short-term need has progressed to entitlement, we have not helped those who are poor. We have not met their needs for respect and dignity. We have not encouraged them to dream or use the gifts and talents God has given them. We are unwittingly fostering a Christian welfare state of ongoing dependency. Parents who exist under this system will not experience the satisfaction of providing for their children. The children will not grow up seeing diligent parents working with their hands. They will not observe or be taught the virtue of hard work. Giving to needy people, which seems helpful on the surface, is not beneficial to the giver or the receiver, and it can be toxic. "There is a way that seems right to a man, but its end is the way to death." (Proverbs 14:12)

Organizations may point to the number of people being fed and the needy children who now have medical care available. These are tangible and measurable results. Unfortunately they miss the intangible harm that is damaging to the whole person. Remember how the poor described their condition: while acknowledging material needs, the words they used were more sociological and psychological. Shame, inferiority, powerlessness, humiliation, fear, hopelessness, depression, social isolation, and voicelessness are hard to measure or demonstrate with graphs. They are the invisible needs.

As Christ followers, we are called to something better. Jesus came to break the cycle of spiritual and physical poverty and set people free. Therefore, let's not create dependency. Instead, let's encourage the poor to use their God-given talents and skills. Let's uphold and affirm their dignity, for they too have been created in the image of God. They have value for who they are, regardless of what they possess.

Breaking Cycles of Poverty Through Work

A cycle of poverty is broken when a person is no longer dependent on charity, but is independent.

> "We should measure welfare's success by how many people leave welfare, not by how many are added."—Ronald Reagan

> "Government's first duty is to protect the people, not run their lives."—Ronald Reagan

> "Jobs are the world's best social service program."—John Perkins

(John M. Perkins is co-founder of the Christian Community Development Association, which is a group of Christians committed to seeing people and communities holistically restored).

I have read my Bible many times, but have missed a similar approach in Paul's inspired advice to the Thessalonian church. Paul spoke strongly about brothers who were idle and not working productively. His succinct advice is: "If anyone is not willing to work, let him not eat." Here is the complete passage.

"Now we command you, brothers, in the name of our Lord Jesus Christ, that you keep away from any brother who is walking in idleness and not in accord with the tradition that you received from us. For you yourselves know how you ought to imitate us, because we were not idle when we were with you, nor did we eat anyone's bread without paying for it, but with toil and labor we worked night and day, that we might not be a burden to any of you. It was not because we do not have that right, but to give you in ourselves an example to imitate. For even when we were with you, we would give you this command: If anyone is not willing to work, let him not eat. For we hear that some among you walk in idleness, not busy at work, but busybodies. Now such persons we command and encourage in the Lord Jesus Christ to do their work quietly and to earn their own living." (2 Thessalonians 3:6–12)

Paul also teaches: "You yourselves know that these hands ministered to my necessities and to those who were with me. In all things I have shown you that by working hard in this way we must help the weak and remember the words of the Lord Jesus, how he himself said, 'It is more blessed to give than to receive.'" (Acts 20:34–35)

Present Lincoln

I discovered a wonderful letter written by Abraham Lincoln to a step-brother, John D. Johnston, around 1850. Johnson had written to him and asked, yet again, for a loan with which to settle some debts. The request is hard to understand in the original document, but the wise response is articulate and illustrates an attempt to break a cycle in the life of a relative.

Said Johnston:

"I am dund & doged to Death so I am all most tired of Living, & I would all most swop my place in Heaven for that much money [...] I would rother live on bread and wotter than to have men allways duning me [...] If you can send me 80 Dollars I am willing to pay you any Intrust you will ask."

(Translation by Steve) "I am done and dogged to death so I am almost tired of living. I would almost swap my place in heaven for that much money. I would rather live on bread and water than to have men always downing me. If you can send me eighty dollars, I am willing to pay you any interest you will ask."

On previous occasions, Lincoln simply would have agreed to such a request. This time, however, sensing an opportunity to impart some wisdom, he responded with the following letter of advice and a proposal.

January 2, 1851

Dear Johnston:

Your request for eighty dollars I do not think it best to comply with now. At the various times when I have helped you a little you have said to me, "We can get along very well now"; but in a very short time I find you in the same difficulty again. Now, this can only happen by some defect in your conduct. What that defect is, I think I know. You are not lazy, and still you are an idler. I doubt whether, since I saw you, you have done a good whole day's work in any one day. You do not very much dislike to work, and still you do not work much merely because it does not seem to you that you could get much for it. This habit of uselessly wasting time is the whole difficulty; it is vastly important to you, and still more so to your children, that you should break the habit. It is more important to them, because they have longer to live, and can keep out of an idle habit before they are in it, easier than they can get out after they are in.

You are now in need of some money; and what I propose is, that you shall go to work, "tooth and nail," for somebody who will give you money for it. Let father and your boys take charge of your things at home, prepare for a crop, and make the crop, and you go to work for the best money wages, or in discharge of any debt you owe, that you can get; and, to secure you a fair reward for your labor, I now promise you, that for every dollar you will, between this and the first of May, get for your own labor, either in money or as your own indebtedness, I will then give you one other dollar. By this, if you hire yourself at ten dollars a month, from me you will get ten more, making twenty dollars a month for your work. In this I do not mean you shall go off to St. Louis, or the lead mines, or the gold mines in California, but I mean for you to go at it for the best wages you can get close to home in Coles County. Now, if you will do this, you will be soon out of debt, and, what is better, you will have a habit that will keep you from getting in debt again. But, if I should now clear you out of debt, next year you would be just as deep in as ever. You say you would almost give your place in heaven for seventy or eighty dollars. Then you value your place in heaven very cheap, for I am sure you can, with the offer I make, get the seventy or eighty dollars for four or five months' work. You say if I will furnish you the money you will deed me the land, and, if you don't pay the money back, you will deliver possession. Nonsense! If you can't now live with the land, how will you then live without it? You have always been kind to me, and I do not mean to be unkind to you. On the contrary, if you will but follow my advice, you will find it worth more than eighty times eighty dollars to you.

Affectionately your brother, A. Lincoln[4]

---

4. *Lincoln and His World*: Volume 3;
Image: Abraham Lincoln, via
http://www.lettersofnote.com/2012/05/you-are-not-lazy-and-still-you-are.html

A Hard Question

A few years ago I was speaking to homeschool families in the Philippines. After my presentation a father stood and asked me how to help young men learn responsibility. I probed a little further and discovered that the young men were graduating from college without knowing how to work or be responsible adults. I also found out after a few more inquiries that many of these young men did not have to dress themselves or take care of their own basic needs, since their family hired servants do these chores. The men were dependent on others to fulfill their basic daily tasks.

I told them that our children had chores, did their own personal care, and were trained to do extra jobs beyond their daily responsibilities for which they were paid. I had not thought it through then, but in hindsight, I realized that I believed my role as a parent was to help each of my sons become independent. I taught them how to drive, mow the lawn, wash a car, and change the oil in a vehicle. My wife had instructed them how to cook, clean, and do their own laundry. It is easier for a parent to do many tasks than to train the children to do the same jobs, but it is not helpful in the long-term development of the children.

It's Easier to Write a Check

Robert Lupton was meeting with a group of people discussing a food pantry that was supported by several churches. The conversation was revealing. After some discussion, all the people present realized that the pantry was not a good solution but seemed bent on perpetuating it even when it was not helpful. Exasperated, Mr. Lupton said "Why do we persist in giving away food when we know it fosters dependency?"

One person responded, "Because it is easier! It costs much less time and money to run a food pantry, and that's what churches want! Churches want their members to feel good about serving the poor, but no one really wants to become involved in messy relationships." [5]

Teachable Westerners

It is blessed to give and help the weak, but we need to be creative in discovering new ways to truly help the weak without creating dependence and entitlement. We need to have a willing compassionate heart with a teachable, inquiring mind. We also need to be humble enough to ask questions and truly listen to the weak and needy.

When you are thinking of giving in the traditional sense, ask yourself if your donation is meeting an emergency need in a crisis, or fostering idleness? What will be the impact of continued gifts coming to a family, a church, or a community?

---

5. page 57, Toxic Charity

Learn to Shift Gears

"After the 1994 genocide in Rwanda, many Christian organizations were motivated to rebuild this broken country. Following the example and admonitions of Jesus to feed the hungry, clothe the naked, and show compassion to the hurting, these organizations and their dedicated people responded. Churches in the United States rebuilt Rwandan churches and schools, sent food aid and supplies, and attempted to address the unimaginable physical and psychological damage inflicted by the hundred days of terror. Several years after the genocide, peace and stability allowed Rwanda to transition from a country needing emergency assistance to one needing long-term development. Unfortunately, many churches and aid organizations failed to recognize this, leading to frustrations like those experienced by a Rwandan named Jean.

After the genocide, Jean seized an opportunity to begin a small poultry business to provide his neighborhood with eggs. He managed to scrape together funds to purchase several fowl, and his business grew. Later, a church in the United States "adopted" the village where Jean lived and worked. The church decided to donate clothes and supplies. They also imported eggs from a neighboring community and gave them away. Suddenly, this one village was flooded with surplus eggs. It is not difficult to imagine what happened to Jean's business: People went first to collect the free eggs and bought Jean's eggs only when the supply of free eggs was depleted. The market price for eggs plummeted in Jean's village, and, as a result, Jean was forced to sell his productive assets, his chickens.

The next year, after Jean had left the poultry business, the church that had supplied the free eggs turned its attention to another disaster in another part of the world. Jean's community had no capacity to produce eggs locally and was forced to import eggs from a neighboring town. The cost of these eggs was higher than the eggs Jean had sold, so both Jean and his village were hurt economically by the good intentions of one U.S. church."[6]

Providing Water, Model 1

With enthusiasm, a church in the United States determined to develop a working partnership with a village in the Honduras. They sent a team for an extended visit and discovered the primary need was water, since the women had to travel several miles each day to supply their families with this precious commodity. With their engineers and the funding from the congregation, the team provided pure water, and there was joy in the village. The team went back to the United States satisfied they had made a significant impact.

The next year the same team returned only to witness the women carrying jugs on their heads in the heat. They wondered what had happened. They learned the pump had broken

---

6. Page 56–57, *Created to Flourish*

down, so they rolled up their sleeves and fixed it. The water was soon flowing once again. This same situation was repeated many times over several years. When the pump would inevitably break down, the women went back to jugs until the Americans returned to save the day and fix "their" well.

Providing Water, Model 2

Another remote village also had a water problem, and they also had a partner church in the United States to come alongside and seek a solution to their needs. This church enlisted the help of Opportunity International, who sent a community developer to help them develop a plan. The villagers were educated about drilling and expenses. They were assisted in formulating a budget and business plan. The community developer arranged for a loan based on their small savings and connected them with an engineer to help set up their own water commission. This commission would set fees, manage the operation, and maintain the wells.

Men from the village did the work of digging, laying water lines, and installing 220 water meters. When the water surged into the homes, the villagers were filled with pride. Their water source proved so abundant that they were able to sell the excess water to an adjacent village. They now owned and managed a valuable money producing asset. The well belonged to 'them'.[7]

Banker to the Poor

"When we want to help the poor, we usually offer them charity. Most often we use charity to avoid recognizing the problem and finding the solution for it. Charity becomes a way to shrug off our responsibility. But charity is no solution to poverty. Charity only perpetuates poverty by taking the initiative away from the poor. Charity allows us to go ahead with our own lives without worrying about the lives of the poor. Charity appeases our consciences."—Muhammad Yunus[8]

---

7. Adapted from Robert Lupton's *Toxic Charity*, (New York: Harper Collins, 2011) pp.11–13
8. Banker to the Poor: Micro-Lending and the battle Against World Poverty

MINISTERING TO THE WHOLE MAN THROUGH CHRISTIAN MICRO-FINANCE

A Hand-Out and a Hand-Up

A single parent was raising several children. A charity came alongside her and sponsored her oldest child. Because of their support, she was able to pay the tuition to the local school and her son was able to graduate. Several years later she was in contact with this charity. She thanked them for their help, and went on to say that another group had come alongside her and provided her a small loan and training. Their assistance enabled her to develop a business in her home. This small home enterprise provided the funds for her to pay the tuition for the other children, who all graduated from school.

Micro-Finance

Thankfully there are many helpful organizations focused on ways to address the physical and sociological needs of their clients. These may be categorized as micro-finance groups. Micro-finance means small loans or financial assistance. These groups are committed to assisting clients develop a stream of income to meet physical needs. But while they help their clients economically, they do not address the need for a transformation of the heart through the gospel of Jesus. A person may become a successful entrepreneur, but without a transformation of his heart, he is still needy, just with more money. His wallet may grow, but what about his relationship with God, his wife, and his children? Will he be a better man who contributes to his church and community, or just a financially prosperous one? "For what does it profit a man to gain the whole world and forfeit his soul?" (Mark 8:36)

Christian Micro-Finance

I believe a better solution that produces good fruit in the long-term is Christian micro-finance. In this model, a dedicated group of believers shares sound business principles with individuals and families to develop independence built on a relationship with God through Jesus Christ. One of my favorite sayings is:

> Give me a fish and I eat for a day,
>
> Teach me to fish and I eat for a lifetime.

Our traditional charitable approach is 'giving a fish,' while a Christ centered emphasis on micro loans and discipleship is 'teaching to fish.' This approach empowers the poor and gives them a hand-up instead of a hand-out. One such organization, which I have been supporting and learning from for several years, is Hope International, based in Lancaster, Pennsylvania.

History of Hope International

Following the fall of the Soviet Union in Ukraine in the early 1990s, Jeff Rutt, a Lancaster, Pennsylvania-based homebuilder, traveled to Ukraine numerous times with his church, transporting containers of food, clothing, and medical supplies to the city of Zaporozhye.

After several of these visits, a local pastor pulled Jeff aside and told him honestly that the shipments were not helping. Instead of handouts, the pastor felt that his community needed a hand up.

Though people were accessing needed supplies, they had become dependent on American charity. In addition, local businesses could not compete with the free handouts. The well-intentioned aid shipments were actually doing more harm than good by depressing local industry and initiative.

Jeff returned from the trip with a strong desire to find a solution. He plunged into research and eventually discovered the concept of micro-enterprise development, then a little-known poverty alleviation strategy, which helps fund and support small business enterprises. https://www.hopeinternational.org

Fleshing Out Teach Me to Fish and Give Me a Fish

I have created a fictitious scenario about a village that has two models of aid coming from the United States. The Raines family determines that they want to make a difference in the world by making a five-hundred-dollar annual contribution to alleviate poverty in the world for five years. They have been learning about the perils of charitable giving and the benefits of Christian micro-finance, so their family decides to make contributions to two organizations representing these different philosophies.

"Help the Needy (HTN)" is a well-known nonprofit organization that gives fish to qualifying families in the form of monthly checks. They represent the "hand-out" approach.

"Building Families of Faith (BFF)" is a new Christian non-profit micro-finance organization which seeks to empower, or teach people to fish, by extending loans. They represent the "hand-up" philosophy.

Help the Needy (HTN)

The Johnsons were interviewed by this organization. The single mother raising two children humbly approached the person in charge and demonstrated that her family was in need of clean water, food, clothing, shelter, and medical care. The HTN representative approved them to be in their program and made arrangements for monthly checks to be sent for their support.

When the Johnsons were accepted, they told their friends, the Turners, about their good fortune. After going through the same process, the Turners applied and were also accepted into the program.

In an effort to put a face to their organization, HTN has sent the Raines' family information about the Johnsons and the Turners. The Raines will be receiving pictures of their families and information about them quarterly. The Johnsons and Turners are looking forward to the charitable gifts and have expressed their thanks for the generosity of the Raines.

Building Families of Faith (BFF)

The Sams heard about "Building Families of Faith" in their church and began meeting with the on-site administrator. He asked them about their dreams and encouraged them to develop a business plan. After some work improving the plan, they were accepted into the program, joined a support group in their town, and were granted a loan. Since the supporters have connections to the local micro-finance ministry, they will be able to track their family's progress over the next five years. The Sams are grateful for a hand-up.

In addition to the money portion, there are also support groups which each person receiving a loan commits to attend. These groups are essential to the success of the program. At each meeting, they greet one another, pray and worship, study God's Word, report on their group savings, manage their loans, and wrap up with prayer. I believe these meetings are the lifeblood of this approach. Bearing one another's burdens, learning Biblical principles of finance, sharing good business practices, and encouraging each other are vital to their joint success.

ROI

The Raines' faithfully give and track their monetary return on their investment each year, which some folks would refer to as an ROI, or Return On Investment. Each organization has the same overhead expenses, which are also referred to as administration costs. These expenses are a combination of all the costs incurred in running a business: staff salaries in the U.S. and abroad, office rent, marketing dollars, travel expenses, phone bills, legal advice for maintaining a non-profit agency, etc. These costs are generally twenty cents on the dollar or 20% of the money received from the giver. From the five-hundred-dollar annual donation, divided between these two organizations, $100.00 (20% of $500) will go to overhead costs.

See the visual representation of years one through five at the end of this lesson.

Year One: Help the Needy

The amount of $250, minus $50 for overhead expenses, is given to two families, the Johnsons and the Turners, who are living in Rwanda. Each family receives $100 and use the money to buy clothes, food, medicine, and pay school fees for their children. At the end of the year the money is gone and they are expectantly looking forward to their next check.

Johnson   Turner

Year One: Building Families of Faith

The amount of $250, minus $50 for overhead expenses, or $200, is given to a Christian partner ministry in Rwanda that has accepted the Sams family, as they have qualified for a loan. Mr. Sams is required to attend weekly meetings with a group of other members who are also receiving loans. He is encouraged to be active member where he will worship, receive instruction on Scriptural business principles, and be a part of this community of believers as they share their journey together.

The Sams receive a $200-dollar loan and agree to pay it back at 8% interest over two years. They are responsible to pay back $108 each year for the next two years. They are also encouraged to save 50¢ per month. After meeting with the loan officer, they have jointly decided that their family is uniquely gifted and motivated to run a small dairy. They invest one hundred dollars to purchase two female goats which will hopefully produce milk and cheese. They budget the remaining $100 for their immediate needs of clothes, medicines, food, and school fees for their children. They are hoping they will begin to generate enough income to grow their dairy business as well as pay back their loans.

Sams

Year Two: Help the Needy

$200 ($250 − $50), is distributed to the Johnsons and the Turners. They use their $100 stipend to buy clothes, food, medicine, and pay school fees for their children. At the end of the year the money is gone and they are expectantly looking forward to their next check.

Johnson   Turner

Year Two: Building Families of Faith

The amount of $200 ($250 + $50) is sent to the Christian partner ministry in Rwanda. The Sams have repaid half of their loan, with interest, which amounts to $108 dollars. They now have a successful family enterprise where each of the members of their family share the work.

With $308 ($200 + $108), the on-site coordinator is able to keep eight dollars for his salary and make another loan to a qualifying family. This time $200.00 is loaned to the Peters family. They use $100 for living expenses and invest $100 into a family business to repair wheel barrows. Like the Sams the year before, they also join a support group, grow spiritually, learn biblical principles, encourage one another, and with God's help and hard work, are able to survive the first year and pay back half of their loan on time. That $100 is back in savings and overseen by the local ministry.

Peters

Year Three: Help the Needy

Same scenario, hopefully. Money is received from America on time. It is not uncommon for those who have become dependent on aid, to begin drinking and carousing because of their low sense of self-worth and lack of dignity in receiving handouts. The family structure is hurt and the children have growing emotional needs. Mr. Turner has been seen drinking in excess and has left the home. School teachers and community services are seeking to help them.

Johnson

Turner

Year Three: Building Families of Faith

$200 ($250 − $50) is sent to the Christian partner ministry in Rwanda. The Sams have repaid the rest of their loan, with interest, which amounts to $108 dollars, as have the Peters. With $516 in hand ($200 + $108 + $108 + $100 in savings), the on-site coordinator is able to keep sixteen dollars for his expenses and make two loans to the Woods and the Kellys.

The Woods have developed a plan to raise chickens and sell the eggs. The Kellys have chosen to open a medical clinic. Following the lead of the Sams and Peters, they too are members of the support group for teaching and fellowship. The Sams have now hired two local people to work in their dairy. The Peters' family has adopted an AIDS orphan.

Woods

Kellys

Year Four: Help the Needy

Money is received from America on time, and the physical needs are being met. Mr. Turner is still not home. The family is ashamed of this situation and they have not been attending church. The church, and the BFF support group are praying for his restoration.

Johnson   Turner

Year Four: Building Families of Faith

Four families are now on their feet, and even if no check from the U. S. is received, there are several hundred dollars at work in the village and continuing to come in for loan payments. Thankfully, $200 ($250 − $50) is received from the United States. In addition, the Peters have repaid $108 dollars, as have the Woods and the Kellys. With a $624 nest egg ($200 + $108 + $108 + $108 + $100 in savings from year 3), the on-site coordinator is able to keep $24 dollars for his expenses and make three additional loans to the Rosses, Walkers, and Coopers.

The Rosses plan on building a bicycle repair shop. The Walkers are opening a small cafe in the center of the village. The Coopers will be looking for work in carpentry and small construction projects.

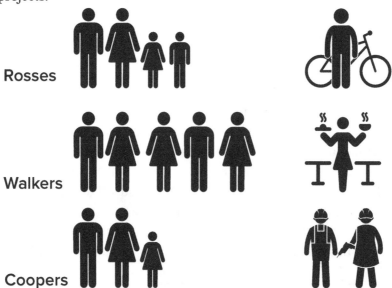

Rosses

Walkers

Coopers

Year Five: Help the Needy

Money is received from America on time and the physical needs are being met. Mr. Turner has repented, been restored, and has applied to BFF to open a business selling mobile phones. The Lemon family has sent their picture to the Raines and are in their first year of receiving aid.

Johnson   Turner

Year Five: Building Families of Faith

Seven families are now on their feet, and thanks be to God, $200 ($250-$50) is received from the United States. The Woods, Kellys, Rosses, Coopers, and Walkers have each repaid $108 dollars on their loans. With $740 in the kitty ($200 + $108 + $108 + $108 + $108 + $108), the on-site coordinator is able to keep $40 dollars for his expenses and can now either make new loans to prospective families, or make new loans to the first seven families who are seeking to expand their businesses.

The Turner home has joined a support group, and they are selling and servicing cellular phones. The Jetts are opening a small preschool, and the Lloyds are opening their home to take in seamstress work which they are able to do, thanks to their new sewing machine.

Turners

Jetts

Lloyds

Life Going On in Rwanda After Five years

Help the Needy is still raising money to give to the Johnsons and Lemons. While their physical needs are being met, their emotional and spiritual needs have not been addressed and family relationships have suffered. They are dependent on foreign donations to subsist and are receiving no instruction and are not being taught skills to provide for their families on their own. Their children will most likely grow up dependent on others with their hands out looking for continued welfare. The families do not walk with their heads held high, neither do they fit into the fabric of their growing community. Sadly, even at church, they feel isolated.

After a rocky first year, Mr. Turner seems to have a new lease on life. His wife and children had to live frugally the first year of their business, but they are full of hope as the look towards the future.

After a prosperous five years, Building Families of Faith has provided a hand up to ten families which now operate thriving local businesses. The families involved have benefited economically, emotionally, and spiritually, and are now self-sustaining. Not only have these ten families found new life and purpose, their village now has a dairy, wheelbarrows, eggs, a medical clinic, a bicycle repair shop, a carpenter, a place to buy cell phones, a preschool, and a seamstress.

The Sams are followers of Jesus, as are the Peters and Woods. They have grown in their faith as they have learned biblical principles during their weekly support group meetings. The Kellys were new to the community, but after they received a loan and joined the support group, they have developed meaningful friendships. They are witnessing God at work and being loved on by the other members. All of the families have experienced minor trials and challenges, but they have become a tight knit group as they grow and learn together.

The Local Church

The local congregation which introduced BFF to the community is benefiting from the spiritual growth of their members. Giving has also increased, which has provided new impetus for outreach to their community. The local church is considering a permanent structure to hold their services.

The Village

Mr. Sams was elected to be a member of the town council, and Mrs. Peters is on the school board. The savings group is making plans to pool their resources and dig a well, so they do not have to walk for water. A committee has begun to study what needs to be done to make this dream come to fruition. They hope to sell the surplus water to the neighboring villages.

Savings

Don't forget the savings which have been accumulating. Each family has been saving 50¢ per month or six dollars per year. Here is the net savings of our seven families pooling their resources together as a group.

Sams	5 years	$30
Peters	4 years	$24
Woods	3 years	$18
Kellys	3 years	$18
Rosses	2 years	$12
Walkers	2 years	$12
Coopers	2 years	$12
Turners	1 year	$6
Jetts	1 year	$6
Lloyds	1 year	$6

Through their individual savings accounts, $144 has been set aside by these frugal families. They can now decide whether to provide loans to reinvest or to maintain a nest egg for emergencies. These loans have the potential to generate interest while expanding their

LESSON 34: MINISTERING TO THE WHOLE MAN THROUGH CHRISTIAN MICRO-FINANCE

businesses.

When the loans of the new three family enterprises have been repaid with interest (as are 98% of such loans) there is $772 in hand, $324 in outstanding loans, and along with the $144 in the savings group, $1,240 dollars is at work on the ground in the country of Rwanda, helping to rebuild families, churches, communities, and ultimately a country.

Reality Check

Does this scenario sound too good to be true? Maybe. Perhaps the Peters suffered a setback when a fire destroyed their wheel barrow shop. Maybe it took some of the families three years to repay their loans. My hope is that you get a taste of the solid fruit that comes from investing in families and of the steady growth from one to ten families in a few short years. While two families on charity are dependent and dealing with an uncertain future, ten families now have hope. With children observing the effects of diligence and a godly work ethic, the future which was bleak now looks fraught with potential. Similar results are being found around the world where Hope International is working with almost a million families being assisted in many of the neediest countries (as of 2017).

Family Evaluation at the End of Five Years with a Report Card

The Raines family has been observing the trends in their five-year investment into the lives of the families in Rwanda. Now they are sitting down for a family meeting to evaluate where they will be giving in the future. They decided to grade different aspects of their giving through these two organizations to help them measure the impact of their investment of $2,500.

	HTN	BFF
Food, clothing, shelter	A	A
Spiritual development	judge not	A
Personal dignity and respect	F	A
Fruit in the family, immediate and future	F	A
Sense of community as a member of a team	F	A
Hope for the future	D	A
Church life	D	A
Impact on the Community	D	A

As they thought about the $500 being sent over each year, they recognized that the money donated to charity through Help for the Needy had yielded questionable fruit at best, and most likely had harmed the families receiving aid in this form.

They were pleasantly surprised by the meaningful fruit of the Christian micro-finance model. They had thought it would be better, but seeing it fleshed out in the lives of ten families helped them to grasp the positive impact of their donations. What most blessed them was knowing that their initial investment of $1,250 had contributed $250 to the parent organization in the U.S., helped financially sustain the local ministry in the village, and there was still $1,240 dollars growing and enriching the lives of families. They also had a positive glimpse into the future, as they contemplated the effect on the children of these pioneers as they observed the hard work and diligence of their parents. Since they are armed with education and resources, the future is bright for these young people and their families.

LESSON 34: MINISTERING TO THE WHOLE MAN THROUGH CHRISTIAN MICRO-FINANCE   221

As a family, the Raines decided to write to the Johnsons and Lemons and encourage them to join the local support group as they wouldn't be contributing to Help for the Needy in the future. They proposed to increase their giving, but to earmark all of the funds for Building Faith Families Christian micro-finance efforts.

For further reading:

You can download the book, *Created to Flourish*, for free at: https://www.hopeinternational.org/#ctf-ebook

Podcast: You can also listen to Steve interview Peter Greer, the president of Hope International, on podcast 195 here http://www.buildingfaithfamilies.org/podcasts/.

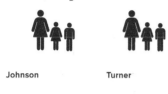

Johnson   Turner

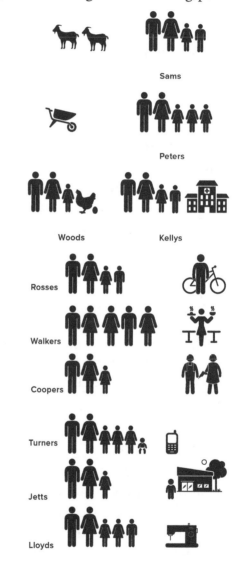

THE GREAT COMMISSION

The Command

The last three verses in Matthew's gospel are called the Great Commission.

> "Jesus came and said to them, 'All authority in heaven and on earth has been given to me. Go therefore and make disciples of all nations, baptizing them in the name of the Father and of the Son and of the Holy Spirit, teaching them to observe all that I have commanded you. And behold, I am with you always, to the end of the age." (Matthew 28:18-20)

These were His last words to the apostles. Similar commands to preach the gospel to the whole world were also recorded in Mark 16:15, Luke 24:46-47, and John 20:21.

The word apostle means "sent one." As the apostles received the Spirit, they were sent to tell people about Jesus in all nations, beginning with Jerusalem. This command, or commission, is for all followers of Jesus. Each of us is to pray, give, go, or do some combination of these three options.

The Need

According to the Joshua Project, https://joshuaproject.net, there are 17,014 people groups in the world. Of these, 3,233 have been significantly reached, 3,728 partially reached, 1,777 superficially reached, and 1,213 minimally reached. That leaves 7,063 people groups that are unreached, amounting to 3.14 billion people or 41.5% of the population of the world, which is 7.5 billion as of this writing. Interestingly, there are fewer than 200 countries in the world.

People Groups and Dr. Ralph Winters

Unless you are a student of missions, your first question might be, "What is a people group?" This language began with a famous talk given by Dr. Ralph Winters at the 1974 Lausanne Congress of World Evangelization.

> "For evangelization purposes, a people group is the largest group within which the Gospel can spread as a church planting movement without encountering barriers of understanding or acceptance" (1982 Lausanne Committee Chicago meeting).

Until that meeting, most earnest believers who were concerned about fulfilling the call to preach the gospel and make disciples of all nations believed that the gospel had reached every nation in the world. The church of God simply needed to pray for an outpouring of the Spirit to inspire believers in each country to reach all their own countrymen. We assumed that if the gospel has been preached in Ecuador, for example, then the Ecuadorean believers would already be familiar with the language and customs of the unreached people in their country, and they would be uniquely equipped to share the good news with their countrymen.

After this address, these missionary statesmen realized this was no longer the situation. If there were a worldwide revival, 41.5% of the population would still be part of unreached people groups. These people groups would be hindered from hearing the good news because of "barriers of understanding or acceptance."

Jerusalem, Judea, Samaria, and the Uttermost Parts of the Earth

In the first chapter of Acts, just before He ascended into heaven, Jesus gave this final command to His disciples. It is similar to the Great Commission but addresses the scope of the great task and gives some examples of people groups.

> "'You will receive power when the Holy Spirit comes upon you. And you will be my witnesses, telling people about me everywhere—in Jerusalem, throughout Judea, in Samaria, and to the ends of the earth.' After saying this, he was taken up into a cloud while they were watching, and they could no longer see him." (Acts 1:8-9 NLT)

For the Jewish apostles, preaching to Judea was the easiest for they shared a common language and culture. In Acts 2, Peter preaches to Judeans and several thousand are converted. But for these same disciples to share the good news with Samaritans posed a different challenge. Although they shared the same language, there was a cultural divide, as evidenced by the encounter with Jesus and the Samaritan woman at the well in John 4. The disciples were shocked to see Jesus, a Jew, speaking to her at all. Prejudice is a significant barrier to be crossed. While their tongues were prepared to speak, their hearts and cultural mindsets needed to be transformed before they could tell Samaritans about Jesus.

To reach and teach and make disciples of people in the "uttermost part of the earth," these early disciples would have to learn a new language, adapt to a new culture, and learn new patterns of thinking. This is a true cross-cultural outreach that will take a significant amount of time, energy, and resources.

Steve's People Groups

Where I live in Lancaster County, Pennsylvania, I can preach to most of my neighbors because I speak English, and we all share the same culture. I also have good friends who are Amish. They speak English, but live in a very different culture. My close neighbors are what I consider my Judeans, and the Amish would be my Samaritans.

We also have a large immigrant population from many countries. I meet them in an ESL (English as a Second Language) class I teach at my church. I have students from Pakistan, Nepal, Bosnia, Brazil, Vietnam, and Brazil. They are learning English, but come from a different country, speak a different language, and culturally think differently than I do.

The First Missionary

Paul certainly obeyed the Great Commission. He is often seen as the first foreign missionary, for he traveled to many places outside the borders of Israel telling people about Jesus. "You yourselves know how I lived among you the whole time from the first day that I set foot in Asia, serving the Lord with all humility and with tears and with trials that happened to me through the plots of the Jews; how I did not shrink from declaring to you anything that was profitable, and teaching you in public and from house to house, testifying both to Jews and to Greeks of repentance toward God and of faith in our Lord Jesus Christ." (Acts 20:18-20)

He not only told them, he stayed with them and made disciples of those who chose to follow Jesus and were converted. The letters of Paul in the New Testament are his instructions to those fledgling churches that he helped plant. He encouraged them to grow in their faith and not be baby Christians, but mature men and women of God.

One of the young men that Paul trained was Timothy. Paul's letters to Timothy and Titus are encouraging exhortations from a mentor to his beloved students. In 2 Timothy 2:2, Paul commissioned Timothy to identify other men who could continue to pass on these eternal truths and keep the Great Commission going from generation to generation. "Now teach these truths to other trustworthy people who will be able to pass them on to others." Clearly these commands to make disciples of all nations still apply to us today.

Make Disciples of All Peoples

In Ralph Winter's original address in 1974, he comments on the difference between reaching a country for Christ, and reaching every group of people, or people group, with the gospel.

> "Why is this fact not more widely known? I'm afraid that all our exultation about the fact that every country of the world has been penetrated has allowed many to suppose that every culture has by now been penetrated. This misunderstanding is a malady so wide-spread that it deserves a special name. Let us call it 'people blindness'—that is, blindness to the existence of separate peoples within countries—a blindness, I might add, which seems more prevalent in the U.S. and among U.S. missionaries than anywhere else. The Bible rightly translated could have made this plain to us. The "nations" to which Jesus often referred were mainly ethnic groups within the single political structure of the Roman government. In the Great Commission as it is found in Matthew, the phrase 'make disciples of all ethne (peoples)' does not let us off the hook once we have a church in every country—God wants a strong church within every people!"

> Ralph Winter's address can be found here in its entirety: https://joshuaproject.net/assets/media/articles/the-highest-priority.pdf

My Story

When I chose to fully follow Jesus and seek first His kingdom, my path intersected with an organization called Operation Mobilization. I was attending a worship service in Akron, Ohio, and heard the founder, George Verwer, speak on the text, "I heard the voice of the Lord saying, 'Whom shall I send, and who will go for us?' Then I said, 'Here I am! Send me.'" (Isaiah 6:8)

God anointed that message, and my heart was stirred to become a foreign missionary and take the good news to the ends of the earth. During the next few years I took classes on world missions at seminary, and learned that we are each commanded to make disciples of all nations.

As I studied cross-cultural missions and evangelism strategies under Dr. J. Christy Wilson Jr., I had the added blessing of meeting several missionary statesmen who came and spoke to the students, but also, I think, to fellowship with Dr. Wilson.

During this period in my life, I also began reading missionary biographies. One of the first books I read was *Through Gates of Splendor* by Elisabeth Elliot. This is the account of five young couples who moved to Ecuador, South America, in an attempt to reach the Auca tribe (Waorani) with the gospel of Jesus. In January, 1956, while attempting to contact this tribe, the five husbands were killed. Miraculously God opened a way for Elisabeth Elliot, her young daughter, and Rachel Saint to live with the Waorani and work with the very natives who had killed their loved ones. Needless to say, my heart was deeply moved. In the providence of God, I had the privilege of renting a room in Elisabeth Elliot's home for one year while I was a student at Gordon-Conwell Theological Seminary. We will learn more about the Waorani later in this lesson.

Cross-Cultural Missionaries are Necessary

There is still a great need for believers to carry the good news to nations where the name of Jesus is not known. When we enter a new and different culture than our own, this effort involves bridging the differences between our culture and the new culture. This dynamic is referred to as being cross-cultural.

When those who respond to the call of God are making the initial beachhead to take the gospel to an unreached people group and engage a new culture that has never heard the good news, they will need all of the expertise, funding, and prayer support they can get. If those five young couples had not raised financial support, been trained, prayed, and learned the language, the Waorani would not have heard about Jesus. Once a new church has been established, the missionaries need to shift gears and work to phase themselves out of a job by appointing elders and deacons from this fledgling church to carry the gospel to their neighbors in Judea, Samaria, and the uttermost parts of the earth. This long-term strategy should be always in their minds as they make disciples.

Paul was the first cross-cultural missionary and an essential part of the work of God in planting churches throughout the world. He went to different cultures than his own, preached the gospel, taught the new believers, and trained leaders like Timothy and Titus. These groups of new converts became the local body of Christ in cities like Laodicea, Colossae, and Philippi.

Then Paul set apart and commissioned the local members of the indigenous church to be elders and deacons. Another word for indigenous is natural. It was natural that local believers should lead their congregations, for they knew the language and the culture.

Teach Them Diligently

I followed the plan of God as revealed in Deuteronomy for discipling and training my own children. Even though I did not grow up in a home that regularly set aside time to read the Word of God as a family, God helped my wife and me to make this a habit in our home. This passage in Deuteronomy shaped my thinking as a parent. I saw two components in it: to teach God's Word intentionally and to be with my children as much as possible.

> "You shall teach them diligently to your children, and shall talk of them
> when you sit in your house, and when you walk by the way, and when
> you lie down, and when you rise." (Deuteronomy 6:7)

In addition to reading Scripture regularly in our home, we also sought to talk of God's ways as we sat in our house, walked by the way, lay down, and when we arose. It was because of this verse and others like it that God led us to home educate our children. I reasoned that I could diligently teach my sons God's word and model it throughout the day when we were together.

Parents First

After many years of seeking to be faithful to this passage, I was asked at a conference why I had not quoted the two previous verses. I did not have an answer, so I opened my Bible and read:

> "You shall love the LORD your God with all your heart and with all your
> soul and with all your might. And these words that I command you
> today shall be on your heart." (Deuteronomy 6:5-6)

I saw clearly that before I could effectively teach my children to love God and His Word, I had to love God and His Word. As the parent teacher it was my responsibility to love God with everything in me, love His Word, and be faithful in my personal relationship with God before I was prepared to train my children to do the same.

I began to seek God that I would indeed love Him with all my heart, soul, mind, and strength. I also asked Him to help me to love the truth. God answered that prayer, and now I can look back to that conference as a very significant turning point in my relationship with God. Being responsible as the parent teacher transformed me, and it enhanced my message to my family. We both benefited by following God's plan as revealed in His inspired advice.

Uniquely Suited

Parents are ideally equipped to teach and train their children. They can teach God's Word and model their faith in their home because they live with them 24/7. Parents know the language and culture of their children. They are intimately involved in their children's day to day activities and are familiar with their world. I remember on many occasions seeking to teach my children a new concept and being able to use appropriate illustrations and draw from a wealth of knowledge that I knew they were familiar with. I also believe there is no one on this earth that loves them or wants them to succeed more than my wife and myself.

Born Disciplers

It is easy for me to understand why God calls parents to "train up their children" for they are uniquely qualified to pass their faith on to the next generation. Parents also know that the amount of time the children will be in their home is limited. They work diligently to train their children to become independent. They teach their sons and daughters to feed themselves, get dressed, read, write, and learn math. They hope they will grow, be married, have children and then disciple them. Every parent wants their children to mature and be solid contributing citizens of heaven and earth. This is a natural model of discipleship.

Missionaries and Christian ministries should emulate parents and help those they are serving to become independent. They should seek to provide scripture in their native language, teach them to read the Word of God, pray, and grow in their faith. Then they will be equipped to disciple others and share the good news to their countrymen.

Apply Principles We Have Been Learning

We are seeking to be faithful stewards of our money, time, and resources. We are choosing to love our neighbor as ourselves and to see how aid and assistance feels from his perspective. We want to discern the impact of our traditional methods in meeting the poverty of body as well as spirit. We don't want to create dependency and give people a fish for a day, but rather encourage them to grow and become independent. This is what making disciples is all about: teaching believers to fish so they can eat for a lifetime and then teach others to fish.

Fulfilling the Great Commission is Transformative

As newly appointed elders and deacons love, pray for, teach, and serve their brethren, they grow into their roles as the leaders of their local fellowship. This process of ministering to others transforms servant leaders and makes them more like Jesus. For Jesus loves, prays for, and continues to serve the Body of Christ.

Anyone who has served as a teacher will agree that they learn and grow more in their own faith walk as they seek to serve and minister others. This method of church planting practiced by Paul enables teachers and students to be mutually sanctified as they pursue Christ together.

Can We Improve on This Model?

You may not enjoy reading this section, but if we are going to examine blind-spots and harmful fruit from our traditional evangelical approach, we need to address "short-term mission trips." I have seen and contributed to many short-term trips of young people who sign up to travel to a different country or culture, in hopes of making a difference for a few weeks in the summer. This concept is endorsed because we hope the people involved will be deeply affected by the needs in a third world culture by being in that country. We secretly embrace the conviction that perhaps some of these individuals will even be led to become long-term missionaries because of their experience. Unfortunately, the research does not support this theory.

Here are a few facts before we look at these well-intentioned excursions in more detail. A March 18, 2008 article in USA Today reported that Princeton University conducted a study that found 1.6 million American church members took mission trips abroad in 2005. The average length being 8 days long, and the total cost was 2.4 billion dollars. This new trend, called "Religious Tourism" continues to grow annually.

Traditional Going

We have spent a good bit of time considering how to improve on the traditional model of charitable giving. Can we do better with traditional going? Perhaps you have participated in such an event or heard reports of trip members upon their return. As glowing as their reports may have sounded, and as hard as it is for me to write, they probably did very little lasting good, and potentially some harm by their efforts.

Consider the impact on the local missionary who had to stop his normal routine to host the group. He spent weeks preparing for their arrival, had special food prepared, took them on some sight-seeing expeditions, and tried to help them have a meaningful experience. One seminary in the Caribbean had earnest young people visit who wanted to make a difference. They arranged for them to lay tile on a floor of a newly constructed building. These volunteers had no experience and the work was shoddy at best and in several places needed to be redone. What the church group did not know was that there were experienced tile workers sitting outside the walls, hoping there would be work left for them to do when the big-hearted but misguided Americans returned home.

One summer a church in Mexico was painted six times by six different short-term mission groups. Think about the cost to the sending churches that raised the money to send these teams of eager volunteers. Consider the local painters who lost the opportunity for earning a meaningful income working with their own hands, and the impact of the loss of work on the local painter's family. This scenario is sad on so many levels, but we continue to perpetuate this approach every summer.

Or what about groups of young people who visited children's homes and orphanages. These tender-hearted folks lavished hugs and affection on these emotionally starved kids. But, what does it feel like to the children when the visitors leave after eight days? If several groups come down in one summer, what is like to have your heart broken three or four times in three months? There is more to a mission trip than how it impacts those who go; we need to think through the impact on those we are seeking to serve and bless.

When I chose to go on a short-term trip to Appalachia, I did not consider the impact on those I was ministering to. I mostly thought about the impact on me. I would have a new experience. I would feel good about helping others. I would have a good time with the other guys and gals on the trip. When I reflect now, the trip was more about me than them!

A New Approach is Needed

We still need to pray, to give, and to go, but with wisdom and discernment. I have asked missionaries about short-term efforts. They appreciate the fellowship. It can be lonely living on foreign soil. But perhaps instead of sending twenty at one time, maybe, space it out so every quarter a couple or family can visit and provide encouragement.

Summer outreaches often revolve around a common need to learn English, and there are needs and opportunities for people to serve at these camps and summer schools. However let's refrain from painting the same building, or laying tile, or taking away from the local workers. Let's not assume we have all the answers, but instead come alongside and serve in a spirit of humility.

The Great Omission

The man who flew the five men into the jungle was Nate Saint. His son Steve was four years old when he said goodbye to his father that morning in January. Forty years later Steve and his family moved back to the jungle to live with this tribe. In February, 2018, I had the opportunity to meet Steve and read his book, *The End of the Spear* about his family's adventures. After two years in the jungles of Ecuador, the Saint family moved back to the United States and subsequently began a ministry called ITEC. These initials represent Indigenous People's Technology and Education Center.

I believe the work of ITEC applies the unique principles we have been learning and applies them to the great commission just as Hope International has significantly improved traditional charity with Christian micro-finance. I have been a financial partner and prayer supporter of this ministry for many years. Steve Saint's book, *The Great Omission*, was instrumental in my thinking about the role of well-meaning churches and individuals in America.

Steve Saint has a unique perspective in our consideration of how to fulfill the great commission without creating dependence or using an ineffective western mission strategy. Since he grew up as the son of missionaries, he has seen both approaches to missions. His parents had responded to the great commission by raising support, assembling a team of prayer partners, moving their family to the jungle of Ecuador, and enrolling in language school to learn the tongue of those tribes where they would be working.

He also lived in Ecuador for many years with his mother on the mission field. When he was a young man, he returned to the States where he was educated and trained. During his lifetime, he saw the good and the not-so-good aspects of how Americans traditionally take the gospel to other nations. Since he has lived with the Waorani during his summers as a boy, and later as an adult, he has seen the fruit of modern missions on this tribe.

Indigenous Church

Just as all parents are commanded, and uniquely equipped, to teach and train their children, all followers of Jesus are similarly called and uniquely prepared to:

> "Go therefore and make disciples of all nations, baptizing them in the
> name of the Father and of the Son and of the Holy Spirit, teaching them
> to observe all that I have commanded you." (Matthew 28:19-20)

The local church is uniquely equipped to not only minister to their own church, but to fulfill the great commission to others in their people group and culture. These believers know the language and the culture. They live side by side with their neighbors for whom Christ also died. They do not need to raise large amounts of support in order to go to a foreign land. They do not need to invest years at a language school to learn a new language. The training they do need in evangelism and discipleship will not only equip them to take make disciples of their countrymen, it will also help them develop and grow in their own walk with God.

Sadly, we have neglected to mobilize the local indigenous group of believers in our efforts to make disciples of all nations. This lack is what Steve Saint calls the "great omission." I agree.

From Dependence to Independence

The Waorani, who have responded to the gospel, now need to be helped to develop sustainability and independence and not continued dependence on the churches and missionaries from America. The new job of the western missionaries should be shifting gears to disciple them and train them to become independent. They should also be encouraged to obey the great commission themselves. As believers, they share our responsibility to make disciples of all nations.

When Steve Saint was in Ecuador, his desire was to see the Waorani grow in their faith and accept responsibility to lead their churches and reach out to their neighbors. With this servant spirit and a desire to help the Waorani and other indigenous tribes become mature disciples, the Saint family formed ITEC. I have interviewed Steve and his son Jaime on several podcasts about their unique ministry to empower the indigenous people and help them fulfill the great commission. You can listen to these podcasts #192-194 here:

http://www.buildingfaithfamilies.org/podcasts/ You can learn more about ITEC at itecusa. org.

This ministry began when the Waorani asked Steve Saint to help them preach and make disciples of their neighboring villages. I-DENT, I-SEE, and I-MED are tools and training which ITEC has developed to meet the needs of people in their community and surrounding communities. When I was at ITEC headquarters this past year, I heard this sentence which is attributed to Theodore Roosevelt: "People don't care how much you know until they know how much you care."

The different services of ITEC meet a need and show that believers care. After they have demonstrated that they care, then believers can speak to their countrymen about Jesus. These services also provide funding for those who are going and help them be self-sufficient. ITEC is about training and equipping followers of Jesus to grow, to mature, and to become disciples and disciple-makers, thus fulfilling the great commission.

The Spirit of a Servant

Sadly, Americans often do not have the reputation of arriving in a new culture with the heart of a servant. Instead of having the attitude as expressed in this passage and saying, "How can I serve with you?" Americans are known for flying in and saying, "Here is our plan for you." We often swoop in with our specialized training, advanced degrees, financial backing, and an organized team of prayer warriors standing behind us. We are usually a member of a well-oiled missionary sending agency which has an established plan and vision. Let's embrace the posture of Jesus.

> "Do nothing from selfish ambition or conceit, but in humility count others more significant than yourselves. Let each of you look not only to his own interests, but also to the interests of others. Have this mind among yourselves, which is yours in Christ Jesus, who, though he was in the form of God, did not count equality with God a thing to be grasped, but emptied himself, by taking the form of a servant." (Philippians 2:3-7)

The Poor, the Crippled, the Lame, the Blind

John and the Summer Family Retreat

> "When you give a dinner or a banquet, do not invite your friends or your brothers or your relatives or rich neighbors, lest they also invite you in return and you be repaid. But when you give a feast, invite the poor, the crippled, the lame, the blind, and you will be blessed, because they cannot repay you. For you will be repaid at the resurrection of the just." (Luke 14:12-14)

Now that our eyes have been opened to the needs of the poor and we have observed the universal need we each feel to be included, valued, treated with dignity, and have a voice, let's consider another group of people, those with special needs. What do you know about the crippled, the lame, and the blind? I confess, until my son John, who was born with Down Syndrome, became a part of our family, I knew very little about these needy people who were also created in the image of God.

When John was eighteen years old, our family was invited to attend a Joni and Friends Family Retreat in Pennsylvania. Our world began to open that week, as we were introduced to the many facets of the world of disability. Each family who attends the camp has at least one member who has been affected by a disability.

Since I have been going to camp and interacting with a part of the church I had not known before, I have learned to be careful how I describe people who have been created in the image of God, but have different needs. These people are not disabled. They have been "affected by a disability," but they are not the disability. When you break an arm, you have a temporary disability, but you are not disabled. Your arm is broken, but you aren't. It is a distinction worth pondering. These gifted people have strengths and weaknesses just as we do. In some ways they are even advanced. My son has more chromosomes than most people! John is also very sensitive to the emotional needs of people. Because of what I have learned from John, I now try to focus on the gifts people with special needs have, and not on their physical limitations.

At camp I met Mike, who has cerebral palsy. He was wearing a t-shirt which read, "Just because I can't speak doesn't mean I don't have anything to say." I had never thought about that aspect, but his shirt was part of my learning curve. Up to this point in my life, whenever I had encountered people with a disability it was only for a few minutes in the back of the church, or in line at the grocery store. Being at camp for the better part of a week allowed me to see past the wheelchairs, slurred speech, and facial indicators, to begin to know the real person. I need to remind myself these people are not defined by their disability or challenge. They too, are created in the image and likeness of God.

Love Your Neighbor as Yourself

One of the ways I am helped to think about John and strive to be a good dad to him is to consider how I would like to be treated if I had a disability. What if I were John? How would I like to be treated? What opportunities would I like to have access to? John did not ask to be born with a different number of chromosomes.

Since these special people are my neighbors, I wondered how I am to love and care for them. How do I love my neighbor as myself? How would I want to be treated if I were in their shoes? Many of my new friends affected by disability were born with their conditions. Some had been in accidents, and other needs are a result of an error in a medical procedure. They did not ask to be different, nor did they choose to have a disability. And they cannot change it.

The objective of this unit is to apply what we have learned about the different aspects of what it means to be poor to see how we can reach out to this needy group of individuals. As we did before, let's look at the statistics and demographics to get a sense of the scope of the population described as having a disability.

The Scope of the Need

One billion people, or 15% of the world's population, experience some form of disability. Of these, 20% of the estimated global total, or approximately 200 million people, experience significant disabilities.

Persons with disabilities are more likely to experience adverse socioeconomic outcomes than persons without disabilities, such as less education, poorer health outcomes, lower levels of employment, and higher poverty rates.

I'm sure you are not surprised to learn that special needs folks are often ostracized in society, do not possess much of a voice, find it difficult to find a meaningful occupation post high school, and will not outgrow their condition. What shocked me was discovering that the disability community is often excluded and unwelcome on Sunday mornings worship services and may be one of the least evangelized people groups.

While many of their physical needs are being addressed, thanks to the American Disabilities Act, they still have significant needs that affect their being. They need to be valued, respected, be able to have productive occupation, and be included instead of stared at and ostracized.

Exceptional People

Since our first summer camp experience with families affected by disability, I have had the privilege of meeting many "exceptional" people. One of them is Joni Eareckson Tada, who in 1967 was injured in a diving accident at 17 years old, leaving her in a quadriplegic state with minimal use of her hands. After two years of rehabilitation, Joni reentered the community with new skills and a fresh determination to help others in similar situations. She formed a ministry called Joni and Friends, which is dedicated to extending the love and message of Jesus Christ to people who are affected by disability around the world. Joni (pronounced Johnny) is an anointed speaker, author, singer, radio personality, and a gifted painter. She is the voice for and of the special-needs world. God has given her amazing gifts and opportunities to exercise those gifts around the world. She has been an instrument of grace to millions. I encourage you to watch her movie, or read her biography, called Joni. You can learn more about her life and ministry here: http://www.joniandfriends.org Steve has tentatively scheduled a podcast with Joni in the near future. Check back to see if this is available at http://www.buildingfaithfamilies.org/podcasts/

Short Term Strategies

To the church's credit, many groups of believers are quick to come to the aid of victims of a broken leg, or a car accident, where those victims will be back on their feet in six to eight weeks. Meals are prepared and delivered to the home for the first few weeks. Arrangements are made to drive their children to school and after-school activities.

While I will give a high grade of "A" to support networks such as these, most churches are not equipped to engage in long term support and care scenarios as with a family who has a child born with Down Syndrome, Autism, or Cerebral Palsy. Their needs will not abate, and they will not outgrow their chromosome count or their permanent movement disorder. There are no medical remedies or short-term solutions, be we are still called to love our neighbor. Paul calls this bearing one another's burdens. "Bear one another's burdens, and so fulfill the law of Christ." (Galatians 6:2)

Long Term Strategies

Perhaps you know someone who is in hospice care with only a short time to live. One small group in a church came up with this strategy. One of the men was in need of companionship in the evening, someone to sit with him and give his wife a much-needed break. Several of his close friends wanted to help and determined to bear this burden, but as they individually pondered the time commitment, the thought of spending several nights a week at the home of their friend discouraged them. While several friends were contemplating carrying this burden themselves and visiting their friend every evening, no one ended up going.

One person got the idea of sharing the care, so they had fourteen people sign up to spend one evening every two weeks with their brother. This was doable, and one of these big-hearted folks was in the home of their friend each evening, until he passed from this life to the next. When one person cannot bear the load themselves, assemble a team!

Value and Inclusion at Church

Inclusion has always been a big issue for the Demmes. We have been fortunate to have attended churches which included our son in the worship experience. We are presently attending Wheatland Presbyterian Church, where John just began serving as an usher, to his delight and our satisfaction. John loves to participate in the life of our local church and to be an integral part of the church. He took the initiative and asked to be an usher. Dave and Rick took him under their wing and showed him how to do it. He is now a part of the usher team. Every Sunday, John greets you at the door to the sanctuary, hands you a bulletin, and helps collect the offering. After a few months, I spoke to the men who worked alongside John and thanked them for treating him with respect. They interacted with him as an adult with value, and did not patronize him. This is huge. I also thanked them for not thinking of him as the cute little guy with Down Syndrome who is kind of like the church mascot or project. They treat him as an equal. He can sense when he is being treated like a child, and it hurts him, just as it would hurt you or me.

Unfortunately, this is not the norm. We know of too many circumstances where our friend's son or daughter was asked to leave Sunday School for being disruptive. In some situations they were not encouraged to attend the main worship service because of noises they made. Still other churches direct everyone with special needs to a room with others who have special challenges.

Special Buddies

Another local church in our area assigns "buddies" to be with special needs students throughout the church service. They come alongside of these folks and take them to their classes and stay with them throughout the morning worship experience. In this way the parents, some of whom are single, have the opportunity to attend church by themselves and have a meaningful worship experience, knowing their child is being cared for. After the service, they have a chance to connect with other adults for encouraging fellowship. For these parents, having an hour or so to seek God and connect with other members of the body of Christ is extremely meaningful. In addition to blessing the parent(s) the young person feels extra special hanging out with someone closer to their age, who is cool.

I have so much more I could share on this topic, but when you seek God, He will show you how to come alongside and love the least of these. Trust Him to lead you and use your own creativity to figure out how to be a friend and treat these wonderful brothers and sisters in Christ as you would want to be treated if you were in their shoes.

More Ideas for Service

"Being affectionately desirous of you, we were ready to share with you not only the gospel of God but also our own selves." (1 Thessalonians 2:8)

When I first attended the Joni and Friends Family Retreat I did not know how to interact with men, women, and children affected by a disability. I read books and got to know other parents in our daily small groups. I heard about their challenges and blessings. During one small group I asked the question, "If someone were to come to you and ask how they could help your family, what would you tell them?"

One man said, "Don't treat our family as an outreach project or the object of a ministry. Get to know us. Spend time so we can get to know you. Listen before speaking. Ask how you might best serve thus."

There may be financial needs in families struggling with a disability, but in many cases I am aware of, these are not the primary concerns. If you really want to help, put away your checkbook, and see how you can give of yourself. Your time, energy, and presence.

Volunteer at a Joni and Friends Family Retreat. You will have to pay for your own room and board but this experience will change you and bless the person with the disability and their family. One parent told me that these STMs (Short Term Missionaries) are so special. I asked why. She said they have a team of therapists, who are special in their own way, but that is their job for which they are compensated. STMs, on the other hand, pay their own way to love on these children. This sacrificial love really blessed the parents. For more information: https://www.joniandfriends.org/ministries/family-retreats/#stm

Remember what we learned in a previous study about the best way to help the poor. It is by asking them what they need. Now is not the time to pretend we have all the answers, don our Superman cape, and swoop in to help. We too are needy. One of the main lessons I have learned in over thirty years of being with my son and other special people is that they are more like me than they are different. John has dreams and desires just like I do.

Do Unto Others

I have often asked myself, how I would like to be treated if I was my son John. I would want to be treated with respect. I would want to be heard and valued. I would want to be included. It is good for me to remember that John did not choose this life. Some of the ways we value our son is by genuinely listening to him. He does not speak clearly, but by asking questions, using some sign language, and being involved in his day to day activities, we generally have a pretty good idea what he is trying to communicate. We maintain eye contact and don't interrupt him. Whenever possible, we try to make his dreams come true, for he has them just as we do.

Going to work Monday through Friday, to the gym Saturday morning, and to church on Sunday keeps him engaged and active. Holiday vacations are tough. Work for John is a place where he belongs. He takes great pride in telling people he is a part of the shipping team and has a picture of the whole team on his iPad. His job assist is wonderful in stretching him and giving him new responsibilities. When the UPS driver arrives each day with a package, John signs the appropriate form. His job is a source of meaning and value. He is included. He has a voice and is a productive member of our business.

He has advocates as well. He speaks, however unclearly, at every monthly company luncheon. Recently several employees were conversing amongst themselves when John, dressed in his tie and suit, was behind the podium. He was visibly hurt, because they were being disrespectful of him by ignoring his presentation. His advocates in the room sensed what was transpiring, and before the next luncheon corrected the situation. John is now heard, for everyone in the room has been asked to be quiet and give him their attention.

Inclusion in the Workplace

In 2013 my daughter-in-law, CassieMarie, learned about a sign language class being offered in our community. She had been helping with our care of John, and as members of his family, we wanted to learn sign language so that we could encourage John to use his signs and be able to communicate his needs to us more clearly.

At the end of the eight-week class, Gwen, our instructor, invited a few of her deaf friends, along with her husband Mike, to join our class so that we could break up into smaller groups and practice communicating using our new skill. In getting to know Mike, I learned that he had experience working in shipping. Since our business had a shipping position open in our warehouse, I encouraged him to apply for the job. Mike has now been with Demme Learning for over five years and is one of our most efficient and dependable workers.

Two years ago, Jen joined the Demme Learning team as a job assistant to our special-needs employees. She also took a sign class from Mike's wife Gwen and has become proficient enough to communicate with Mike and Jeff (another deaf man with our company) as well as with John.

This spring, seven employees of Demme Learning are enrolled in a sign class on Tuesday evenings. During Wednesday lunch we have upwards of ten more employees learning sign language during lunch at a slower pace. The fact that hearing people are making the effort to learn sign language speaks volumes to those who are hearing impaired. Being able to communicate is the first step in building a deeper relationship. It is loving as we would want to be loved.

I need to say that I would not classify Mike and Jeff as having special needs or intellectual disabilities. While they are unable to hear, their other senses make up for a lack in the ears. They are intelligent, sharp, diligent, very observant, and valuable employees who were created in the image and likeness of God.

The inclusion of John and others with physical challenges and limitations has impacted the whole company. Not only have we at Demme Learning acquired reliable and hard-working employees, but they in return are valued and respected for their contribution to our company. It is a win-win relationship. If you would like to watch a video of John at work go to: https://youtu.be/jI0nmpzYlCg

Lighthouse Vocational Services

MathUSee also has several products that need to be assembled. We have chosen to give this work to two local businesses that employ only special needs adults. They are paid for their work and find meaning and self-respect doing a job well. In addition, they experience the camaraderie of interacting with their supervisors and fellow workers.

Several years ago, our family toured a ministry called Lighthouse Vocational Services. We saw the work they were doing, met the leadership, and entered into a partnership with them. Our plastic blocks are sent from our supplier directly to Lighthouse, where they are assembled by the adults affected by disability. I have been told the workers like working with the "Lego blocks." For more information: https://www.lighthousevoc.org

EARS

A few weeks ago, another ministry began bringing their mobile unit to do assembly work in our warehouse. They are from EARS, Ephrata Adult Rehab Services, https://www.ephratarehab.org.

They love coming to work with us, and we enjoy having them. We had been delivering product to them to assemble at their facility. When the kits were completed, they were delivered to our warehouse. This new arrangement enables us to get to know the workers, and several of their team are joining us for our sign language classes on Wednesdays. Our journey continues.

Gifted and Created in God's Image

According to scripture we are all created in the image and likeness of God. "Then God said, 'Let us make man in our image, after our likeness.' ... So God created man in his own image, in the image of God he created him; male and female he created them." (Genesis 1:26-27)

God formed us. We didn't just happen. "You made all the delicate, inner parts of my body and knit me together in my mother's womb. Thank you for making me so wonderfully complex! Your workmanship is marvelous—how well I know it. You watched me as I was being formed in utter seclusion, as I was woven together in the dark of the womb. You saw me before I was born. Every day of my life was recorded in your book. Every moment was laid out before a single day had passed." (Psalms 139:13-16 NLT)

As members of the Body of Christ, we each have been given a gift. "God has given each of you a gift from his great variety of spiritual gifts. Use them well to serve one another." (1 Peter 4:10)

I have done my best to talk about the needs of the disability community and how we can serve them and love them as we would like to be loved if we were in their shoes. What I have not done is talk about their unique strengths and gifts. I have been blessed on many occasions by these extraordinary individuals.

David is a young man with cerebral palsy who is confined by a wheelchair. He has a friend who is non-verbal. On his own initiative he purchased a sign language course and taught himself to speak in sign language so he could communicate with his friend. David is now an interpreter at his workplace.

My son John is one of the kindest, most loving people I have ever met. He loves my wife and me unconditionally. He loves God, his family, and the people with whom he works. He looks forward to attending church and going to work. His warm and hearty greetings to fellow workers and UPS drivers alike are legendary. People love his smile and his hugs. He is generally "fine" and rarely complains.

These exceptional people are my heroes. They are honest, authentic, loving souls. Yes, they have limitations, but they also have incredible gifts that they are using to edify the church and build God's kingdom.

When I attended the funeral of Chris, the pastor closed the two-hour service, during which the church was packed with people whose lives Chris had touched, with this wise observation. The pastor commented that we in the audience, who are "typical," assume that when we get to heaven, Chris will be more like us. After listening to all of the testimonials of how extraordinary Chris was, the reverend made the observation that when we enter heaven, we may find ourselves more like Chris.

Sharing Each Other's Burdens

Perhaps you have a friend, or know someone in your church, who is affected by a disability, and you are wondering what is the best way is to help or serve them. God does direct us each to "Share each other's burdens, and in this way obey the law of Christ." (Galatians 6:2 NLT)

First pray and ask God to help you see this individual as He sees him or her. Then remember that we are more alike than unlike. Unfortunately, we often focus on what makes us different, but there are so many more ways that we are the same.

As the parent of a special-needs son, it warms my heart to see people just hang out with John because they like him for who he is. We have had many people who have come into John's life, taken him to ballgames, played video games, or gone mini-golfing with him. John is just like us, he likes to belong, to be included, to be treated with respect, and to be with people.

The Least of These

When we minister to those who are needy, we may find ourselves ministering to Jesus Himself.

> "When the Son of Man comes in his glory, and all the angels with him,
> then he will sit upon his glorious throne. All the nations will be gathered
> in his presence, and he will separate the people as a shepherd
> separates the sheep from the goats. He will place the sheep at his right
> hand and the goats at his left.

Then the King will say to those on his right, 'Come, you who are blessed by my Father, inherit the Kingdom prepared for you from the creation of the world. For I was hungry, and you fed me. I was thirsty, and you gave me a drink. I was a stranger, and you invited me into your home. I was naked, and you gave me clothing. I was sick, and you cared for me. I was in prison, and you visited me.'

Then these righteous ones will reply, 'Lord, when did we ever see you hungry and feed you? Or thirsty and give you something to drink? Or a stranger and show you hospitality? Or naked and give you clothing? When did we ever see you sick or in prison and visit you?'

And the King will say, 'I tell you the truth, when you did it to one of the least of these my brothers and sisters, you were doing it to me!'" (Matthew 25:31-45)

Redeemer

I am often asked to speak about my life with John and the lessons God has taught me on our journey together. If you would like to listen to a talk, you can access it by clicking on this link or pasting in this URL http://www.buildingfaithfamilies.org/videos-2/ and then selecting the talk entitled "Finding Hope and Redemption in the Valleys of Life."

About ten years ago, I was speaking on this topic in Columbus, Ohio, and a young couple stood in front of the podium after the workshop. With tears in her eyes, the mother said, "Don't you think you have a child with a disability because of sin in your life?" I had never been asked that before. I paused and then said, "Absolutely not, and here is the scripture upon which I base my conviction: 'He does not deal with us according to our sins, nor repay us according to our iniquities.'" (Psalm 103:10)

In fact, I think the opposite is true. John has been the source of so much good in my life and in the life of my family. I consider John a blessing, and a gift from God. You would not be working through this curriculum if John had not joined our home in 1987. At that season in my life, I was a pastor and a high school math teacher, with several other responsibilities. In the ensuing 10 months, John battled a virus and was in the hospital in an oxygen tent for several days. While there, the doctors discovered a heart condition, for which John had two catheterizations and eventually open-heart surgery at eight months of age. Two months later he had surgery to repair a blockage in his intestine. He gained a pound the first year of his life.

I burned out and had an emotional breakdown which made it difficult for me to interact with people. My wife was also hurting, so we resigned from all of our responsibilities and moved to a different state, so we could regroup as a family. I began tutoring individual students as well as small groups of children, in an effort to provide an income for our family. While teaching these students, I created my own worksheets and materials for the young scholars. These early efforts grew into the program we now know as MathUSee. One of my favorite names for God is Redeemer. For truly our good, sovereign, loving God works all things together for our good.

Because of John, my eyes have been opened to the world of the less fortunate, and now you too have had a taste of the special need's world. May God bless you and make you a blessing, as you serve and encourage the least of these, His brethren. Amen.

For More Study

If you would like to learn more and dig deeper into the world of disability, consider taking the course "Beyond Suffering" from Joni and Friends. The course was "created to transform the way Christians view God's plan for disability and suffering." You can learn more about it here: www.joniandfriends.org/ministries/christian-institute-on-disability/beyond-suffering/

I interviewed Joni Erickson Tada and you can listen to it here: www.BuildingFaithFamilies.org/podcasts/ the podcast is #201.

SOLUTIONS TO WORKSHEETS

1.1

Practice Questions

1. 34 hr × 6.00/hr = $204.00

2. Time and a half is $6/hr × 1.5 hr = $9/hr
   40 hr × $6/hr + 3.5 × $9/hr = $271.50

3. 40 hr × $6/hr + 7 hr × 1.5 × $6/hr =
   $240 + $63 = $303

4. 34 hr + 43.5 hr + 47 hr = 124.5 hr
   $204.00 + $271.50 + $303.00 = $778.50
   $778.50 ÷ 124.5 hr = $6.25/hr

5. 2,000 hr × $11.75/hr = $23,500

6. $27,000 ÷ 2,000 hr = $13.50/hr

7. $179,500.00 × 0.015 = $2,692.50

8. 8 case × 100 DVD/case × $0.11/DVD= $88.00
   $88.00 ÷ 6 hr = $14.67/hr

Bible and Discussion Questions

9. Your choice :-)

10. "All Scripture is inspired by God and is useful
    to teach us what is true and what is wrong in
    our lives. It corrects us when we are wrong
    and teaches us to do what is right. God uses
    it to prepare and equip his people to do every
    good work." (2 Timothy 3:16–17 NLT)

11. Enjoy the information and the story.

1.2

Practice Questions

1. 38.5 hr × $10.75/hr = $413.88

2. 40 hr × $10.75/hr + 11 hr × 1.5 × $10.75/hr =
   $430.00 + $177.375 = $607.38

3. 40 hr × $10.75/hr + 8.25 hr × 1.5 × $10.75/hr =
   $430.00 + $133.03125 = $563.03

4. 38.5 hr + 51 hr + 48.25 hr = 137.75 hr
   $413.88 + $607.38 + 563.03 = $1,584.29
   $1,584.29 ÷ 137.75 hr = $11.50/hr

5. 2,000 hr × $18.33/hr = $36,660

6. $44,500 ÷ 2,000 hr = $22.25/hr

7. 1.5% + 1.5% = 3% = 0.03
   $112,000 × 0.03 = $3,360.00

8. 47 kit × $0.60/kit = $28.20
   $28.20 ÷ 3.25 hr = $8.68/hr

Bible and Discussion Questions

9. Adam and Eve were commissioned to "Be
   fruitful and multiply. Fill the earth and govern
   it. Reign over the fish in the sea, the birds
   in the sky, and all the animals that scurry
   along the ground." (Genesis 1:26–28 NLT)

10. God's word is able to be readily obeyed. It is doable.

11. A fun and informative discussion
    question for your family.

1.3

Practice Questions

1. 25 hr × $7.50/hr = $187.50
   40 hr × $7.50/hr + 1 hr × 1.5 × 7.50/hr =
   $300.00 + $11.25 = $311.25

2. 50 wk × 40 hr/wk × $8.25/hr = $16,500.00

3. $52,500 ÷ 2,000 hr = $26.25/hr

4. $950 × 0.15 = $142.50

5. 83 set × $0.45/set = $37.35
   $37.35 ÷ 3.5 hr = $10.67/hr

6. When I receive a salary I can budget better
   knowing I can count on a set amount of money
   each paycheck. If I receive a commission I will
   work more diligently and effectively since my
   salary is based on the results of my efforts but
   if I do not produce, I go hungry and may miss
   rent payments. Having a combination allows me
   to count on part of my income for my primary
   responsibilities while encouraging me to work
   harder and smarter to make more money.

7. 7 car × $1,260/car × 0.25 = $2,205

8. 4 wk × $450/wk + $2,205 = $4,005

Bible and Discussion Questions

9. Someone who faithfully takes care of what belongs to someone else.

10. "I saw heaven opened, and behold, a white horse! The one sitting on it is called Faithful and True, and in righteousness He judges and makes war. His eyes are like a flame of fire, and on His head are many diadems, and He has a name written that no one knows but Himself. He is clothed in a robe dipped in blood, and the name by which He is called is The Word of God." (Revelation 19:11–13) "In the beginning was the Word, and the Word was with God, and the Word was God. [...] And the Word became flesh and dwelt among us, and we have seen his glory, glory as of the only Son from the Father, full of grace and truth." (John 1:1, 14)

11. Did they?

1.4

Lesson Practice Questions

1. 38 hr × $9.25/hr = $351.50
   40 hr × $9.25/hr + 8 hr × 1.5 × $9.25/hr = $370.00 + $111.00 = $481.00

2. 2,000 hr × $23.00/hr = $46,000.00

3. $75,000 ÷ 2,000 hr = $37.50/hr

4. $375 × 0.24 = $90.00

5. 28 set × $1.25/set = $35.00
   45 min/60 min = 0.75
   2 hr 45 min = 2.75 hr
   $35.00 ÷ 2.75 hr = $12.73/hr

6. Answers should vary, but I personally prefer being paid by the piece since I have a greater incentive to work faster and more efficiently.

7. Option 1 = $50,000
   Option 2 = $10,000 + 0.01 × 65,000,000 = $10,000 + $65,000 = $75,000
   Option 2 is larger in this case

8. 0.015 × 6,500,000 = $97,500

Bible and Discussion Questions

9. That they be faithful.

10. Every word is eternal and life-giving, the words of God are eternal, the word of Christ builds faith, the truth makes us clean, God-breathed truth is liberating, holy words sanctify.

11. This will be interesting.

1.5

Lesson Practice Questions

1. 38 hr × $12.80/hr = $486.40 (first week)
   40 hr × $12.80/hr + 5 hr × 1.5 × $12.80 = $512.00 + $96.00 = $608.00 (second week)

2. 40 hr × $12.80/hr + 2.5 hr × 1.5 × $12.80 = $512.00 + $48.00 = $560.00 (third week)
   $486.40 + $608.00 + $560.00 = $1,654.40
   $1,654.40 ÷ 3 wk = $551.47/wk (average)

3. 2,000 hr × $13.25/hr = $26,500

4. $39,000 ÷ 2,000 = $19.50/hr

5. 180,000 dinars × 0.03 = 5,400 dinars

6. 0.015 × 13,950 shekels + 240 shekels = 209.25 shekels + 240 shekels = 449.25 shekels

7. 236 goats × 0.25 dinar/goat = 59 dinars

8. $160.00 × 0.35 = $56.00

Bible and Discussion Questions

9. When my life is full of good things, I am tempted to forget that the good land, God's blessing, and the power to get wealth all come from God.

10. a. "Learn to fear the LORD"
    b. Become more obedient "by keeping all the words of this law [...] and doing them"
    c. Develop humility and "prevent him from becoming proud and acting as if he is above his fellow citizens"
    d. Help to be careful and "prevent him from turning away from these commands in the smallest way"
    e. When the Word of God is diligently read daily, the family will also benefit, as "descendants will reign for many generations in Israel"

11. Notice how different this is from today on one level, and yet similar on another level.

2.1

Lesson Practice Questions

1. $37.25 \times 0.18 = \$6.71$
$37.25 \times 0.05 = \$1.86$

2. $37.25 + \$1.86 + \$6.71 = \$45.82$
I would add 18¢ because
$37.25 + \$1.86 + \$6.71 + \$0.18 = \$46.00$

3. $26.95 \times 0.2 = \$5.39$
$26.95 \times 0.07 = \$1.89$

4. $26.95 + \$5.39 + \$1.89 = \$34.23$
I would add 77¢ because
$26.95 + \$5.39 + \$1.89 + \$0.77 = \$35.00$

5. $0.99 \times \$874.50 = \$865.76$

6. No, since it has been more than 15 days. If it had been less than 15 days he could have saved $0.02 \times \$1,358.00 = \$27.16$

7. $100\% - 5\% = 95\% = 0.95$
$0.95 \times \$2,573.92 = \$2,445.22$

8. $100\% + 1\% = 001\% = 1.01$
$1.01 \times \$2,573.92 = \$2,599.66$

Bible and Discussion Questions

9. You shall love God with all your heart, soul, mind, and strength.

10. 1 Corinthians 13 talks about love, Hebrews 11 talks about faith, and Psalm 1, 19, and 119 talk about God's Word.

11. Answers will vary

2.2

Lesson Practice Questions

1. $76.85 \times 0.16 = \$12.30$
$76.85 \times 0.0675 = \$5.19$

2. $76.85 + \$12.30 + \$5.19 = \$94.34$
I would add 66¢ because
$76.85 + \$12.30 + \$5.19 + \$0.66 = \$95.00$

3. $93.20 \times 0.15 = \$13.98$
$93.20 \times 0.0725 = \$6.76$

4. $93.20 + \$13.98 + \$6.76 = \$113.94$
I would add 6¢ because
$93.20 + \$13.98 + \$6.76 + \$0.06 = \$114.00$

5. $1,299.00 because it is one day too late for the discount.

6. $265.00 - (2\% \times \$265.00) =$
$265.00 - \$5.30 = \$259.70$

7. $1,802.73 - (2\% \times 1,802.73) =$
$1,802.73 - \$36.05 = \$1,766.68$

8. $1,802.73

Bible and Discussion Questions

9. No. Either you will hate the one and love the other or vice versa.

10. "Do not be conformed to this world, but be transformed by the renewal of your mind." (Romans 12:2)

11. If the amount of your tip is based on your performance you might work harder and more efficiently to provide better service to the customer. You may think of other benefits.

2.3

Lesson Practice Questions

1. $29.60 \times 0.16 = \$4.74$
$29.60 \times 0.06 = \$1.78$

2. $29.60 + \$4.74 + \$1.78 = \$36.12$
rounded down to $36.00

3. $1,075.00

4. $1,075.00 \times 0.02 = \$21.50$
$1,075.00 - \$21.50 = \$1,053.50$

5. $3 \times \$2.00$ for parking and $3 \times \$2.00$ at the curbside check-in, so $12.00.

6. If the invoice is paid within 15 days 2% can be deducted, and if you choose to not use this discount, the entire bill is due in 30 days.

7. $3,573.92 \times 0.05 = \$178.70$

8. $3,573.92 \times 0.01 = \$35.74$

Bible and Discussion Questions

9. An idol is anything in which someone looks to supply what only God is designed to provide. Answers may include, self, another person, money, a sports team, insurance, possessions, etc.

10. Your answer will vary. I like meditating

on the character qualities of God.

11. Uber, Lyft, and taxi drivers. Parking shuttles, curbside check-in, etc.

2.4

Lesson Practice Questions

1. $\$9.50 \times 4 = \$38.00$

2. $\$38.00 \times 0.065 = \$2.47$ for the tax
$\$38.00 \times 0.05 = \$1.90$ for the tip
$\$38.00 + \$2.47 + \$1.90 = \$42.37$

3. $\$147.50 \times 0.07 = \$10.33$ for the tax

4. $\$147.50 \times 0.18 = \$26.55$ for the tip

5. $\$147.50 + \$10.33 + \$26.55 = \$184.38$
This amount divided into three parts is $\$61.46$.

6. $\$2,857.00 \times 0.02 = \$57.14$

7. $\$1,902.73 \times 0.02 = \$38.05$

8. $\$1,902.73$

Bible and Discussion Questions

9. Money can provide a sense of security. It can provide food, clothing, and shelter. Money can become a source of pride, and acquiring more and more of it may become a lifelong passion. Working for money and seeing it as the source of all of our needs is making money an idol.

10. Being transformed in his mind. Thinking biblically. Seeing God for who He is and not who he had been told He is.

11. Answers will vary.

2.5

Lesson Practice Questions

1. $\$23.80 \times 0.06 = \$1.43$
$\$23.80 + \$1.43 = \$25.23$

2. $\$23.80 \times 0.17 = \$4.05$

3. $\$23.80 + \$1.43 + \$4.05 = \$29.28$
which rounds to $\$30.00$

4. By April 13th—within 10 days.

5. $\$736.00 \times 0.02 = \$14.72$

6. 25 days or by April 28th

7. $\$3,895.00 \times 5\% = \$194.75$
$\$3,895.00 - \$194.75 = \$3,700.25$

8. $\$3,895.00 + (1\% \times \$3,895.00) =$
$\$3,895.00 + \$38.95 = \$3,933.95$

Bible and Discussion Questions

9. The love of money.

10. We are each unique and have the privilege/ opportunity to be individually tutored by God Himself. We need to find out what works for us and helps us follow Jesus fully.

11. Answers are different for each family.

3.1

Lesson Practice Questions

1. Gross Weekly Pay $= \$22,800.00 \div 52 = \$438.46$
Federal Witholding $= \$40.00$
State $= 3.07\% \times \$438.46 = \$13.46$
County $= 1\% \times \$438.46 = \$4.38$
FICA $= 7.65\% \times \$438.46 = \$33.54$
SUI $= 0.06\% \times 438.46 = \$0.26$
Total $= \$40.00 + \$13.46 + \$4.38 +$
$\$33.54 + \$0.26 = \$91.64$

2. FICA $= \$33.54$

3. SUI $= \$0.26$

4. $\$438.46 - \$91.64 = \$346.82$

5. $10\% \times \$438.46 = \$43.85$

6. Employer Contributions
FUTA $= 6\% \times \$438.46 = \$26.31$
FICA $= 7.65\% \times \$438.46 = \$33.54$
SUI $= 2\% \times 438.46 = \$8.77$
Total $= \$26.31 + \$33.54 + \$8.77 = \$68.62$

7. What percent (W_p) of $\$438.46$ is $\$346.82$?

$W_p \times \$438.46 = \$346.82$

$W_p = \dfrac{\$346.82}{\$438.46}$

$W_p = 0.79 = 79\%$

Bible and Discussion Questions

8. Love is giving. God so loved the world that He gave His Son to die for us so that we have eternal life.

9. Parents are to teach their children diligently when they sit in their home, go for a

walk, lie down, and when they rise.

10. Listen well!

3.2

Lesson Practice Questions

1. $78,000.00 \times 52 = 4,056,000.00$

2. $4,056,000.00 \times 1.5\% = \$60,840.00$
   $\$60,840.00 \div 52 = \$1,170.00$

3. Federal W/H is given at $0.00.
   State $\$1,170.00 \times 3.07\% = \$35.92$
   County $\$1,170.00 \times 1\% = \$11.70$
   FICA $\$1,170.00 \times 7.65\% = \$89.51$
   SUI $\$1,170.00 \times 0.06\% = \$0.70$
   Total $137.83

4. $\$1,170.00 - \$302.83 = \$1,032.17$

5. $\$1,032.17 \times 10\% = \$103.22$

6. Answers are your own.

7. W_p of $1,170.00 is $1,032.17?
   $$W_p = \frac{\$1,032.17}{\$1,170.00} = 88\%$$

Bible and Discussion Questions

8. Coveting is selfish. Coveting is present in several of the Ten Commandments.

9. Honoring is an attitude of the heart. When I honor someone, I respect them and treat them with deference.

10. Answers will vary.

3.3

Lesson Practice Questions

1. $1,485 \times \$0.11 \times 100 = \$16,335.00$

2. $\$16,335.00 - \$12,000.00 = \$4,335.00$

3. $\$4,335.00 \times 15.3\%$ (7.65% of employer and 7.65% for employee) $= \$663.26$
   $\$663.26 \div 4 = \$165.82$

4. For the 2019 calendar year these dates were April 15, June 17, September 16, January 15

5. $\$4,335.00 \times 10\% = \$433.50$

6. $\$4335.00 \times 4.07\%$ (3.07% + 1%) $= \$176.43$

7. This is not an exact science, but if she estimates her annual income to be around $16,500.00 then multiply this by 10% and divide it by 12 for monthly payments or by 52 for weekly or by 4 for quarterly payments as God would lead. At the end of the year after she knows exactly how much she has made, she can make a year end adjustment.

Bible and Discussion Questions

8. Loving is unselfishly giving and thinking of others ahead of yourself. Coveting is selfish and thinking of self first.

9. No we are to honor our parents even when they are flawed as in Noah and David's life. There are no perfect parents, or children, in the Bible. We all make mistakes.

10. Answers will vary from family to family.

3.4

Lesson Practice Questions

1. Answers may vary depending on the estimate. If you guessed that the percentage withheld for taxes would be 25%, you might answer $54,000 \times 75\% = \$40,500$

2. $1\% \times \$54,000.00 = \$540.00$
   $3\% \times \$54,000.00 = \$1,600.00$
   $8\% \times \$54,000.00 = \$4,300.00$

3. $\$54,000.00 \div 52 =$ a little over $1,000.00

4. Weekly exact is $\$54,000.00 \div 52$ is $1,038.46
   Federal Withholding given as $132.00
   State $31.88 ($3.07\% \times \$1,038.46 = \$31.88$)
   County $10.38 ($1\% \times \$1,038.46 = \$10.38$)
   FICA $79.44 ($7.65\% \times \$1,038.46 = \$79.44$)
   SUI $0.62 ($0.06\% \times \$1,038.46 = \$0.62$)
   Total $254.32
   ($132.00 + $31.88 + $10.38 + $79.44 + $0.62 = $254.32)

5. FUTA $62.31 ($6\% \times \$1,038.46 = \$62.31$)
   FICA $79.44 ($7.65\% \times \$1,038.46 = \$79.44$)
   SUI $20.77 ($2\% \times \$1,038.46 = \$20.77$)
   Total $162.52 ($62.31 + $79.44 + $20.77 = $162.52)

6. $\$54,000.00 \div 12 = \$4,500.00$ is his monthly pay times 10% = $450.00.

7. FICA stands for Federal Insurance

Contribution Act and is comprised of Social Security (6.2%) and Medicare (1.45%).

Bible and Discussion Questions

8. Loving God and loving your neighbor as yourself

9. Honor your father and mother. It is found in Exodus 20, Deuteronomy 5, and Ephesians 6.

10. A good accountant can save you money. They will also be sitting at the table with you if the IRS wants to audit your taxes.

3.5

Lesson Practice Questions

1. $81,000.00 − $24,000.00 = $57,000.00

2. The first $19,050.00 will be taxed at a rate of 10%, which is $1,905.00
   Subtracting $19,050.00 from $57,000.00 yields a balance of $37,950.00
   This amount is taxed at the 12% rate.
   $37,950.00 × 0.12 = $4,554.00.
   Adding the two amounts, $4,554.00 + $1,905.00 = $6,459.00
   $6,459.00 ÷ 4 = $1,614.75.

3. $81,000.00 ÷ 52 = $1,557.69

4. Federal W/H given as $0.00
   FICA $119.16 (7.65% × $1,557.69 = $119.16)
   County $15.58 (1% × $1,557.69 = $15.58)
   SUI $0.93 (0.06% × $1,557.69 = $0.93)
   Total withheld $119.16 + $15.58 + $0.93 = $135.67

5. Gross weekly pay is $1,557.69
   W_p of $1,557.69 is $135.67

   $$W_p = \frac{\$135.67}{\$1,557.69} = 9\%$$

6. How much will their employer contribute?
   FUTA $93.46 (6% × $1,557.69 = $93.46)
   FICA $119.16 (7.65% × $1,557.69 = $119.16)
   SUI $31.55 (2% × $1,557.69 = $31.15)
   Total $93.46 + $119.16 + $31.15 = $243.77

7. A flat tax is one percentage rate for all workers who are being taxed. The graduated tax has brackets or income levels with different percentage rates based on the amount of annual income. Currently there are seven such brackets in the U.S. tax code.

Bible and Discussion Questions

8. Jesus did not think of Himself first but came to serve and to give His life for us. Even though He was God, He still emptied himself and took the form of a servant.

9. Absolutely, because this request is according to His will. And as we ask in accordance with His will, He hears and answers. "This is the confidence that we have toward Him, that if we ask anything according to His will He hears us. And if we know that He hears us in whatever we ask, we know that we have the requests that we have asked of Him." (1 John 5:14–15)

10. This will be interesting.

4.1

Lesson Practice Questions

1. The functions may include: checking, savings, loans, mortgages, ATM, etc.

2. Members of your local community

3. Some of the ways banks earn money include: fees, investments, interest on loans, etc.

4. W_p of $300.00 is $1.50?

   $$W_p \times \$300.00 = \$1.50$$

   $$W_p = \frac{\$1.50}{\$300.00}$$

   $$W_p = 0.005 = 0.5\%$$

5. 100% (meal) + 8.5% (tax) + 16% (tip) = 124.5%
   $36.00 × 1.245 = $44.82

6. Answers may vary, but usually it means you will have a large enough minimum balance in the bank.

7. $290.00/week × 25%/person = $72.50/(person·week)

Bible and Discussion Questions

8. What do you think? I think in the kingdom of God, godliness is more valuable than lots of cash.

9. God began revealing how much He loved Steve through sermons, radio broadcasts, books, and scriptures. Then Steve recalled 1 John 4:19, "We love because He first loved us."

10. This will be interesting.

4.2

Lesson Practice Questions

1. The bank has to pay for a building, wages of the employees, and fees to do business. If your money is not generating enough interest then you have to help pay for these services.

2. In the old days before computers, these little books kept track of your savings.

3. When you begin paying off your mortgage, a percent goes to interest and the rest to the original amount of the home. This amount is called your equity and is what you own.

4. Answers will vary, but one big reason is if you need cash.

5. 100% (meal) + 6% + 15% = 121%.
$88.00 × 121% = $106.48.

6. I am hoping it is free. But ask the bank to be sure before being charged a fee.

7. $400.00 × 2 = $800.00 ÷ 3 = $266.66 (and two of you make an extra penny)

Bible and Discussion Questions

8. Thankfulness and contentment.

9. John 15:9 "As the Father has loved me, so have I loved you."

10. This will vary from home to home. I have used checking, savings, ATM, home equity loan, and the security deposit box.

4.3

Lesson Practice Questions

1. The bank :-)

2. When you open a savings account, the bank saves your money and pays you interest.

3. The money you choose to put into the bank.

4. $45.00 × 3 = $135.00 × 40% = $54.00.
$135.00 − $54.00 = $81.00.

5. $135 × 0.6 = $81.00
0.6 is 60% which is 100% minus the 40% discount.

6. George is 40% times $2,400.00 = $960.00.
Johnny is 60% times $2,400.00 = $1,440.00
To check, $960.00 + $1,440.00 = $2,400.00

7. 100% (meal) + 5% + 20% = 125%,
$24.80 × 125% = $31.00,
$31.00 ÷ 2 = $15.50 each

Bible and Discussion Questions

8. Count your blessings, name them one by one, and it will surprise you what the Lord hath done.

9. The more he marinates in the truth of God's love and affection, the more he loves God. The more he is loved by God, the more he is equipped to love others as he is being loved.

10. This order of services often changes as we move through different seasons of our life.

4.4

Lesson Practice Questions

1. Security, Trust, Fidelity, and others

2. The lender, often a bank, loans money. The borrower asks to get a loan and pay the bank interest in exchange for the funds.

3. Automated Teller Machine

4. Mortgage

5. 80% × $288.00 = $230.40

6. $16,500.00 × 40% = $6,600.00
$16,500.00 × 30% = $4,950.00
$16,500.00 × 15% = $2,475.00

7. 5.8% + 12% + 1.2% = 19%.
100% − 19% = 81%.
$6,600.00 × 0.81 = $5,346.00.

Bible and Discussion Questions

8. "Keep your life free from love of money, and be content with what you have."

9. Search your heart.

10. I wish I was a fly in your home when you were having these special conversations.

4.5

Lesson Practice Questions

1. The loan officer represents the people who have deposited money in the bank, that the person borrowing the money will be able to pay this amount back, in full, on time, and with interest.

2. Defaulting on the loan

3. If you default, the bank takes over possession of the car or home and will sell it to recover the cost of the loan.

4. Collateral is something of value which the bank can sell to recover their costs if the loan is not paid in full and on time.

5. Usually a savings account.

6. $21,975.00 − $3,400.00 =
   $18,575.00 is the net profit.
   $18,575.00 × 34% = $6,315.50,
   $18,575.00 × 28% = $5,201.00,
   $18,575.00 × 19% = $3,529.25 for Brad and Nate.

7. 5.8% + 9% + 1.7% = 16.5%,
   100% − 16.5% = 83.5% × $5,201.00 = $4,342.84

Bible and Discussion Questions

8. "I will never leave you nor forsake you."

9. It is an awesome truth to try and assimilate. God loved us and chose us before the foundation of the world to be His children. Amen.

10. Listen to what banks provide for your grandparents.

5.1

Lesson Practice Questions

1. Joseph B. Unit

2. Manny Tens

3. $125.00 in the box, "One hundred twenty-five and 00/100" on the line

4. 1556

5.

Joseph B. Unit 369 Decimal Street Place Value, PA 17606	**NEIGHBOR'S BANK** 1557 12 Main Street Goodtown, PA 17601 60–1234/0313	DATE _July 12, 2019_

PAY TO THE ORDER OF _Jack Taylor_ _____ $ _279.00_

Two hundred seventy-nine and 00/100 _____ DOLLARS

MEMO _Guitar payment_ _____ _Joseph B. Unit_
AUTHORIZED SIGNATURE

⑆031312343⑆1557 089876540 2⑈

6.

ENDORSE HERE

Pay to the order of
Steven P. Unit

Joseph B. Unit

DO NOT WRITE, SIGN, OR STAMP BELOW THIS LINE

Reserved for Financial Institution use

7.

ENDORSE HERE

For Deposit Only
Joseph B. Unit

DO NOT WRITE, SIGN, OR STAMP BELOW THIS LINE

Reserved for Financial Institution use

8.

*AD-Automatic Deposit *AP-Automatic Payment *ATM-Teller Machine *DC-Debit Card *T-Tax Deductible *TT-Telephone Transfer

NUMBER OR CODE	DATE	TRANSACTION DESCRIPTION	PAYMENT AMOUNT	✓	FEE	DEPOSIT AMOUNT	BALANCE	
							305	40
475	5/20	Guitar lesson	25 00	✓			280	40
476	5/25	Swimming class	15 00	✓			265	40
	5/27	Deposited paycheck		✓		360 00	625	40
477	5/27	Focus on the Family	50 00	✓			575	40
478	6/13	Car insurance	60 00				515	65
479	6/15	Cell phone	34 75				480	65
480	6/18	Cash	25 00	✓			455	65

9.

BALANCE THIS STATEMENT		550	40
Add Deposits made since this statement		0	00
SUBTOTAL		550	40
Checks issued but not on the statement			
Number	Amount		
478	60	00	
479	34	75	
TOTAL OUTSTANDING CHECKS		94	75
Subtract (total outstanding checks from subtotal)		455	65
CURRENT BALANCE		455	65

Bible and Discussion Questions

10. Our treasure is an indicator of what is in

our heart. Our treasure is a window into our priorities and what we consider important.

11. "Satisfy us in the morning with your steadfast love, that we may rejoice and be glad all our days." (Psalm 90:14)
"Let me hear in the morning of your steadfast love, for in you I trust." (Psalms 143:8)

12. This will be enlightening.

5.2

Lesson Practice Questions

1. 031312343

2. below the memo line and below the bank's address

3. 12 Main Street, Goodtown, PA 17601

4. to state the purpose of a check

5.

Joseph B. Unit 369 Decimal Street Place Value, PA 17606		NEIGHBOR'S BANK 12 Main Street Goodtown, PA 17601 60–1234/0313			**1558**

PAY TO THE ORDER OF *Ricky Ricardo* $ *1,595.84*

DATE *July 12, 2019*

One thousand five hundred ninety-five and 84/100 DOLLARS

MEMO *bongo drums*   *Joseph B. Unit*
AUTHORIZED SIGNATURE

⑆031312343⑆1558 089876540 2⑈

6.

ENDORSE HERE

Pay to the order of
Jeffrey C. Unit
Joseph B. Unit

DO NOT WRITE, SIGN, OR STAMP BELOW THIS LINE
Reserved for Financial Institution use

7.

ENDORSE HERE

Joseph B. Unit

DO NOT WRITE, SIGN, OR STAMP BELOW THIS LINE
Reserved for Financial Institution use

8.

■AD-Automatic Deposit ■AP-Automatic Payment ■ATM-Teller Machine ■DC-Debit Card ■T-Tax Deductible ■TT-Telephone Transfer

NUMBER OR CODE	DATE	TRANSACTION DESCRIPTION	PAYMENT AMOUNT	✓	FEE	DEPOSIT AMOUNT	BALANCE	
							455	65
481	6/20	Barnes and Noble	69 96	✓			385	19
482	6/25	Radio Shack	102 50	✓			283	19
	6/27	Deposited paycheck		✓		360 00	643	19
483	6/27	Calvary Church	36 00				607	19
484	7/13	Library fees	4 20	✓			602	99
485	7/15	Video rental	8 55				594	44
	7/19	Deposited tax refund				178 21	772	65

9.

BALANCE THIS STATEMENT		638	99
Add Deposits made since this statement		178	21
SUBTOTAL		817	20
Checks issued but not on the statement			
Number	Amount		
483	36 00		
485	8 55		
TOTAL OUTSTANDING CHECKS		44	55
Subtract (total outstanding checks from subtotal)		772	65
CURRENT BALANCE		772	65

Bible and Discussion Questions

10. Prayerfully select one or several. Consider recording them in a journal.

11. Unconditionally means with out conditions. God loves us irrespective of what we have done or will do. He loved us when we were sinners. There is nothing we can do to add to His love or take away from His affection.

12. This will be informative.

5.3

Lesson Practice Questions

1.

■AD-Automatic Deposit ■AP-Automatic Payment ■ATM-Teller Machine ■DC-Debit Card ■T-Tax Deductible ■TT-Telephone Transfer

NUMBER OR CODE	DATE	TRANSACTION DESCRIPTION	PAYMENT AMOUNT	✓	FEE	DEPOSIT AMOUNT	BALANCE	
							264	70
203	3/07	Computer software	45 00	✓			219	70
204	3/10	Singing lessons	75 00				144	70
	3/10	Deposited bday check		✓		240 00	384	70
205	3/12	Joni and Friends	100 00	✓			284	70
206	3/19	Flowers for Morris bday	32 45	✓			252	25
207	3/27	Cash	50 00				202	25
	3/31	Deposited tax refund				125 76	328	01

2. No, checks 204, 207, and a deposit haven't cleared

3.

BALANCE THIS STATEMENT		327	25
Add			
Deposits made since this statement		125	76
SUBTOTAL		453	01
Checks issued but not on the statement			
Number	Amount		
204	75	00	
207	50	00	
TOTAL OUTSTANDING CHECKS		125	00
Subtract (total outstanding checks from subtotal)		328	01
CURRENT BALANCE		328	01

4. Your statement tells you all of the activity that the bank has a record of for the preceding month. It will tell you your balance, all the checks and deposits which have cleared, ATM withdrawals, and any fees you have incurred.

5. An overdraft is when a check is written for more than is in your account.

6. A foreign ATM is any one which is not a branch of your own bank.

7. Use your own bank or credit union to avoid ATM fees.

Bible and Discussion Questions

8. The heart of a man is the real person inside of us. It is the hidden man. It is our essence.

9. This may be Steve's favorite life-changing verse. Use your own words to describe how the Father loves the Son and how Jesus loves us.

10. Just an estimate is fine

5.4

Lesson Practice Questions

1.

■AD-Automatic Deposit ■AP-Automatic Payment ■ATM-Teller Machine ■DC-Debit Card ■T-Tax Deductible ■TT-Telephone Transfer

NUMBER OR CODE	DATE	TRANSACTION DESCRIPTION	PAYMENT AMOUNT		✓	FEE	DEPOSIT AMOUNT		BALANCE	
									441	25
356	8/01	Strasburg mini-golf	17	50	✓				423	75
357	8/05	Circuit city	53	95	✓				369	80
	8/08	Deposited paycheck			✓		475	00	844	80
358	8/10	1st Community Church	47	50	✓				797	30
359	8/24	Goodwill	18	70					778	60
360	8/25	Wawa gas station	40	00					738	60

2. No, two checks haven't cleared, 359 and 360

---

3. yes

BALANCE THIS STATEMENT		797	30
Add			
Deposits made since this statement			
SUBTOTAL		797	30
Checks issued but not on the statement			
Number	Amount		
359	18	70	
360	40	00	
TOTAL OUTSTANDING CHECKS		58	70
Subtract (total outstanding checks from subtotal)		738	60
CURRENT BALANCE		738	60

4. Fees appear as debits since they are being taken out of or deducted from your balance.

5. Interest will show up as a credit since it is being added or credited to your account.

6. A credit union is owned by its members and exists to serve them. Fees for services are normally less than for a bank.

7. A bank is seeking to make money for a profit and distribute dividends to its shareholders. A credit union puts the profits back into the business.

Bible and Discussion Questions

8. Our heart is what makes decisions, decides how we invest our treasure, and governs our tongue. It is the most important part of our spiritual man. "Keep your heart with all vigilance, for from it flow the springs of life." (Proverbs 4:23)

9. "God's love has been poured into our hearts through the Holy Spirit who has been given to us." (Romans 5:5)

10. Every family has their own methods.

5.5

Lesson Practice Questions

1. Joseph B. Unit

2. Christian Freedom International

3. $275.00, in numerals to the far right of the check and in the line directly below the numerals, written out as "Two hundred seventy-five and 00/100 dollars."

4. 2981

5. 031312343

6. 12 Main Street, Goodtown, PA 17601

7. A reminder of the purpose of the check ("for the resettlement of the Karen people")

Bible and Discussion Questions

8. "The LORD sees not as man sees: man looks on the outward appearance, but the LORD looks on the heart." (1 Samuel 16:7)

9. No. Romans 8:38–39 "I am sure that neither death nor life, nor angels nor rulers, nor things present nor things to come, nor powers, nor height nor depth, nor anything else in all creation, will be able to separate us from the love of God in Christ Jesus our Lord."

10. Every generation does things a little differently than their predecessors.

6.1

Lesson Practice Questions

1. Money that is coming in. Salary, self-employment, commissions, etc.

2. Wants are things that you can get along without. Needs may include food, clothing, shelter, and transportation, etc.

3. Savings, emergencies, and giving

4. Your answer. Saving money in an envelope for a specific need

5. Using the chart at the end of Lesson 6 in the instruction manual, figure out the aproximate amount of money for each category based on an annual salary of $25,000.00

Gross Income	$25,000.00
Tithe	$2,500.00
Taxes	$3,750.00
Net Spendable	$18,750.00
Housing	$7,125.00
Food	$2,250.00
Auto	$2,812.50
Insurance	$937.50
Debts	$937.50
Recreation	$937.50
Clothing	$937.50
Savings	$937.50
Medical/Dental	$937.50
Miscellaneous	$937.50

6. Which figures are a cause for concern, and why?

Gross Income	$25,000.00	
Tithe	$2,500.00	
Taxes	$3,750.00	
Net Spendable	$18,750.00	
Housing	$7,144.00	a little above, ok
Food	$2,286.00	a little above, ok
Auto	$2,643.00	a little below, ok
Insurance	$880.00	a little below, ok
Debts	$1,200.00	too high, concerned
Recreation	$1,400.00	too high, concerned
Clothing	$895.00	a little below, ok
Savings	$350.00	too low, concerned
Medical/Dental	$410.00	too low, concerned
Miscellaneous	$917.00	a little above, ok

7. 65% is the suggested limit.

Bible and Discussion Questions

8. When a person incurs debt I think he is presuming that everything will be the same in the future as it was in the past. We do not know what the future will bring.

9. He saved us from our sins, which separate us from God.

10. Ask and listen well :-)

6.2

Lesson Practice Questions

1. Outgo is money being spent.

2. Knowing what your spending tendencies are will help project what your needs will be.

3. A budget helps us be faithful stewards and prepare for savings, emergencies, and giving.

4. No two families or individuals are the same. We can learn and adapt principles for us.

5. Using the chart at the end of Lesson 6 in the instruction manual, figure out the approximate amount of money for each category based on an annual salary of $40,000.00.

Gross Income	$40,000.00
Tithe	$4,000.00
Taxes	$7,200.00
Net Spendable	$28,800.00
Housing	$8,640.00
Food	$3,456.00
Auto	$3,456.00
Insurance	$1,440.00
Debts	$1,440.00
Recreation	$2,016.00
Clothing	$1,440.00
Savings	$1,440.00
Medical/Dental	$1,152.00
Miscellaneous	$2,016.00
Investments	$2,304.00

6. Now that you have some guidelines from #5, here are actual numbers for those same categories over the course of a year. Which figures are a cause for concern, and why?

Gross Income	$40,000.00	
Tithe	$4,000.00	
Taxes	$7,200.00	
Net Spendable	$28,800.00	
Housing	$8,640.00	good
Food	$3,380.00	a little below but ok
Auto	$4,134.00	$678.00 above, concern
Insurance	$1,437.00	good
Debts	$1,250.00	very good
Recreation	$2,009.00	good
Clothing	$1,975.00	$525.00 above, concern
Savings	$1,440.00	good
Medical/Dental	$1,044.00	good
Miscellaneous	$1,241.00	good
Investments	$2,250.00	a little low but ok

7. Unless you track your spending for several months, you will not have a handle on where your money is going.

Bible and Discussion Questions

8. No. Debts were incurred in the Bible. But often going into debt is unwise.

9. Because Jesus has taken away their sin and now they are clean new creatures.

10. Everyone has recurring expenses and financial obligations. You will too someday.

6.3

Lesson Practice Questions

1. Answers will vary.

2. Recording your expenses gives you real data of what you actually spend.

3. Using the chart at the end of Lesson 6 in the instruction manual, figure out the approximate amount of money for each category based on an annual salary of $15,000.00.

Gross Income	$15,000.00
Tithe	$1,500.00
Taxes	$1,200.00
Net Spendable	$12,300.00
Housing	$4,305.00
Food	$1,845.00
Auto	$1,845.00
Insurance	$615.00
Debts	$615.00
Recreation	$615.00
Clothing	$615.00
Savings	$615.00
Medical/Dental	$615.00
Misc.	$615.00

4. Now that you have some guidelines from #3, here are actual numbers for those same categories over the course of a year. Which figures are a cause for concern, and why?

Gross Income	$15,000.00	
Tithe	$1,500.00	
Taxes	$1,200.00	
Net Spendable	$12,300.00	
Housing	$4,305.00	good
Food	$1,850.00	good
Auto	$2,000.00	a little high, ok
Insurance	$600.00	good
Debts	$845.00	230 above, concern
Recreation	$550.00	a little low but ok
Clothing	$1,115.00	500 above, concern
Savings	$200.00	very low, concern
Medical/Dental	$425.00	a little low
Misc.	$395.00	ok

5. Answers will vary.

6. Answers will vary, but I hope you have some kind of regular employment or chores.

7. Answers will vary.

Bible and Discussion Questions

8. Sin separates us from God.

9. Lord willing we will do this or that.

10. Listen, don't judge or assume. There is no one correct response.

6.4

Lesson Practice Questions

1. Answers will vary.

2. Answers will vary.

3. Using the chart at the end of Lesson 6 in the instruction manual, figure out the approximate amount of money for each category based on an annual salary of $50,000.00. Use the same percentages on the chart as $40,000.

Gross Income	$50,000.00
Tithe	$5,000.00
Taxes	$9,000.00
Net Spendable	$36,000.00
Housing	$10,800.00
Food	$4,320.00
Auto	$4,320.00
Insurance	$1,800.00
Debts	$1,800.00
Recreation	$2,520.00
Clothing	$1,800.00
Savings	$1,800.00
Medical/Dental	$1,440.00
Misc.	$2,520.00
Investments	$2,880.00

4. Now that you have some guidelines from #5, here are actual numbers for those same categories over the course of a year. Which

figures are a cause for concern, and why?

Gross Income	$50,000.00	
Tithe	$5,000.00	
Taxes	$9,000.00	
Net Spendable	$36,000.00	
Housing	$11,000.00	good
Food	$4,150.00	good
Auto	$4,975.00	655 above, concern
Insurance	$1,750.00	ok
Debts	$1,900.00	ok
Recreation	$2,700.00	180 above, little concern
Clothing	$2,400.00	600 above, concern
Savings	$2,100.00	300 above, good
Medical/Dental	$1,275.00	a little low, ok
Misc.	$2,300.00	a little low, ok
Investments	$2,550.00	a little low, ok

5. Only you know!

6. This is your best guess.

7. Were you close to what you guesstimated in #6?

Bible and Discussion Questions

8. To assume that we know what the future holds when only God does.

9. Zero. Nada. Zilch. None.

10. This will be wise advice.

6.5

Lesson Practice Questions

1. Their salary from work.

2. Answers will vary.

3. Answers will vary. But Steve thinks now is a good time! "Indeed, the 'right time' is now. Today is the day of salvation." (2 Corinthians 6:2 NLT)

4. Pray about this and start small and aim to develop a regular discipline.

5. My wife is an enveloper, but I am not. Try saving for one thing and see if this method works for you.

6. Answers will vary.

7. Answers will vary.

Bible and Discussion Questions

8. God gave us His word in hopes that we would practice it and our lives and the lives of our children would be well.

9. Pick one or more. I like them all!

10. This will be rich.

7.1

Lesson Practice Questions

1. Retail is the cost to the supplier plus his profit; the final customer.

2. Brings products from many different places to a convenient location for you to purchase.

3. Rent, salaries, utilities, and advertising.

4. 40%

5. 4%–5%

6. $59.00 − 35.00 = $24.00

7. W_p of $59.00 is $24.00?
$W_p = $24.00/$59.00 ≈ 41%$ of retail

W_p of $35.00 is $24.00?
$W_p = $24.00/$35.00 ≈ 69%$ of wholesale

Bible and Discussion Questions

8. God! "You shall remember the LORD your God, for it is he who gives you power to get wealth." (Deuteronomy 8:18)
"Every good gift and every perfect gift is from above, coming down from the Father of lights." (James 1:17)

9. Give this your best shot!

10. John Wanamaker believed that since we are all equal before God we should be equal before price.

7.2

Discussion Questions (answers to 1–3 may vary)

1. The price the retailer pays for an item

2. Provides products in quantity at good prices; brings products from distant locations

3. Transportation, warehouse rental, salaries, possibly travel

4. $9.00 ÷ $16.00 ≈ 56%$

5. $7.00 ÷ $9.00 ≈ 78%$

6. $2.89 − (12% × $2.89) ≈ $2.54
or 100% − 12% = 88%, so 88% × $2.89 ≈ $2.54

7. $2.89/gal − $2.54/gal = $0.35/gal
2,400 gal × $0.35/gal = $840.00

Bible and Discussion Questions

8. Absolutely not!! The saints in Hebrews 11:37–40, John the apostle, and Jesus Himself.

9. "The armies of heaven, arrayed in fine linen, white and pure, were following him on white horses." (Revelation 19:14)

10. Ask your family!

7.3

Lesson Practice Questions

1. Profit 85¢ − 25¢ = 60¢
W_p of 85¢ is 60¢?
$W_p = 60¢ ÷ 85¢ = 71%$

2. $W_p × $0.89 = $0.20
$W_p = $0.20 ÷ $0.89 ≈ 22%$

3. They will encourage customers to purchase the lemonade since it brings a greater profit.

4. Again, the lemonade since they have more room to offer a discount and still make a profit.

5. $14.99 × 0.65 ≈ 9.74

6. 40% of Retail is $5.00
$0.40 × R = $5.00
R = $5.00 ÷ 0.40 = 12.50

7. $1.79 − $1.25 = $0.54 profit for each gallon of water.
$2.99 − $1.83 = $1.16 profit for each pound of cheese.
120 gallons of water times $0.54 = $64.80. Water wins!
40 pounds of cheese times $1.16 = $46.40.

Bible and Discussion Questions

8. "Gains the whole world and loses or forfeits himself." (Luke 9:25)
"But those who desire to be rich fall into temptation, into a snare, into many senseless and harmful desires that plunge people into ruin and destruction." (1 Timothy 6:9)
"When you have eaten and are full and have built good houses and live in them, and when your herds and flocks multiply and your silver and gold is multiplied and all that you have is multiplied, then

your heart be lifted up, and you forget the LORD your God, who brought you out of the land of Egypt, out of the house of slavery." (Deuteronomy 8:11–14)

9. Joshua, (Zechariah 3:4–5)

"I will rejoice greatly in the LORD, My soul will exult in my God; For He has clothed me with garments of salvation, He has wrapped me with a robe of righteousness." (Isaiah 61:10)

10. You will know :-)

7.4

Lesson Practice Questions

1. $1,700 ÷ 500 = $3.40

2. A. $7.50 − $3.40 = $4.10
   B. $14.99 − $7.50 = $7.49

3. $1,700 ÷ $4.10 = 414.6, so 415 books

4. A. $14.99 − $3.40 = $11.59
   $1,700 ÷ $11.59 ≈ 146.7 so 147 books
   B. W_p × $14.99 = $11.59
   W_p = $11.59/$14.99
   W_p ≈ 77%

5. A. $3,500 ÷ 28 = $125
   B. W_p of $595 is $125?
   W_p × $595 = $125
   W_p = $125/$595 ≈ 21%

6. Retail: friends and neighbors; Wholesale: Mr. Evans; Middleman: Boy Scouts

7. Mr. Evans' profit = $4.00 − $2.50 = $1.50
   W_p × $2.50 = $1.50
   W_p = $1.50/$2.50 = 0.6 = 60%
   Scouts' profit = $7.00 − $4.00 = $3.00
   W_p × $4.00 = $3.00
   W_p = $3.00/$4.00 = 0.75 = 75%
   Scouts' percentage was higher

Bible and Discussion Questions

8. "As for the rich in this present age," Paul writes to Timothy, "Charge Them Not to Be Haughty, Nor to Set Their Hopes on the Uncertainty of Riches, But on God, Who Richly Provides Us with Everything to Enjoy. They Are to Do Good, to Be Rich in Good Works, to Be Generous and Ready to Share, Thus Storing Up Treasure for Themselves as a Good Foundation for the

Future, So That They May Take Hold of That Which Is Truly Life." (1 Timothy 6:17–19)

9. This will be unique to you.

10. Brick and mortar represents a real building.

7.5

Lesson Practice Questions

1. The retail price is $5.95.

2. W_p of $5.95 is $3.10
   W_p = $3.10/$5.95 = 0.52 = 52%

3. $105.00 − $58.00 = $47.00

4. A.
   W_p of $105.00 = $47.00
   W_p = $47.00/$105.00 = 0.45 = 45%
   B.
   W_p of $58.00 = $47.00
   W_p = $47.00/$58.00 = 0.81 = 81%

5. $1.45 − $1.05 = 0.40 markup
   W_p of $1.45 = $0.40
   W_p = $0.40/$1.45 = 0.28 = 28%

6. The volume of eggs sold is much higher than the number of sandals sold during the same time period.

7. 60% of $15.97 = $9.58
   $15.97 − $9.58 = $6.39 or you could say
   100% − 60% = 40% and 40% of $15.97 is $6.39

Bible and Discussion Questions

8. This is your observation.

9. Romans 5

10. I wish I could listen!

8.1

Lesson Practice Questions

1. Purchasing online. Answers will vary.

2. Overspending. Answers will vary.

3. There is a 3–5% transaction fee each time an item is charged in addition to late fees and interest on unpaid balances.

4. Visa, Mastercard, American Express, and Discover

5. If the consumer pays in cash, there

is no 3% transaction fee.

6. A young first time user has no credit history and is an unknown quantity. Until they demonstrate they are able to pay back a loan they are a high risk of not paying back their balance.

7. You should be 18 and either be a student or have a steady job.

Bible and Discussion Questions

8. Malachi 3:10 "Bring the full tithe into the storehouse, that there may be food in my house. And thereby put me to the test, says the LORD of hosts, if I will not open the windows of heaven for you and pour down for you a blessing until there is no more need."

9. "For godly grief (conviction) produces a repentance that leads to salvation without regret, whereas worldly grief (condemnation) produces death." Conviction is godly sorrow, which leads to repentance, forgiveness, and life. Condemnation on the other hand, is grief with despair, and leads to death. Conviction is hopeful. Condemnation is hopeless.

10. The result of your interview.

8.2

Lesson Practice Questions

1. Answers will vary, but perhaps Lowes, Walmart, Coscto, or Target.

2. The way the bank records drafts from largest to smallest may trigger $30.00 overdrafts.

3. As soon as you swipe your card there is a hold of $25.00 or $50.00 placed on your card. Even if the amount you charge is only $15.00, which is adjusted when you have completed the transaction, the hold may have caused an overdraft fee.

4. Keep a careful look at your balance and make sure you have enough money in your account. If you do incur fees, talk to your bank and they may be taken off your account.

5. A credit card wants to sound good. Make a list of each aspect of the card and compare the interest rate, the fee structures, the annual fee, etc. Then you can compare with intelligence.

6. This is like a report card which measures how likely you are to pay back the credit card company.

7. Use the card regularly and then pay back the balance monthly when it is due. Keep your credit utilization ratio low.

Bible and Discussion Questions

8. Returning a tenth acknowledges that God owns everything and is Lord of all he has.

9. Conviction is uncomfortable but it leads to a restored relationship with God and others which leads to a sense of peace and harmony. Conviction has an element of hope.

10. The result of your interview.

8.3

Lesson Practice Questions

1. You can shop online, rent a car, make a hotel reservation, and use UBER or LYFT.

2. The money is taken out of your bank account so you cannot spend more than you have in the bank.

3. The ratio of how much you use your card or the amount of your balance, to your spending limit.

4. A low ratio is better.

5. You are on a trial period with the credit card company and seeking to look good in their eyes by paying off your balance in a timely fashion so you can be married and get a better card. :-)

6. Some cards have 5% cash back rebate while others give rewards for accumulating miles which reflect dollars in purchases.

7. To receive a secured card you need to make a deposit first and then use credit against this amount. This is very much like a debit card since you have already made a deposit to put money into your bank account.

Bible and Discussion Questions

8. God is Lord of all and he is the source of all we own.

9. King David, Psalm 51.

10. The result of your interview.

8.4

Lesson Practice Questions

1. A credit card is a loan which is being extended by the credit card company which they are hoping you will pay back. A debit card is you borrowing money against what you already have in the bank. A credit card has the risk of going into debt. A debit card has much less risk of this happening.

2. As you build your credit score, you may be able to have a home mortgage some day to purchase your first home.

3. A joint account is one where you are added to the account of someone who already has a credit card. A potential problem may arise if the other person's name on the card has a credit history which is not good as this could reflect negatively on you.

4. $38,000.00

5. credit card balance

6. Non-Sufficient funds.

7. To reimburse the bank for the extra work and to deter you from doing this again.

Bible and Discussion Questions

8. Tithes belong to God and are already His. Contributions or offerings are a free choice which you make when you decide to give more than what is your responsibility.

9. Guilt is what you do and does not change who you are in Jesus. Shame is feeling like you, your person, and your identity are flawed.

10. The result of your interview.

8.5

Lesson Practice Questions

1. If you are enrolled as a student in a college or university you may receive an invitation to open a credit card account.

2. Usually at least $30.00 maybe more.

3. 23%

4. $1,000.00

5. credit cards, student loans, mortgages, car loans, personal loans

6. Student loans and credit cards

7. I hope you learned something interesting and applicable!

Bible and Discussion Questions

8. A need is essential, food, shelter, clothing, and transportation. A want is something you would like to have but don't need for basic survival.

9. Mine is Romans 8:1, "there is no condemnation for those who belong to Christ Jesus." Yours may be different.

10. The result of your interview.

9.1

Lesson Practice Questions

1. Steve thought salt pellets for his water softener were cheaper at Home Depot until he found the cost per pound. Compare ounce to ounce or pound to pound to make an accurate comparison.

2. Answers may vary, but should be between 25¢ and 75¢ depending on the type of vehicle.

3. The Grocery Outlet is 12¢ per egg.

4.

	Stauffers	Target
24 eggs	$3.10	$3.38
Milk	$3.58	$4.49
Cheerios	$14.30	$11.00
Auto	$2.30	$2.60
Total	$23.28	$21.47

conclusion: Target is the cheaper option

5.

	Grocery Outlet	Costco
24 eggs	$2.98	$3.19
Milk	$3.58	$3.58
Cheerios	$6.99	$6.79
Auto	$4.30	$9.00
Total	$17.85	$22.56

conclusion: the outlet is the cheaper option

6. The Grocery Outlet has the best price per ounce at 11¢.

7. Sheetz does not carry almond butter, coconut oil, cinnamon, or apples.

Bible and Discussion Questions

8. When it comes to any occupation which God leads us to, it is not what we do but who we do it

for! When we love and serve the King of Kings, whether we eat, write math books, or teach God's Word, we are laboring for the glory of God.

9. We pick each other up when we fall. We are stronger together. We sharpen one another and become wise as we walk with wise people.

10. I hope these edified you.

9.2

Lesson Practice Questions

1. How long of a drive takes time and costs money per mile for your vehicle.

2. The cost of driving to several stores was far more costly than the few pennies they saved on the items.

3. Answers may vary, but it probably isn't Target.

4. Sheetz: $\dfrac{\$2.99}{38.465 \text{ in}^2} = \$0.08/\text{in}^2$

   Stauffers: $\dfrac{\$5.55}{78.5 \text{ in}^2} = \$0.07/\text{in}^2$

   Target: $\dfrac{\$4.29}{28.26 \text{ in}^2} = \$0.15/\text{in}^2$

   Costco: $\dfrac{\$9.95}{254.34 \text{ in}^2} = \$0.04/\text{in}^2$

   Costco has the lowest price per square inch

5. Sheetz, six pizzas, $6 \times \$2.99 + \$2.60 = \$20.54$ (for 230.79 sq in)
   Stauffers, three pizzas, $3 \times \$5.55 + \$2.30 = \$18.95$ (for 235.5 sq in) (closer by 18 minutes)
   Target, eight pizzas, $8 \times \$4.29 + \$2.60 = \$36.92$ (for 226.08 sq in)
   Costco, one pizza, $1 \times \$9.95 + \$9.00 = \$18.95$ (for 254.34 sq in, the most pizza)
   The family needs to decide between a shorter drive (Stauffers) or more pizza at the same price (Costco)

6. Sheetz, six pizzas, $6 \times \$2.99 + \$2.60 = \$20.54$
   $\$20.54 + 2 \times \$4.99 = \$30.52$, but no apples
   Stauffers, three pizzas, $3 \times \$5.55 + \$2.30 = \$18.95$
   $\$18.95 + 4 \times \$0.99 + 2 \times \$3.58 = \$30.07$ and closer
   Target, eight pizzas, $8 \times \$4.29 + \$2.60 = \$36.92$
   $\$36.92 + 4 \times \$1.53 + 2 \times \$4.49 = \$52.02$
   Costco, one pizza, $1 \times \$9.95 + \$9.00 = \$18.95$
   $\$18.95 + 4 \times \$2.00 + 2 \times \$3.58 = \$34.11$
   Stauffers is the option with the lowest total cost

7. Sheetz, six pizzas, $6 \times \$2.99 + \$2.60 = \$20.54$
   $\$20.54 + 2 \times \$4.99 + 4 \times \$1.50 = \$36.52$
   Stauffers, three pizzas, $3 \times \$5.55 + \$2.30 = \$18.95$
   $\$18.95 + \$0.99 + 2 \times \$3.58 = \$30.07$
   Target, eight pizzas, $8 \times \$4.29 + \$2.60 = \$36.92$
   $\$36.92 + 4 \times \$1.53 + 2 \times \$4\$49 = \$52.02$
   Costco, one pizza, $1 \times \$9.95 + \$9.00 = \$18.95$
   $\$18.95 + 4 \times \$2.00 + 2 \times \$3.58 = \$34.11$
   Stauffers is tied with Costco in total cost, so I would go to Stauffers (buy local!)

Bible and Discussion Questions

8. He thought being a full time pastor or missionary was more spiritual than being a math teacher.

9. I like, "Encourage one another and build one another up." (1 Thessalonians 5:11) You are free to pick your own.

10. I'm sure these were helpful and deep.

9.3

Lesson Practice Questions

1. Whether it is the size of the glass at the Dairy Mart, or the size of the can of apple juice, measure and use your math to find the price per ounce or a similar unit of measure.

2. Larger quantities for cheaper prices.

3. Costco at $0.12 per ounce

4. Grocery Outlet $0.31 and Costco $0.30

5. Stauffers $0.13, Target $0.14, Costco $0.13, Grocery Outlet $0.12.

6. Stauffers $2.30, Sheetz, CVS, and Target $2.60, Grocery Outlet $4.30, Costco $9.00.

7. Since the different sizes make this hard to compare, compute by using the price per ounce without taking into consideration the size of the container.

	Stauffers	Target	Costco	Grocery Out
5 lbs Apples	$4.95	$7.65	$10.00	$4.95
12 oz cinnamon	$9.24	$6.36	$3.36	$3.60
Milk 2 gal.	$7.16	$8.98	$7.16	$7.16
Auto	$2.30	$2.60	$9.00	$4.30
Total	$23.65	$25.59	$29.52	$20.01

The Grocery Outlet is the best bargain and it does not have a membership fee.

Bible and Discussion Questions

8. Steve thinks honesty, church attendance, loving God, and loving our neighbors and enemies.

9. Paul and Barnabas, the other companions, and Silas.

10. Listen well.

9.4

Lesson Practice Questions

1. The annual fee. The distance to the store.

2. Large quantities of perishable items may spoil before being used.

3. There are 16 ounces per pound.

4.

	Stauffers	Target	Costco	Groc. Out.	CVS
2.5 lbs coco. oil	$19.20	$14.80	$6.80	$7.60	$30.00
48 oz yogurt	$5.76	$7.68	$5.79	$5.28	$16.32
1 lb alm. butter	$13.12	$5.92	$4.80	$4.99	$9.92
Auto	$2.30	$2.60	$9.00	$4.30	$2.60
Total	$40.38	$31.00	$26.39	$22.17	$58.84

The Grocery Outlet has the lowest total cost.

5. If the other stores are closed and there is no other option, or perhaps you are in the store for a prescription and just need one item. Convenience.

6. Costco is $0.28 per ounce.

7. These stores have wonderful bargain prices, but check their expiration date to be careful. Answers will vary if they are near your home.

Bible and Discussion Questions

8. No occupation is more spiritual than another. All work is God's work when our hearts are committed to glorifying God.

9. When believers fellowship together, God is present in a special way. We are also encouraged by each other.

10. This should be interesting.

9.5

Lesson Practice Questions

1. The size of the glass can be deceiving. In this case the larger glass had similar amount of fluid capacity.

2. From your experience.

3. Milk

4. The grocery store, Stauffers

5. Costco

6. According to your taste. Frozen yogurt and a hot dog?

7. This is your story.

Bible and Discussion Question

8. I hope you had more than one, but what is the biggest one?

9. Jesus asks the Father to make all followers of Jesus be one, just like the Trinity is one. The result of this unity will be that the world will know that God sent Jesus to the earth.

10. They might be old enough to have seen the rise of buying clubs.

10.1

Lesson Practice Questions

1. The atmosphere, customer service, and the overall experience of shopping there.

2. He wants to keep small businesses afloat and profitable. He appreciates their expertise and knowledge. They are often closer and an alternative to the big chains.

3. He has a relationship with them. They know his lawn equipment and can fix it at their location. Over the years, the same people are still at the store. They have records of all his purchases and repairs.

4. He talks with people when he calls, a user-friendly website, fun and professional flight attendants, no hidden expenses and no cancellation fees.

5. $2,300.00 + (3 \times \$45.00) +$ $(3 \times \$150.00) = \$2,885.00$

6. $\$75.00 \times 30 \times 3 = \$6,750.00$

7. Expertise and integrity.

Bible and Discussion Questions

8. God in the Garden of Eden.

9. Reflect :-)

10. Their insights are valuable.

10.2

1. A warranty is an insurance policy that a company offers on the sale of their product.

2. Sears Craftsman tools

3. Being responsible, productive, giving us a sense of purpose and sharing in the upkeep of our family's estate.

4. $2,300.00 + (9 × $45.00) + (9 × $150.00) + (2 × $50.00) = $4,155.00
$4,155.00 ÷ 9 = $461.67 per year

5. 9 years times 30 mowings per year is 270.
$4,155.00 ÷ 270 = $15.39 per mowing

6. Two bike shops, one consumer, one couple who rented them, youtube videos, his son.

7. Your own sources.

Bible and Discussion Questions

8. After the first couple sinned, work was accompanied with sweat and toil.

9. David sought God in the morning, while Daniel prayed three times a day.

10. This should be enlightening.

10.3

Lesson Practice Questions

1. You may already know this, but maybe how they first discovered this place will be interesting.

2. Did you expect that many?

3. Have fun doing the math.

4. We all have different views.

5. $161.00 + $32.00 + $44.00 + 46.00 = $283.00

6. SWA $318.96, GAMMA GO $271.60 + $60.00 + $60.00 = $391.60

7. If you have no luggage, need to make a quick trip, and will not be cancelling the ticket. Then the only cost would be the airfare of $161.00.

Bible and Discussion Questions

8. We serve parents and students. The whole family benefits when students begin to experience success.

9. Answers are yours alone. My favorite

passage is 1 John 5:14–15.

10. This may be different than your networking skills, but I wish I had asked my folks when I had the opportunity.

10.4

Lesson Practice Questions

1. He knows the manager. They are near and provide services when he needs them. Good customer service.

2. It is easy and convenient. You can make purchases without leaving your chair. No transportation expense. Wide variety of products.

3. ACME $161.00 + $32.00 = $193.00
GAMMA GO $271.60
SWA $318.96
ACME wins for having the lowest price

4. ACME $161.00 + 2 × $44.00 + $46.00 = $295.00
GAMMA GO $271.60 + $60.00 + $40.00 + $60.00 = $431.60
SWA $318.96

5. SWA, no cancellation fee; GAMMA GO, $200.00.

6. Shoes and a bed.

7. Good, quality, reliable, dependable

Bible and Discussion Questions

8. Our home and vehicles are our garden of Eden. By keeping them neat and attractive the atmosphere of our home is enhanced and our spirits are uplifted.

9. Adoration-Confession-Thanksgiving-Supplication

10. You may need to take notes.

10.5

Lesson Practice Questions

1. Your opinion.

2. Also your opinion.

3. You can't try on the item. You can order and return, but that is aggravating to me, but not to others.

4. Estimate.

5. I hope so :-)

6. They may be bogus and written by the company or their employees.

7. Good service, quality, reliability, dependability

Bible and Discussion Questions

8. Diligence. A positive work ethic, and commitment to complete a project.

9. The Holy Spirit

10. These should be edifying and encouraging.

11.1

Lesson Practice Questions

1. This is up to you.

2. Walk, ride a bike, take a bus.

3. Pray and ask God to help.

4. Used cars are older and they have had problems in the past.

5. Craigslist, bulletin boards in your town, by asking family and friends, talking with your mechanic.

6. ($6,100 + $1,600) + ($1,200 + $35) + ($1,000 + $35) = $9,970
$3 \times 365 = 1,095$
$9,970 \div 1,095 = $9.11 per day

7. $9,970 \div 45,000 = $0.22 per mile

Bible and Discussion Questions

8. It is the responsibility of the family to care for relatives.

9. Our Lord gave this prayer for the use of the Disciples.

10. Pretty self-explanatory but can also be food for thought.

11.2

Lesson Practice Questions

1. Over a year. Even though it looked like a bargain, he wanted someone to look it over and take it for a test drive.

2. Carfax

3. Toyota Camry

4. The sales tax is 6% of the cost of the car in

PA, plus there are registration and title fees

5. We pay the cost up front to buy the car then are mostly focused on regular expenses like gasoline costs.

6. ($6,100 + $1,600) + ($1,200 + $35) = $8,935
$2 \times 52 = 104$
$8,935 \div 104 = $85.91 per week

7. $8935 \div 30,000 = $0.30 per mile

Bible and Discussion Questions

8. fathers and mothers

9. "When you pray, you must not be like the hypocrites. For they love to stand and pray in the synagogues and at the street corners, that they may be seen by others. Truly, I say to you, they have received their reward. But when you pray, go into your room and shut the door and pray to your Father who is in secret. And your Father who sees in secret will reward you. And when you pray, do not heap up empty phrases as the Gentiles do, for they think that they will be heard for their many words. Do not be like them, for your Father knows what you need before you ask him." (Matthew 6:5–8)

10. Listen well, especially to their reasons for choosing this source.

11.3

Lesson Practice Questions

1. An individual selling their vehicle and not a business or dealership.

2. This will be interesting.

3. This will be edifying.

4. The cost of the depreciation in the first year or two is so high.

5. Answers may vary

6. ($6,100 + $1,600) + ($1,200 + $35) + ($1,000 + $35) + ($950 + $35) = $10,955
$4 \times 12 = 48$
$10,955 \div 48 = $228.23 per month

7. $10,955 \div 60,000 = $0.18 per mile

Bible and Discussion Questions

8. When someone is worthy of being thanked, respected, and honored, it is our joy, privilege, and responsibility to see that they receive this honor.

9. He takes portions of the prayer and uses them in prayer, such as give us our daily bread and deliver us from evil.

10. This should be interesting.

11.4

Lesson Practice Questions

1. 2014

2. The cost was only a little over half the price for the same model brand new.

3. He called the Ford dealership to learn the best buy they could offer me and then had his mechanic take it for a test drive and examine it.

4. When an item increases in value over time. A home generally appreciates.

5. Cars lose their value over time.

6. ($6,100 + $1,600) + ($1,200 + $35) + ($1,000 + $35) + ($950 + $35) + ($850 + $35) = $11,840
$5 \times 365 = 1,825$
$11,840 \div 1,825 = \$6.49$ per day

7. $11,840 \div 75,000 = \$0.16$ per mile

Bible and Discussion Questions

8. "You know that you ought to imitate us. We were not idle when we were with you. We never accepted food from anyone without paying for it. We worked hard day and night so we would not be a burden to any of you. We certainly had the right to ask you to feed us, but we wanted to give you an example to follow." (2 Thessalonians 3:7–9)

9. I like them all :-)

10. This sounds like fun!

11.5

Lesson Practice Questions

1. Depreciation happens very quickly.

2. $35,000 − $21,500 = $13,500

3. He still had $21,500!!!

4. Many, if not most, young adults will drive a car owned previously from family and friends.

5. I wish I could hear it!

6. $11,840 is the cost for 5 years and continuing the pattern the next two years may look like this: + ($750 + $35) + ($650 + $35) = $13,310

7. $13,310 \div 105,000 = \$0.13$ per mile

Bible and Discussion Questions

8. Let's live out our faith and be doers and not just talkers.

9. I like them all :-)

10. After reading through this lesson, you may want to consider thanking your parents for a car to drive. Just a suggestion :-)

12.1

Lesson Practice Questions

1. $87,959 − 87,765 = 194 \div 12.6 = 15.4$ mpg

2. Even with the savings on fuel cost, the repairs and maintenance expenses made the operating cost the same for both cars.

3. There should be no repairs the first few years.

4. Depreciation!

5. The increased expenses of maintenance and repairs.

6. 50 cents per mile

7. When an item loses value over time.

Bible and Discussion Questions

8. "You shall not muzzle an ox when it is treading out the grain." (Deuteronomy 25:4) Jesus says, "The laborer deserves his wages." (Luke 10:7)

9. David was a man after God's own heart.

10. This is for your parents to tell you.

12.2

Lesson Practice Questions

1. Subtract the readings on the odometer to find how many miles you have traveled, then divide this number by how many gallons were needed to fill the tank.

2. $54,532 - 54,183 = 349 \div 17.3 = 20.2$ mpg

3. Approximately $1.27 plus vet bills

4. $22.00 \div 191 = \$0.12$ per mile

5. Fuel is 191 miles $\div$ 26 mpg = 7.3 gallons.
   $7.3 \times \$3.00$ per gallon is $21.90.
   Tolls are $26.75.
   $\$26.75 + \$21.90 = \$48.65$
   $\$48.65 \div 191$ mi = $0.25/mi

6. This is your opinion but I would think if you each chipped in $25.00 that would be lovely.

7. Operating expense is the fuel, maintenance, repairs and insurance expenses. These are more readily seen and paid more frequently. Ownership cost is the price of the vehicle plus fees.

Bible and Discussion Questions

8. Thanks but no thanks. For the duration of your time at this church, you will have nothing in terms of an appreciating asset for retirement but the church does. Ask for a housing allowance instead.

9. Samuel had his eyes on their outward appearance and how tall they were.

10. Hopefully pretty good!

12.3

Lesson Practice Questions

1. $\$20.00 + \$15.00 + \$25.00 + \$12.00 = \$72.00$
   $\$72.00 \div \$3.00 = 24$ gallons of gas

2. $72,606 - 72,150 = 456 \div 24 = 19$ mpg

3. $5,095

4. Year 2 $3,370
   $\$5,095 - \$3,370 = \$1,725$

5. The older the car or truck, the greater the cost of maintenance and repair bills.
   $\$3,230 + \$3,370 + \$3,810 = \$10,410$

6. $10,410 \div 45,000$ miles = $0.23 per mile

7. Liability insurance.

Bible and Discussion Questions

8. The first of all their harvest produce and dough were to go to the priests.

9. Out of the abundance of the heart the mouth speaks. The tongue and the heart are connected. A soft heart leads to godly speech, while a hard heart leads to conflict.

10. This is an individual choice for each family.

12.4

Lesson Practice Questions

1. $2,796 \div 52.5$ gallons = 53.3 mpg

2. $\$3,230 + \$3,370 + \$3,810 + \$5,095 = \$15,505$
   $\$15,505 \div 60,000 = \$0.26$

3. Ownership costs

4. Operating expenses
   $5,310 is greater than $885
   The car is mostly paid for, so ownership costs are lower while the operating expenses are higher due to the age of the car and all the miles it has been driven.

5. $203 \div 191 = \$1.06$

6. It is restful, you can read or rest. It takes longer due to the many stops.

7. If you had an old clunker which did not require very much money to fix

Bible and Discussion Questions

8. Pay them a livable salary and don't ask them to live in a parsonage.

9. Hypocrisy is when our talk does not match our walk. It is easy to spot this condition in others, but difficult to acknowledge in ourselves.

10. Highway miles per gallon are usually higher than around town miles per gallon.

12.5

Lesson Practice Questions

1. Greyhound bus is $22.00 and the Megabus is $29.99.

2. 4 on the Megabus is 4 × $29.99 = $119.96. The cost of driving the car is 191 × $0.50 = $95.50 + $18.97 = $114.47 The more people who are traveling the better the deal to drive.

3. $3,230 + $3,370 + $3,810 + $7,700 + $1235 + $1,035 = $20,380

4. When should you stop making repairs and just buy a new vehicle.

5. an actuary

6. Your opinion

7. Also your opinion

Bible and Discussion Questions

8. Something like, be generous to everyone, but make sure you are generous to your church staff.

9. When our heart and spirit are clean and renewed in our inner man, our outer man will find it much easier to love and serve God and others.

10. These will be unique to your home.

13.1

Lesson Practice Questions

1. $18,000, $162,000

2. $845.07

3. $641.25

4. $142,224.73

5. 320 payments, and save $142,224.73 − $123,541.55 = $18,683.18

6. Were you close?

7. Your opinion.

Bible and Discussion Questions

8. Emergency fund, nest egg, inheritance for family.

9. David

10. This should be interesting.

13.2

Lesson Practice Questions

1. $12,500, $237,500

2. $1,470.68

3. $841.15

4. $115,463.65

5. 217 payments, save $115,463.65 − $103,192.67 = $12,270.98

6. Hope you were close!

7. Your thoughts.

Bible and Discussion Questions

8. To continue serving God as long as he is able. He is being re-fired not re-tired.

9. "Grant to Solomon my son a whole heart that he may keep your commandments, your testimonies, and your statutes, performing all, and that he may build the palace for which I have made provision." (1 Chronicles 29:19)

10. I'm sure this is sage counsel.

13.3

Lesson Practice Questions

1. $28,000, $112,000

2. $835.48

3. $385.00

4. $38,387.06

5. 173 payments, save $38,387.06 - $36,737.07 = $1,649.99

6. 5.75% ÷ 12 = .479%

7. The 15 year mortgage

Bible and Discussion Questions

8. It seemed to contribute to his downfall.

9. Don't multiply gold and silver, don't go to Egypt for horses, don't have many wives or they will turn your heart away from God.

10. Listen well and take notes.

13.4

Lesson Practice Questions

1. $19,500, $175,500

2. $915.49

3. $694.69

4. $154,076.79

5. 279 payments, save
   $154,076.79 − $114,634.55 = $39,442.24

6. The right to repossess our personal property.

7. 1% of the amount of the loan, which are paid up front and will generally lower the rate of our loan $\frac{1}{8}$ of a percent per point.

Bible and Discussion Questions

8. That they will love God with all their heart, soul, mind, and strength and follow Jesus fully.

9. The wisest man was not wise enough to obey the simplest commands and his heart was turned away from following God as a result.

10. This should be interesting.

13.5

Lesson Practice Questions

1. $25,000, $100,000

2. $733.44

3. $322.92

4. $32,019.11

5. 168 payments, save
   $32,019.11 − $29,653.29 = $2,365.82

6. Your monthly payments will be lower. You may receive a better interest rate. You will not have to pay PMI.

7. To amortize is to pay down your balance over a specified period of time by making regular payments. The amortization table is a record of each monthly payment with how much is dedicated to interest and how much to the principal.

8. We will always have a tension between providing for the physical needs of our family, while also seeking lay up treasures in heaven.

9. This is unique to each one of us, but for Steve, I spend time in God's word regularly as well as communing with God in prayer and having regular times of fellowship.

10. I would be interested in their answer.

14.1

Lesson Practice Questions

1. Transfer taxes are 2% of the purchase price divided between the seller and the buyer. So 1% of the purchase price. Title insurance is $750 per 100,000, or 0.75% of the purchase price.

2. The same, $3,191

3. Private Mortgage Insurance Their down payment was less than 20%

4. $301.97 on Principal and Interest and $140.92 on PMI

5. Jacksons $177,185.99, Hills, $149,209.25, Jacksons paid the most by $27,976.74

6. $16,901.40

7. A monetary deposit demonstrating you are in good faith and earnest about buying a home. It is skin in the game.

Bible and Discussion Questions

8. Instead of telling their friends and church when they had a need they prayed and asked God to meet their needs.

9. It is the real person deep inside of each of us. It is our essence.

10. I hope this is interesting :-)

14.2

Lesson Practice Questions

1. Escrow is money held by a third party.

2. This is money accumulated monthly and set aside

to pay for property taxes and home insurance.

3. The lender because he has the most to lose if these fees are not paid in a timely fashion.

4. The research the history of a title and deed to make sure there are no liens against the property, sometimes as far back as 80 years.

5. If a lien slips through the research or red tape and needs to be paid, the insurance will cover it.

6. Transfer taxes, prepaid reserves, title insurance, and fixed fees.

7. Some say 45% of your gross pay and others 30% of your take home pay.

Bible and Discussion Questions

8. When we seek first the kingdom, God will see that ALL our needs are met.

9. God's desire is for life to go well with us and our children. That is why he yearns for us to keep His commandments.

10. If you feel like emailing them to me, I am interested!

14.3

Lesson Practice Questions

State	Monthly Mortgage Payment	Monthly Rent
Alabama	$995	$1,010
Hawaii	$2,750	$2,200
Illinois	$1,150	$1,625
Montana	$1,500	$1,175
Pennsylvania	$1,008	$1,374

1. Hawaii and Montana.

2. Illinois and Pennsylvania.

3. Alabama has similar rents and ownership costs. You will have to make a decision based on intangibles and not purely economic.

4. 37 out of 50, or 74%.

5. Since closing costs are so significant you won't want to pick up and move every two or three years unless you get a really good buy on a house and will make a significant profit to cover these fees.

6. Stability. Build equity. Forced savings for retirement.

7. 1%

Bible and Discussion Questions

8. Romans 15:26, Galatians 2:10, as well as 2 Corinthians 8 and 9

9. Where your treasure is, there will your heart be also. They are inextricably interwoven together and can't be separated.

10. Then thank them for room and board :-)

14.4

Lesson Practice Questions

1. By their home which is referred to as their personal estate.

2. This is the amount you have invested in your home. It is your money and what you own.

3. Mobility. A chance to learn about an area. No responsibility to fix, make repairs, or pay property taxes.

4. $3,088

5. It is better to invest smaller amounts over a long period of time, than big chunks over a smaller period of time.

6. Work to accumulate a large down payment.

7. I hope so. ;-)

Bible and Discussion Questions

8. God expects me to live by faith AND work diligently when he provides opportunities for labor.

9. He asked his professor for help, read an article by Charles Finney, then asked God to create in him a soft clean heart.

10. Take note.

14.5

Lesson Practice Questions

1. $844.99

2. $844.99 + $110 + $280 = $1,234.99

3. $280

4. 12 × $280 = $3,360

5. Transfer Tax = $1,500

   Title Insurance = $150,000 × 0.0075 = $1,125

6.

Down payment	(10%) $15,000
Prepaid Reserves	$3,360
Transfer Taxes	$1,500
Title Insurance	$1,125
Fixed Fees	$3,191
Closing Costs	$24,176

7. Your opinion.

Bible and Discussion Questions

8. What is the essence of 2 Thessalonians 3:6–12?

9. Reflect and consider.

10. This is a bunch of dough.

15.1

Lesson Practice Questions

1. 400 ft^2

2. 100 ft^2

3. Your experience, but for Steve, painting, landscaping, cutting the grass, washing cars, and washing windows.

4. 24 (watch the video to see how this is computed)

5. The labor is the largest part of a job. You may have to do the job sooner if the paint or siding is not a good quality.

6. 2(28 ft × 14 ft) + 2(24 ft × 14 ft) + 2($\frac{1}{2}$ × 9 ft × 24 ft) = 784 ft^2 + 672 ft^2 + 216 ft^2 = 1,672 ft^2
   1,672 ft^2 ÷ 100 ft^2/square = 16.72 squares
   16.72 squares ÷ 2 squares/carton = 8.36 cartons, so 9 cartons

7. 2(28 ft × 22 ft) = 1,232
   1,232 ft ÷ 100 ft^2/square = 12.32 squares
   13 squares will do it

Bible and Discussion Questions

8. The heart and the treasure are interconnected, when issues of money are discussed life issues are being addressed at a deep heart level.

9. "The Holy Spirit will come upon you, and the power of the Most High will overshadow you; therefore the child to be born will be called Holy— the Son of God." (Luke 1:35)

10. This is unique to your family.

15.2

Lesson Practice Questions

1. This will vary from family to family, but for Steve it was electrical, plumbing, and gas lines.

2. An estimate is general and can be flexible, while a bid is like a contract and is fixed. We all hear things a little differently and having the documents in writing avoids confusion.

3. Choose from the 11 in the Instruction Manual.

4. 15 ft × 8.5 ft × 2 sides + 14 ft × 8.5 ft × 2 sides = 255 ft^2 + 238 ft^2 = 493 ft^2 It will be close, but one gallon (400 ft^2) plus one quart (100 ft^2) should do the job. $21.00 + $54.00 = $75.00.

5. 15 ft × 14 ft × 2 coats = 420 ft^2
   Just by the numbers we would need one gallon plus one quart, but since we are putting two coats on, I would try to get by with one gallon. $17.50 + $42.00 = $59.50 or $42.00 if we are careful.

6. 25 ft × 10 ft × 2 sides + 16 ft × 10 ft × 2 sides + 15ft × 25 ft × $\frac{1}{2}$ × 2 sides = 500 ft^2 + 320 ft^2 + 375 ft^2 = 1,195 ft^2 divided by 200 (2 squares per carton) = 5.975, rounded to 6 cartons

7. 19 ft × 16 ft ×2 sides = 608 ft^2 divided by 100 = 6.08, so 7 squares.

Bible and Discussion Questions

8. Steve does not think that spiritual headship extends to economic headship because of these two Scriptures: "Submitting to one another out of reverence for Christ." (Ephesians 5:21) and "Husbands, love your wives, as Christ loved the church and gave himself up for her." (Ephesians 5:25)

9. Isaiah 61:1 "The Spirit of the Lord GOD is upon me, because the LORD has anointed me to bring good news to the poor; he has sent me to bind up the brokenhearted, to proclaim liberty to the captives, and the opening of the prison to those who are bound."

10. These vary for each couple.

15.3

Lesson Practice Questions

1. 20 × $34 + 26 × $33 = $680 + $858 = $1,538

2. 20 × $24 + 26 × $33 = $480 + $858 = $1,338.
   You saved $200 on the cost of materials.

3. 20 × $24 + 25 × $33 = $480 + $825 = $1,305

4. $1,305 ÷ 4 = $1,305 = $326.25 per year

5. 20 × $34 + 25 × $33 = $680 + $825 =
   $1,505 ÷ 7 = $215 per year. No, it does
   not pay to skimp on quality materials.

6. 28 ft × 14 ft × 2 sides + 24 ft × 14 ft × 2
   sides + 9 ft × 24 ft × $\frac{1}{2}$ × 2 sides = 784
   ft^2 + 672 ft^2 + 216 ft^2 = 1,672 ft^2 divided
   by 200 (2 squares per carton) = 8.36, so 9
   cartons at $150 per carton = $1,350

7. Corner pieces are 14 ft × 4 corners =
   56 ft × $2.25 = $126
   Channel pieces are 22ft × 4 (the hypotenuses of the
   triangles under the roof on the gable ends) + 28
   ft × 2 (under the roof near where the gutter would
   be) + 24 ft + 28 ft + 24 ft + 28 ft (the four bottom
   pieces) = 88 ft + 56 ft + 104 ft = 248 ft × $0.50 =
   $124. Corner plus Channel is $126 + $124 = $250.

Bible and Discussion Questions

8. "Husbands, love your wives, as Christ
   loved the church and gave himself up for
   her." (Ephesians 5:25). Jesus is the perfect husband.

9. The word "Christ" can also be rendered "Anointed."

10. Listen well and enjoy the stories. You will have
    your own to pass on to your children someday.

15.4

Lesson Practice Questions

1. (46 × $25) + $175 = $1,150 + $175 =
   $1,325 + 20% = $1,325 + $265 = $1,590

2. (48 × $25) + $148 = $1,200 + $148 = $1,348

3. $1,590 − $148 = $1,442 ÷ 48
   hours = $30.04 per hour
   $1,590 − $1,348 = $242 you would have saved

4. 13.5 ft × 6 ft × 2 walls + 11.5 ft × 6 ft × 2

walls = 162 ft^2 + 138 ft^2 = 300 ft^2
Three quarts which would be 3 × $6.50 =
$19.50. A whole gallon is only $15.00.

5. 300 square feet × 2 coats is 600 square feet
   which is one gallon plus 2 quarts. $38.00 +
   2 × $15.50 = $69.00. For seven more
   dollars I can buy two gallons ($38.00 × 2 =
   $76.00), which is what I would do.

6. 25 ft × 2 sides + 16 ft × 10 ft × 2 sides + 15
   ft × 25 ft × $\frac{1}{2}$ × 2 sides = 500 ft^2 + 320 ft^2 + 375
   ft^2 = 1,195 ft^2 divided by 200 (2 squares) = 5.975,
   so 6 cartons. 6 times $130 per carton is $780.

7. 10 ft × 4 corners = 40 feet × $2.25 = $90
   Channel pieces are 19 ft × 4 (under the roof on
   the gable triangle ends) + 16 ft × 2 (under the
   roof near where the gutter would be) + 25 ft +
   16 ft + 25 ft + 16 ft (the four bottom pieces) =
   76 ft + 32 ft + 82 ft = 190 ft × $0.50 = $95.
   Corner plus Channel is $90 + $95 = $185.

Bible and Discussion Questions

8. Submit to one another out of reverence
   for Christ and treat each other's
   views with dignity and respect.

9. Jesus will send the Holy Spirit to be with us forever.
   "It is to your advantage that I go away, for if I do
   not go away, the Helper will not come to you. But
   if I go, I will send Him to you." (John 16:7)

10. Take notes :-)

15.5

Lesson Practice Questions

1. You save money and have the satisfaction
   of accomplishing meaningful
   improvements on your home.

2. This is your opinion.

3. This will vary, but Steve does everything
   from mowing the lawn, to building
   retaining walls, to painting rooms.

4. 9 ft × 8 ft × 2 walls + 12 ft × 8 ft × 2
   walls = 144 ft^2 + 192 ft^2 = 336 ft^2
   336 ft^2 × 2 coats = 672 ft^2 which would be one
   gallon (400) plus 3 quarts (300) so it is best to
   buy 2 gallons for a total cost of $100.00.

5. 9 ft × 12 ft = 108 ft² × 2 coats = 216 ft²
3 quarts (300) or 3 × $19 = $57. It is
best to buy 1 gallon for $50.00.

6. 28 ft × 14 ft × 2 sides + 24 ft × 14 ft × 2
sides + 9 ft × 24 ft × $\frac{1}{2}$ × 2 sides = 784
ft² + 672 ft² + 216 ft² = 1,672 ft²
1,672 ÷ 400 = 4.18 gallons or 4 gallons and
1 quart which is 4 × $23 + $9 = $101

7. 1,672 × 2 coats = 3,344 ÷ 400 = 8.36 gallons
or 8 gallons and 2 quarts which is 8 ×$65 +
2 × $27 = $574. Although it is nice to have a
little more than you need and for $11 you can
buy 9 gallons for $585. It is your choice.

Bible and Discussion Questions

8. Learn more about communication, predict your
regular income, keep track of your expenses.

9. "While staying with them He ordered them not
to depart from Jerusalem, but to wait for the
promise of the Father, which, He said, 'you
heard from Me; for John baptized with water,
but you will be baptized with the Holy Spirit
not many days from now.'" (Acts 1:4–5)

10. This advice can be very helpful.

16.1

Lesson Practice Questions

1. $\frac{\$0.68}{1\ ft^2} \times \left(\frac{3\ ft}{1\ yd}\right)^2 =$
$\frac{\$0.68}{1\ ft^2} \times \frac{9\ ft^2}{1\ yd^2} =$
$\frac{\$0.68 \times 9}{1\ yd^2} = \frac{\$6.12}{1\ yd^2}$
$\frac{\$6.00}{1\ yd^2} < \frac{\$6.12}{1\ yd^2}$

2. 9 ft × 12 ft = 108 ft²

108 ft² × $\frac{\$0.49}{1\ ft^2}$ = $52.92 (for padding)
9 ft × 12 ft × $\left(\frac{1\ yd}{3\ ft}\right)^2 =$
9 ft × 12 ft × $\frac{1\ yd^2}{9\ ft^2}$ = 12 yd²
12 yd² × $\frac{\$9.95}{1\ yd^2}$ = $119.40 (for carpet)
$119.40 + $52.92 = $172.32

3. Maple hardwood pieces on skids
and 6 ft sticks of trim.

4. 200 ft × $\frac{1\ stick}{6\ ft}$ = 34 sticks

34 sticks × $\frac{\$1.00}{stick}$ = $34.00
200 ft × $\frac{\$0.79}{1\ ft}$ = $158.00
$158.00 − $34.00 = $124.00

5. He made several phone calls and the
companies kept lowering their prices.

6. 4 yds flatfold × $\frac{\$1.99}{1\ yd\ flatfold}$ = $7.96
4 yds broadcloth × $\frac{\$5.89}{1\ yd\ broadcloth}$ = $17.67
$7.96 + $17.67 = $25.63
$25.63 × 1.06 = $27.17

7. 54 in × $\frac{1\ ft}{12\ in}$ × $\frac{1\ yd}{3\ ft}$ = 1.5 yd
(4 yd × 1.5 yd) + (3 yd × 1.5 yd) =
6 yd² + 4.5 yd² = 10.5 yd²

Bible and Discussion Questions

8. Prayer invites God's participation. When
we ask and commit our activities to God,
He will act and establish our plans.

9. The Spirit of God convicts us of sin, helps us say
Jesus is Lord, enables us to enter the kingdom of
God, gives us new life, righteousness, peace, and joy.

10. Were you surprised by their answer?

16.2

Lesson Practice Questions

1. 5 events × $\frac{\$75}{1\ event}$ = $375 so it would
be better to buy one for $250

2. $250 × $\frac{1\ event}{\$75}$ = 3.$\overline{3}$ events so it
would pay for itself in 4 events

3. If you break it you have to buy a new one to
replace it and you still won't have one yourself.

4. 7.5 yd fabric × $\frac{\$3.69}{1\ yd\ fabric}$ = $27.68
$27.68 × 1.06 = $29.34

5. $12 \text{ ft} \times 18 \text{ ft} = 216 \text{ ft}^2$

$216 \text{ ft}^2 \times \dfrac{1 \text{ yd}^2}{27 \text{ ft}^2} = 24 \text{ yd}^2$

$24 \text{ yd}^2 \times \dfrac{\$15.00}{1 \text{ yd}^2} = \$360.00$ (for carpet)

$216 \text{ ft}^2 \times \dfrac{\$0.90}{\text{ft}^2} = \$194.40$ (for padding)

$216 \text{ ft}^2 \times \dfrac{\$0.60}{\text{ft}^2} = \$129.60$ (for installation)

$\$36.00 + \$194.40 + \$129.60 = \$684.00$

6. $\$684.00 \times \dfrac{1}{24 \text{ yd}^2} = \dfrac{\$28.50}{1 \text{ yd}^2}$

7. $\$684.00 \times \dfrac{1}{216 \text{ ft}^2} = \dfrac{\$3.17}{1 \text{ ft}^2}$

Bible and Discussion Questions

8. Try to pick one. Steve likes them all.

9. This is special to each believer.

10. This should be fun.

16.3

Lesson Practice Questions

1. It is cheaper than buying one (and may be a good tool).

2. If you will continue to use this item many times.

3. $20 \text{ yd felt} \times \dfrac{\$4.29}{1 \text{ yd felt}} = \$85.80$

$20 \text{ yd} \times 72 \text{ in} \times \dfrac{1 \text{ ft}}{12 \text{ in}} \times \dfrac{1 \text{ yd}}{3 \text{ ft}} = 40 \text{ yd}^2$

4. $5 \text{ yd flatfold} \times \dfrac{\$1.89}{1 \text{ yd flatfold}} = \$9.45$

$5 \text{ yd broadcloth} \times \dfrac{\$5.89}{1 \text{ yd broadcloth}} = \$29.45$

$\$9.45 + \$29.45 = \$38.90$

$\$38.90 \times 1.055 = \$41.04$

5. $2 \times 5 \text{ yd} \times \dfrac{3 \text{ ft}}{1 \text{ yd}} = 30 \text{ ft}$

$54 \text{ in} \times \dfrac{1 \text{ ft}}{12 \text{ in}} = 4.5 \text{ ft}$

$30 \text{ ft} \times 4.5 \text{ ft} = 135 \text{ ft}^2$

You could also do this in one step

$2(5 \text{ yd}) \times 54 \text{ in} \times \dfrac{3 \text{ ft}}{1 \text{ yd}} \times \dfrac{1 \text{ ft}}{12 \text{ in}} = 135 \text{ ft}^2$

6. $4\frac{1}{3} \text{ yd fabric} \times \dfrac{\$3.79}{1 \text{ yd fabric}} =$

$\dfrac{13}{3} \text{ yd} \times \dfrac{\$3.79}{1 \text{ yd fabric}} = \$16.42$

$\$16.42 \times 1.0625 = \$17.45$

7. $\dfrac{\$18.00}{1 \text{ yd}^2} \times \dfrac{1 \text{ yd}^2}{9 \text{ ft}^2} = \dfrac{\$2.00}{1 \text{ ft}^2}$

$\dfrac{\$2.00}{1 \text{ ft}^2} + \dfrac{\$0.70}{1 \text{ ft}^2} + \dfrac{\$0.95}{1 \text{ ft}^2} = \dfrac{\$3.65}{1 \text{ ft}^2}$

$11 \text{ ft} \times 15 \text{ ft} \times \dfrac{\$3.65}{1 \text{ ft}^2} = \$602.25$

There are other ways to solve a problem like this one. Feel free to use different strategies based on what makes the most sense to you.

Bible and Discussion Questions

8. A gentleman wants to be asked. He does not force His way into our life.

9. The Spirit helps us understand how much God loves each of us. "God's love has been poured into our hearts through the Holy Spirit who has been given to us." (Romans 5:5)

10. This will be unique to each family.

16.4

Lesson Practice Questions

1. A power washer. He spent $140 per year instead of $2,000 and the rental place kept it well serviced.

2. $\$1,200 \times \dfrac{1 \text{ day}}{\$29} = 41.38$ days (rounds up to 42)

$\$1,200 \times \dfrac{1 \text{ week}}{\$87} = 13.8$ weeks (rounds up to 14)

3. $20 \text{ ft} \times 14 \text{ ft} \times 1 \text{ yd}^2/9 \text{ ft}^2 = 31.\overline{1}$ yd^2 (rounds up to 32)

4. $32 \text{ yd}^2 \times \dfrac{\$7.50}{\text{yd}^2} = \$240$

5. $280 \text{ ft}^2 \times \dfrac{\$0.54}{1 \text{ ft}^2} = \$151.20$

6. $32 \text{ yd}^2 \times \dfrac{\$16.50}{1 \text{ yd}^2} = \$528$

$\$528.00 + \$151.20 + \$240.00 = \$919.20$

7. Will you buy one or rent one? It is your decision.

Bible and Discussion Questions

8. The Gibeonite's ruse and the leaders who did not ask God for wisdom.

9. In-spired means in-spirited or in the spirit. The Spirit of God is responsible for the Bible since "men spoke from God as they were carried along by the Holy Spirit." (2 Peter 1:21)

10. These are always edifying stories.

16.5

Lesson Practice Questions

1. Keep your eyes open, pray, and what else?

2. In Jerusalem when he purchased a few little hand-carved camels.

3. $\dfrac{\$24.95}{1 \text{ yd}^2} \times \dfrac{1 \text{ yd}^2}{9 \text{ ft}^2} = \dfrac{\$2.77}{1 \text{ ft}^2}$

4. $14 \text{ ft} \times 18 \text{ ft} \times \dfrac{1 \text{ yd}^2}{9 \text{ ft}^2} = 28 \text{ yd}^2$

$28 \text{ yd}^2 \times \left(\dfrac{\$16.25}{1 \text{ yd}^2} + \dfrac{\$7.15}{1 \text{ yd}^2}\right) =$
$28 \text{ yd}^2 \times \dfrac{\$23.40}{1 \text{ yd}^2} = \$655.20$

5. $252 \text{ ft}^2 \times \dfrac{\$0.85}{1 \text{ ft}^2} = \$214.20$

6. $2{,}600 \text{ ft}^2 \times \left(\dfrac{\$4.95}{1 \text{ ft}^2} + \dfrac{\$4.00}{1 \text{ ft}^2}\right) =$
$2{,}600 \text{ ft}^2 \times \dfrac{\$8.95}{1 \text{ ft}^2} = \$23{,}270$

7. $2{,}600 \text{ ft}^2 \times \dfrac{\$4.95}{1 \text{ ft}^2} = \$12{,}870$

$\$12{,}870 + \$700 = \$13{,}570$

$\$23{,}270 - \$13{,}570 = \$9{,}700$

Bible and Discussion Questions

8. God encourages us to pray and ask Him to give us our daily bread in Matthew 6:11.

9. The Spirit will testify about Jesus.

10. This will be interesting. Bless you for asking and listening.

17.1

Lesson Practice Questions

1. $95

2. $12 \text{ ft} \times 60 \text{ ft} \times 6 \text{ in} \times \dfrac{1 \text{ ft}}{12 \text{ in}} \times \dfrac{1 \text{ yd}^3}{27 \text{ ft}^3} = 13.3 \text{ yd}^3$

3. $13.3 \text{ yd}^3 \times \dfrac{1 \text{ truckload}}{11 \text{ yd}^3} = 1.2 \text{ truckloads}$
Two truckloads will need to be delivered (only part of the second truckload will be used and paid for)

4. $13.3 \text{ yd}^3 \times \dfrac{\$105}{1 \text{ yd}^3} = \$1{,}396.50$

5. $15 \text{ ft} \times 30 \text{ ft} \times 4 \text{ in} \times \dfrac{1 \text{ ft}}{12 \text{ in}} \times \dfrac{1 \text{ yd}^3}{27 \text{ ft}^3} = 5.56 \text{ yd}^3$
$5.56 \text{ yd}^3 < 11 \text{ yd}^3$ so only one (partial) truckload will be needed

6. $5.56 \text{ yd}^3 \times \dfrac{\$100}{1 \text{ yd}^3} = \$556$

7. $W_p \times 3{,}500 = 500$

$W_p = \dfrac{500}{3{,}500}$

$W_p = 14.3\%$

Bible and Discussion Questions

8. "God, who richly provides us with everything to enjoy." (1 Timothy 6:17)

9. Acts of the Apostles Empowered by the Holy Spirit

10. Every couple is different.

17.2

Lesson Practice Questions

1. $6 \text{ ft} \times 4 \text{ ft} \times 2 \text{ ft} = 48 \text{ ft}^3$

$48 \text{ ft}^3 \times \dfrac{100 \text{ lbs}}{1 \text{ ft}^3} = 4{,}800 \text{ lbs}$

$4{,}800 \text{ lbs} \times \dfrac{1 \text{ ton}}{2{,}000 \text{ lbs}} = 2.4 \text{ tons}$

2. $14 \text{ ft} \times 85 \text{ ft} \times 8 \text{ in} \times \dfrac{1 \text{ ft}}{12 \text{ in}} \times \dfrac{1 \text{ yd}^3}{27 \text{ ft}^3} = 29.4 \text{ yd}^3$

3. $29.4 \text{ yd}^3 \times \dfrac{1 \text{ truckload}}{11 \text{ yd}^3} = 2.67 \text{ truckloads}$
Three truckloads will be needed

4. $29.4 \text{ yd}^3 \times \dfrac{\$110}{1 \text{ yd}^3} = \$3{,}234$

5. $10 \text{ ft} \times 22 \text{ ft} \times 5 \text{ in} \times \dfrac{1 \text{ ft}}{12 \text{ in}} \times \dfrac{1 \text{ yd}^3}{27 \text{ ft}^3} = 3.4 \text{ yd}^3$

$3.4 \text{ yd}^3 \times \dfrac{\$95}{1 \text{ yd}^3} = \$323$

6. $W_p \times 3{,}500 = 1{,}200$

$W_p = \dfrac{1{,}200}{3{,}500}$

$W_p = 34.3\%$

7. $6.25 \text{ tons} \times \dfrac{1 \text{ yd}^3}{1.4 \text{ tons}} \times \dfrac{27 \text{ ft}^3}{1 \text{ yd}^3} = 120.54 \text{ ft}^3$

Bible and Discussion Questions

8. Lust, desire, strong desire, passion

9. "He presented himself alive to them after his suffering by many proofs, appearing to them during forty days and speaking about the kingdom of God." (Acts 1:3)

10. Listen well.

17.3

Lesson Practice Questions

1. $\dfrac{1}{20} \text{ mi} \times \dfrac{5{,}280 \text{ ft}}{1 \text{ mi}} \times 15 \text{ ft} \times 1 \text{ ft} \times \left(\dfrac{1 \text{ yd}}{3 \text{ ft}}\right)^3 =$
$3{,}960 \text{ ft}^3 \times \dfrac{1 \text{ yd}^3}{27 \text{ ft}^3} = 146.\overline{6} \text{ yd}^3 \approx 147 \text{ yd}^3$

2. The amount of sand in one cubic yard is about 1,200 lbs and gravel is about 1,800 lbs, thus the total weight of the cubic yard is around 3,000 pounds

$147 \text{ yd}^3 \times \dfrac{3{,}000 \text{ lbs}}{1 \text{ yd}^3} = 441{,}000 \text{ lbs}$

3. $147 \text{ yd}^3 \times \dfrac{1 \text{ truckload}}{11 \text{ yd}^3} = 13.36 \text{ truckloads}$

so 14 truckloads will be needed

4. $147 \text{ yd}^3 \times \dfrac{\$105}{1 \text{ yd}^3} = \$15{,}435$

5. $3{,}750 \text{ lbs} - 3{,}500 \text{ lbs} = 250 \text{ lbs}$

$250 \text{ lbs} \times \dfrac{1 \text{ gal}}{8.35 \text{ lb}} = 30 \text{ gal}$

6. $W_p \times 3{,}500 = 1{,}800$

$W_p = \dfrac{1{,}800}{3{,}500}$

$W_p = 51.4\%$

7. $15 \text{ in} \times \dfrac{1 \text{ ft}}{12 \text{ in}} = \dfrac{5}{4} \text{ ft}$

$2 \text{ ft} \times 5 \text{ ft} \times \dfrac{5}{4} \text{ ft} \times \dfrac{62.5 \text{ lbs}}{1 \text{ ft}^3} = 781.25 \text{ lbs}$

$781.25 \text{ lb} \times \dfrac{1 \text{ trip}}{80 \text{ lbs}} = 9.8 \text{ trips or } 10 \text{ trips}$

Bible and Discussion Questions

8. Your spouse, or if you are single, your parents.

9. "The Spirit of Jesus did not allow them." (Acts 16:7)

10. Did you have fun?

17.4

Lesson Practice Questions

1. $5 \text{ ft} \times 30 \text{ ft} \times \dfrac{1}{3} \text{ ft} = 50 \text{ ft}^3$

2. $50 \text{ ft}^3 \times \dfrac{1 \text{ yd}^3}{27 \text{ ft}^3} = 1.85 \text{ yd}^3$

If the patio is light duty then the 3,000 grade would be appropriate, which is \$95/yd³

$1.85 \text{ yd}^3 \times \dfrac{\$95}{1 \text{ yd}^3} = \$175.75$

3. The volume of the pool is the area of the base times the height
If the diameter is 12 ft then the radius is 6 ft

$\pi r^2 \times h = \pi (6 \text{ ft})^2 \times 3 \text{ ft} = 108\pi \text{ ft}^3$

$108\pi \text{ ft}^3 \times \dfrac{7.48 \text{ gal}}{1 \text{ ft}^3} = 8{,}07.84\pi \text{ gal} \approx 2{,}538 \text{ gal}$

4. $2{,}538 \text{ gal} \times \dfrac{1 \text{ min}}{24 \text{ gal}} \times \dfrac{1 \text{ hr}}{60 \text{ min}} = 1.7625 \text{ hr}$

or 1 hour 45 minutes and 45 seconds

5. $25 \text{ tons} \times \dfrac{1 \text{ yd}^3 \text{ gravel}}{1.4 \text{ tons}} = 17.9 \text{ yd}^3 \text{ gravel}$

6. $4 \text{ yd}^3 \text{ gravel} \times \dfrac{1.4 \text{ tons}}{1 \text{ yd}^3 \text{ gravel}} = 5.6 \text{ tons}$

$185 \text{ ft}^3 \text{ water} \times \dfrac{62.5 \text{ lbs}}{1 \text{ ft}^3 \text{ water}} \times \dfrac{1 \text{ ton}}{2{,}000 \text{ lbs}} = 5.8 \text{ tons}$

5.8 tons (water) > 5.6 tons (gravel)

7. $6{,}000 \text{ gal} \times \dfrac{1 \text{ ft}^3}{7.48 \text{ gal}} = 802.14 \text{ ft}^3$

Bible and Discussion Questions

8. His wife and a few friends whose insights he respected.

9. The Spirit is referred to as He in chapters 14–16 of John 13 times and Him 4 times.

10. I hope so :-)

17.5

Lesson Practice Questions

1. The higher the grade, the more concrete is in the mix, which makes the final concrete mix stronger and more durable.

2. $18 \text{ tons} \times \dfrac{1 \text{ yd}^3}{1.4 \text{ tons}} = 12.9 \text{ yd}^3$

3. $275 \text{ ft}^3 \times \dfrac{100 \text{ lbs}}{1 \text{ ft}} = 27{,}500 \text{ lbs}$

   $27{,}500 \text{ lbs} \times \dfrac{1 \text{ ton}}{2{,}000 \text{ lbs}} = 13.75 \text{ tons}$

4. $2{,}500 \text{ gal} \times \dfrac{1 \text{ ft}^3}{7.48 \text{ gal}} = 334 \text{ ft}^3$

5. $30 \text{ ft} \times 50 \text{ ft} \times \frac{1}{4} \text{ ft} = 375 \text{ ft}^3$

   $375 \text{ ft}^3 \times \dfrac{1 \text{ yd}^3}{27 \text{ ft}^3} = 13.9 \text{ yd}^3$

   $13.9 \text{ yd}^3 \times \dfrac{1.4 \text{ ton}}{1 \text{ yd}^3} = 19.5 \text{ tons}$

6. $19.5 \text{ tons} \times 40/\text{ton} = \$780$
   $\$780 + \$25 = \$805$

7. 3,000 grade is probably fine for the weight, but for just a few more dollars I would lean towards 3,500 because of the size of the court.

   $30 \text{ ft} \times 50 \text{ ft} \times \frac{1}{3} \text{ ft} = 500 \text{ ft}^3$

   $500 \text{ ft}^3 \times \dfrac{1 \text{ yd}^3}{27 \text{ ft}^3} = 18.5 \text{ yd}^3$

   $18.5 \text{ yd}^3 \times \dfrac{\$95}{1 \text{ yd}^3} = \$1{,}757.50$ for the 3,000 grade

   $18.5 \text{ yd}^3 \times \dfrac{\$100}{1 \text{ yd}^3} = \$1{,}850.00$ for the 3,500 grade

Bible and Discussion Questions

8. Having counsel from several different sources helps you make an informed decision.

9. He has a mind. He prays. He loves. He has feelings. He speaks.

10. I hope you learned some interesting information.

18.1

Lesson Practice Questions

1. Area of duct A is $\pi r^2 = \pi(4 \text{ in})^2 = 16\pi \text{ in}^2 \approx 50.27 \text{ in}^2$
   Area of duct B is $6 \text{ in} \times 8 \text{ in} = 48 \text{ in}^2$
   More air will pass through duct A
   because $50.27 \text{ in}^2 > 48 \text{ in}^2$

2. The circumference of duct A is $2\pi r = 2\pi(4 \text{ in}) = 8\pi \text{ in} \approx 25.13$ while the perimeter of duct A is $6 \text{ in} + 8 \text{ in} + 6 \text{ in} + 8 \text{ in} = 28 \text{ in}$
   Duct B uses more sheet metal
   because $28 \text{ in} > 25.13 \text{ in}$

3. $V \times A = W$
   $120 \text{ V} \times A = W$
   $A = 60 \text{ W}/120 \text{ V} = 0.5 \text{ A}$

4. $120 \text{ V} \times 50 \text{ A} = 6{,}000 \text{ W}$

5. $A_{max} \times 80\% = A_{safe}$
   $20 \text{ A} \times 0.8 = A_{safe}$
   $16 \text{ A} = A_{safe}$
   $120 \text{ V} \times 16 \text{ A} = W_{safe}$
   $1{,}920 \text{ W} = W_{safe}$

6. $W = 1{,}050 \text{ W} + 4(100 \text{ W}) + 5(60 \text{ W}) = 1{,}750$ W, which is less than 1,920 and this is safe.

7.

Customer Charge		$8.00
	200 kWh at 2.193¢ per kWh	$4.39
	550 kWh at 1.984¢ per kWh	$10.91
Transmission Charge		
	750 kWh at 0.564¢ per kWh	$4.23
Transition Charge		
	200 kWh at 1.329¢ per kWh	$2.66
	550 kWh at 1.178¢ per kWh	$6.48
Generation Charge		
	200 kWh at 5.182¢ per kWh	$10.36
	550 kWh at 4.554¢ per kWh	$25.05
Total Charges		$72.08

Bible and Discussion Questions

8. Free gifts are in mousetraps. Free gifts allowed the Greeks to enter Troy. These gifts influence him to feel like he should buy something in return for the gift.

9. Because as soon as He returned from the wilderness the devil was going to attack these truths and try and make Jesus doubt He was the Son of God.

10. You will have to ask.

18.2

Lesson Practice Questions

1. Area of duct A is $\pi r^2 = \pi(3 \text{ in})^2 = 9\pi \text{ in}^2 \approx 28.27 \text{ in}^2$
   The area of duct B is $4.5 \text{ in} \times 7 \text{ in} = 31.5 \text{ in}^2$
   More air will pass through duct B
   since $31.5 \text{ in}^2 > 28.27 \text{ in}^2$

2. The circumference of duct A is $2\pi r = 2\pi(3 \text{ in}) = 6\pi \text{ in} \approx 18.85 \text{ in}$ while the perimeter of duct B
   is $4.5 \text{ in} + 7 \text{ in} + 4.5 \text{ in} + 7 \text{ in} = 23 \text{ in}$
   Duct B uses more sheet metal since $23 \text{ in} > 18.85 \text{ in}$

3. $V \times A = W$
   $120 \text{ V} \times A = W$
   $A = 75 \text{ W}/120 \text{ V} = 0.63 \text{ A}$

4. $120 \text{ V} \times 30 \text{ A} = 3{,}600 \text{ W}$

5. $A_{max} \times 80\% = A_{safe}$
   $30 \text{ A} \times 0.8 = A_{safe}$
   $24 \text{ A} = A_{safe}$
   $120 \text{ V} \times 24 \text{ A} = W_{safe}$
   $2{,}880 \text{ W} = W_{safe}$

6. $W = 2(500 \text{ W}) + 800 \text{ W} + 5(100 \text{ W}) = 2{,}300 \text{ W}$
   $W_{safe} = 2{,}880$ and $2{,}300 \text{ W} < 2{,}880 \text{ W}$ so it is safe

7.

Customer Charge	$8.00
200 kWh at 2.193¢ per kWh	$4.39
600 kWh at 1.984¢ per kWh	$11.90
700 kWh at 1.862¢ per kWh	$13.03
Transmission Charge	
1,500 kWh at 0.564¢ per kWh	$8.46
Transition Charge	
200 kWh at 1.329¢ per kWh	$2.66
600 kWh at 1.178¢ per kWh	$7.07
700 kWh at 1.088¢ per kWh	$7.62
Generation Charge	
200 kWh at 5.182¢ per kWh	$10.36
600 kWh at 4.554¢ per kWh	$27.32
700 kWh at 4.178¢ per kWh	$29.25
Total Charges	$130.06

Bible and Discussion Questions

8. When we see something attractive we may be tempted to purchase it at that moment. But after a night's sleep and some conversation it will look differently. It is better to move carefully than waste money on impulse spending.

9. He quoted scripture and responded to each temptation with "It is written!"

10. Every home has different preferences.

18.3

Lesson Practice Questions

1. Area of duct A is $s^2 = (5 \text{ in})^2 = 25 \text{ in}^2$
   The area of duct B is $4 \text{ in} \times 6 \text{ in} = 24 \text{ in}^2$
   More air will pass through duct A
   since $25 \text{ in}^2 > 24 \text{ in}^2$

2. The perimeter of duct A is $4s = 4(5 \text{ in}) = 20 \text{ in}$
   The perimeter of the rectangle is
   $4 \text{ in} + 6 \text{ in} + 4 \text{ in} + 6 \text{ in} = 20 \text{ in}$
   They use the same amount of sheet metal.

3. $V \times A = W$
   $120 \text{ V} \times A = W$
   $A = 40 \text{ W}/120 \text{ V} = 0.33 \text{ A}$

4. $120 \text{ V} \times 40 \text{ A} = 4{,}800 \text{ W}$

5. $A_{max} \times 80\% = A_{safe}$
   $15 \text{ A} \times 0.8 = A_{safe}$
   $12 \text{ A} = A_{safe}$
   $120 \text{ V} \times 12 \text{ A} = W_{safe}$
   $1{,}440 \text{ W} = W_{safe}$

6. $1{,}440 \text{ W} = 500 \text{ W} + 1{,}050 \text{ W} + x(40 \text{ W/bulb})$
   $1{,}440 \text{ W} - 500 \text{ W} - 1{,}050 \text{ W} = x(40 \text{ W/bulb})$
   $-110 \text{ W} = x(40 \text{ W/bulb})$
   $-2.75 \text{ bulbs} = x$
   We can't have any more 40-watt bulbs since we are already 110 watts over the safe capacity.

7.

Customer Charge	$8.00
200 kWh at 2.193¢ per kWh	$4.39
600 kWh at 1.984¢ per kWh	$11.90
200 kWh at 1.862¢ per kWh	$3.72
Transmission Charge	
1,000 kWh at 0.564¢ per kWh	$5.64
Transition Charge	
200 kWh at 1.329¢ per kWh	$2.66
600 kWh at 1.178¢ per kWh	$7.07
200 kWh at 1.088¢ per kWh	$2.18
Generation Charge	
200 kWh at 5.182¢ per kWh	$10.36
600 kWh at 4.554¢ per kWh	$27.32
200 kWh at 4.178¢ per kWh	$8.36
Total Charges	$91.60

Bible and Discussion Questions

8. When Steve's head was filled with all the positives from the slick sales approach he did not have time to reflect and see the whole picture.

9. All Christians

10. This should be interesting. Learn from them.

18.4

Lesson Practice Questions

1. Area of duct A is $\pi r^2 = \pi(2.5 \text{ in})^2 =$
   $6.25\pi \text{ in}^2 = 19.63 \text{ in}^2$
   The area of duct B is $s^2 = (4.5 \text{ in})^2 = 20.25 \text{ in}^2$
   More air will pass through duct B
   since $20.25 \text{ in}^2 > 19.63 \text{ in}^2$

2. The circumference of duct A is
   $2\pi r = 2\pi(2.5 \text{ in}) = 5\pi \text{ in} \approx 15.7 \text{ in}$
   The perimeter of duct B is $4s = 4(4.5 \text{ in}) = 18 \text{ in}$
   Duct B uses more material since $18 \text{ in} > 15.7 \text{ in}$

3. $V \times A = W$
   $120 \text{ V} \times A = W$
   $A = 25 \text{ W}/120 \text{ V} = 0.21 \text{ A}$

4. $120 \text{ V} \times 75 \text{ A} = 9,000 \text{ W}$

5. $A_{max} \times 80\% = A_{safe}$
   $20 \text{ A} \times 0.8 = A_{safe}$
   $16 \text{ A} = A_{safe}$
   $120 \text{ V} \times 16 \text{ A} = W_{safe}$
   $1,920 \text{ W} = W_{safe}$

6. $1,920 \text{ W} = 1.050 \text{ W} + x(60 \text{ W/bulb})$
   $1,920 \text{ W} - 1.050 \text{ W} = x(60 \text{ W/bulb})$
   $870 \text{ W} \div (60 \text{ W/bulb}) = 14.5 \text{ bulbs}$
   We can have 14 of the 60-watt bulbs
   to be within the safe capacity.

7. Have fun!

Bible and Discussion Questions

8. Annual maintenance fees but a regular scheduled vacation in a nice resort!

9. Yes!!
   "In this is love, not that we have loved God but that he loved us and sent his Son to be the propitiation for our sins." (1 John 4:10)
   "We love because he first loved us." (1 John 4:19)
   "As the Father has loved me, so have I loved you. Abide in my love." (John 15:9)
   "God, being rich in mercy, because of the great love with which he loved us, even when we were dead in our trespasses, made us alive together with Christ." (Ephesians 2:4–5)
   "The LORD takes pleasure in those who fear him, in those who hope in his steadfast love." (Psalm 147:11)
   "The LORD takes pleasure in his people; he adorns the humble with salvation." (Psalm 149:4)

10. Take notes and look up the verses :-)

18.5

Lesson Practice Questions

1. When there is more current moving though the wire than its capacity.

2. Safe capacity is 80% of the maximum capacity which is the amount that can be sustained before breaking. Maximum capacity is 100% while safe capacity is 20% less or 80%, to give a cushion and be safe.

3. Heating, Ventilation, and Air Conditioning

4. A, for amperes or amps.

5. Most homes in the U. S. have a 100 amp service.

6. Volts or voltage.

7. One kilowatt hour represents 1,000 watts per hour.

Bible and Discussion Questions

8. After you have done your homework, prayed, and consulted with your spouse or family.

9. Steve's favorite is "As the Father has loved me, so have I loved you. Abide in my love." (John 15:9) Please choose one or more for yourself.

10. I'm sure their advice is wise.

19.1

Lesson Practice Questions

1. $3\frac{1}{2}$ inches by $5\frac{1}{2}$ inches

2. $\frac{3}{4}$ inches by $3\frac{1}{2}$ inches

3. $3\frac{1}{2}$ inches times $4 = 14$ inches

   14 inches high, $3\frac{1}{2}$ inches wide

4. R-20

5. $5\frac{1}{2}$ inches $- 1\frac{1}{2}$ inches (1.5 inches) $= 4$ inches

   1.5 inches of foam × R-8 = R-12 and 4 inches of cellulose is 4 inches × R-3.7 = R-14.8.
   R-12 + R-14.8 = R-26.8

6. Light red or pink :-)

7. $\frac{20 \text{ liters}}{1} \times \frac{1 \text{ qt}}{0.95 \text{ liter}} = 21.1 \text{ qt}$

   $\frac{21.1 \text{ qt}}{1} \times \frac{1 \text{ gal}}{4 \text{ qt}} = 5.3 \text{ gal}$

Bible and Discussion Questions

8. God speaks to us through another individual, through His written word, and sometimes He communicates with us directly.

9. It is possible to know much about God without meeting Him personally and having a relationship with Him.

10. Ask your parents. Most likely they are 2 inches × 8 inches but you can estimate.

19.2

Lesson Practice Questions

1. A two by six

2. $5\frac{1}{2}$ inches by $5\frac{1}{2}$ inches

3. $4 \times 1\frac{1}{2}$ inches $= 6$ inches

4. R-34

5. $7\frac{1}{4}$ inches $- 1\frac{3}{4}$ inches (1.75 inches) $= 5\frac{1}{2}$ inches

   1.75 in of foam × R-8 = R-14 and $5\frac{1}{2}$ inches of fiberglass is $5\frac{1}{2}$ inches × R-3.7 = R-20.4.
   R-14 + R-20.4 = R-34.4

6. 12 inches × R-3.7 = R-44.4

7. $\frac{1 \text{ mi}}{1} \times \frac{1.6 \text{ km}}{1 \text{ mi}} = 1.6 \text{ km}$

   $\frac{1.6 \text{ km}}{1} \times \frac{1,000 \text{ m}}{1 \text{ km}} = 1,600 \text{ m}$

Bible and Discussion Questions

8. A sense of peace. Proverbs 3:17, 2 Thessalonians 3:16, Colossians 3:15

9. I like all of them, but find the one you like the most right now.

10. Don't take off the sheetrock to find out :-). Ask or find a wall that has not been finished.

19.3

Lesson Practice Questions

1. A one-by-six

2. $1\frac{1}{2}$ inches by $7\frac{1}{4}$ inches

3. $3\frac{1}{2}$ inches $+ 5\frac{1}{2}$ inches $+ 7\frac{1}{4}$ inches $+ 7\frac{1}{4}$ inches $= 23\frac{1}{2}$ inches

4. R-44

5. $3\frac{1}{2}$ inches $- 1$ inch $= 2\frac{1}{2}$ inches

   1 inch of foam is R-8 and $2\frac{1}{2}$ inches of cellulose is $2\frac{1}{2}$ inches × R-3.7 = R-9.3.
   R-8 + R-9.3 = R-17.3

6. $9\frac{1}{2}$ inches $- 2$ inches $= 7\frac{1}{2}$ inches

2 inches of foam is R-16 and $7\frac{1}{2}$ inches of

cellulose is $7\frac{1}{2}$ inches $\times$ R-3.7 = R-27.8.

R-16 + R-27.8 = R-43.8

7. $\frac{1\,\text{mi}}{1} \times \frac{1\,\text{mi}}{1} \times \frac{1.6\,\text{km}}{1\,\text{mi}} \times \frac{1.6\,\text{km}}{1\,\text{mi}} = 2.56$ or $2.6\,\text{km}^2$

Bible and Discussion Questions

8. Sheep can be led, but goats need to be driven.

9. He has learned to know more about God, recognize His voice, and develop a relationship with Him.

10. I have only installed fiberglass myself and it is nasty and requires gloves and goggles.

19.4

Lesson Practice Questions

1. $3\frac{1}{2}$ inches $\times 3\frac{1}{2}$ inches

2. A one-by-four

3. $(3 \times \frac{3}{4}$ inches$) + (2 \times 1\frac{1}{2}$ inches$) + (3\frac{1}{2}$ inches$)$

$= 8\frac{3}{4}$ inches

4. $7\frac{1}{4}$ inches $\times$ R-3.7 = R-26.8 or R-27 as in the table.

5. $7\frac{1}{4}$ inches $- 1.5$ inches $= 5.75$ inches or $5\frac{3}{4}$ inches

1.5 inches $\times$ R-8 and 5.75 inches of cellulose is 5.75 inches $\times$ R-3.7 = R-21.3.
R-12 + R-21.3 = R-33.3

6. $9\frac{1}{4}$ in $- 2.5$ in $= 6\frac{3}{4}$ in

2.5 inches $\times$ R-8 = R-20 and $6\frac{3}{4}$ inches of

cellulose is 6.75 inches $\times$ R-3.7 = R-25.

R-20 + R-25 = R-45

7. $\frac{1.5\,\text{inches}}{1} \times \frac{2.5\,\text{cm}}{1\,\text{inch}} = 3.75\,\text{cm},$

$\frac{3.5\,\text{inches}}{1} \times \frac{2.5\,\text{cm}}{1\,\text{inch}} = 8.75\,\text{cm}$

3.75 cm by 8.75 cm

Bible and Discussion Questions

8. No. Moses heard God in a burning bush, God communicated to Abraham through dreams, Elijah heard the voice of God as a low whisper.

9. These disciples had done impressive works and actions for God, but they did not know Him.

10. Listen with both ears.

19.5

Lesson Practice Questions

1. $1\frac{1}{2}$ inches $\times 3\frac{1}{2}$ inches

2. A four-by-six

3. $(2 \times 3\frac{1}{2}$ inches$) + (3 \times 5\frac{1}{2}$ inches$) + (9\frac{1}{4}$ inches$) =$

7 inches $+ 16\frac{1}{2}$ inches $+ 9\frac{1}{4}$ inches $= 32\frac{3}{4}$ inches

4. R-28

5. From #4, the 2 $\times$ 4 is R-28. A 2 $\times$ 10 is R-34. The 2 $\times$ 10 is better but not by a lot.

6. $5\frac{1}{2}$ inches $- 1$ inch $= 4\frac{1}{2}$ inches

1 inch $\times$ R-8 = R-8 and $4\frac{1}{2}$ inches of

cellulose is 4.5 inches $\times$ R-3.7 = R-16.7.

R-8 + R-16.7 = R-24.7

7. How many kilometers in a 3.1 mile race?

$\frac{3.1\,\text{mi}}{1} \times \frac{1.6\,\text{km}}{1\,\text{mi}} = 5\,\text{km}$. This

race is referred to as a 5k.

Bible and Discussion Questions

8. After a strong wind, an earthquake, and a fire, God spoke in a low whisper.

9. Yes. "If you knew me, you would know my Father also." (John 8:19)
"If you had known me, you would have known my Father also. From now on you do know him and have seen him." (John 14:7)

10. This will be valuable advice.

20.1

Lesson Practice Questions

1. $5.00 minus $1.45 equals $3.55.
   Start with "one forty-five."
   Give one nickel and say "one fifty."
   Give two quarters and say "one seventy-five and two dollars."
   Give three dollar bills and say "three, four, and five."
   (There are other combinations and sequences that are also correct.)

2. $10.00 minus $3.64 equals $6.36.
   Start with "three sixty-four."
   Give one penny and say "three sixty-five."
   Give one dime and say "three seventy-five."
   Give one quarters and say "four."
   Give one dollar bill and say "five."
   Give a five-dollar bill and say "and five is ten."
   (There are other combinations and sequences that are also correct.)

3. Garage sales, yard sales, estate sales, newspaper and penny savers, thrift stores, consignment stores, and Craigslist.

4. Doubling 25° is 50° and then adding 30° makes 80°.

5. $25°C \div 5 \times 9 + 32° = 77°$

6. $\dfrac{90 \text{ kph}}{1} \times \dfrac{1 \text{ mph}}{1.6 \text{ kph}} = 56 \text{ mph}$ or

   $\dfrac{90 \text{ kph}}{1} \times \dfrac{5 \text{ mph}}{8 \text{ kph}} = 56 \text{ mph}.$

7. 90 kph = 55.92 mph rounded it becomes 56 mph.

Bible and Discussion Questions

8. A tithe belongs to God and usually is given to your local church. A contribution is a gift or offering given in addition to the tithe.

9. Compassionate, gentle, kind, loving, generous, practical

10. Some parents may want to keep this to themselves and this is understandable. "When you give to someone in need, don't let your left hand know what your right hand is doing." (Matthew 6:3 NLT) But if they do share, listen well.

20.2

Lesson Practice Questions

1. $20.00 minus $9.20 equals $10.80
   Start with "nine twenty."
   Give one nickel and say "nine twenty-five."
   Give three quarters and say "ten."
   Give a ten-dollar bill and say "twenty."
   (There are other combinations and sequences that are also correct.)

2. $50.00 minus $35.31 equals $14.69
   Start with "thirty-five thirty-one."
   Give four pennies and say "thirty-five thirty-five."
   Give one nickel and say "thirty-five forty."
   Give one dime and say "thirty-five fifty."
   Give two quarters and say "thirty-six."
   Give four dollar bills and say "forty."
   Give a ten-dollar bill and say "fifty."
   (There are other combinations and sequences that are also correct.)

3. Drink water, ask what specials are available, request no ice or a very little

4. $37°C \times 2 + 30° = 104°$

5. $37°C \div 5 \times 9 + 32° = 98.6°$

6. $\dfrac{75 \text{ mi}}{1} \times \dfrac{1 \text{ km}}{0.62 \text{ mi}} = 121 \text{ km}$ or

   $\dfrac{75 \text{ mi}}{1} \times \dfrac{8 \text{ km}}{5 \text{ mi}} = 120 \text{ km}$

7. 75 miles = 121 km

Bible and Discussion Questions

8. Friends, relatives, co-workers, people who live nearby

9. Be edified and encouraged.

10. This will be unique to each family.

20.3

Lesson Practice Questions

1. $5.00 − $3.58 = $1.42
   Start with "three fifty-eight."
   Give two pennies and say "three sixty."
   Give one dime and say "three seventy."
   Give one nickel and say "three seventy-five."
   Give one quarter and say "four."
   Give one dollar bill and say "five."
   (There are other combinations and sequences that are also correct.)

2. $10.00 − $6.09 = $3.91
   Start with "six oh nine."
   Give one penny and say "six ten."
   Give one dime and say "six twenty."
   Give one nickel and say "six twenty-five."
   Give three quarters and say "seven."
   Give three dollar bills and say "ten."
   (There are other combinations and sequences that are also correct.)

3. Used items in the classified section of the newspaper, penny savers, or Craigslist

4. $15°C \times 2 + 30° = 60°$

5. $15°C \div 5 \times 9 + 32° = 59°$

6. $\dfrac{60 \text{ kph}}{1} \times \dfrac{1 \text{ mph}}{1.6 \text{ kph}}$ or $\dfrac{5 \text{ mph}}{8 \text{ kph}} = 38$ mph

7. 37 mph

Bible and Discussion Questions

8. "Religion that is pure and undefiled before God, the Father, is this: to visit orphans and widows in their affliction, and to keep oneself unstained from the world." (James 1:27) I hope you have the privilege of engaging with a widow or an orphan.

9. This would be very tough for me since I find all of these passages edifying.

10. I wish I could hear their answer.

20.4

Lesson Practice Questions

1. $20.00 − $17.73 = $2.27
   Start with "seventeen seventy-three."
   Give two pennies and say "seventeen seventy-five."
   Give one quarter and say "eighteen."
   Give two dollar bills and say "twenty."
   (There are other combinations and sequences that are also correct.)

2. $50.00 − $22.12 = $27.88
   Start with "twenty-two twelve."
   Give three pennies and say "twenty-two fifteen."
   Give one dime and say "twenty-two twenty-five."
   Give three quarters and say "twenty-three."
   Give two dollar bills and say "twenty-five."
   Give a five dollar bill and say "thirty."
   Give a twenty dollar bill and say "fifty."
   (There are other combinations and sequences that are also correct.)

3. Drinks and desserts

4. $10°C \times 2 + 30° = 50°F$

5. $10°C \div 5 \times 9 + 32° = 50°F$

6. You need to drive $\dfrac{500 \text{ km}}{1} \times \dfrac{1 \text{ mi}}{1.6 \text{ km}}$

   or $\dfrac{5 \text{ mi}}{8 \text{ km}} = 313$ miles

7. 310 miles

Bible and Discussion Questions

8. I hope so. It is a good habit to have. It is easy to criticize, but more challenging to love and support. A thank you card once in a while, can be a huge blessing to those in church leadership. "'You shall not muzzle an ox when it treads out the grain,' and, 'The laborer deserves his wages.'" (1 Timothy 5:18)

9. I find it is helpful to not only read, but write out a passage of scripture. Every word is inspired and profitable.

10. This will be interesting.

20.5

Lesson Practice Questions

1. $100.00 - $65.87 = 34.13
   Start with "sixty-five eighty-seven."
   Give three pennies and say "sixty-five ninety."
   Give one dime and say "sixty-six."
   Give four dollar bills and say "seventy."
   Give a ten dollar bill and say "eighty."
   Give a twenty dollar bill and say "one hundred."

2. $10.00 - $2.96 = 7.04
   Start with "two-ninety six."
   Give four pennies and say "three."
   Give two dollar bills and say "five."
   Give a five dollar bill and say "ten."

3. If tax is 5% and the tip is 15% they add up to 20%.

4. $100°C \times 2 + 30° = 230°F$

5. $100°C \div 5 \times 9 + 32° = 212°F$

6. $\dfrac{45 \text{ mph}}{1} \times \dfrac{1.6 \text{ kph}}{1 \text{ mph}} = 72 \text{ kph}$, or
   $\dfrac{60 \text{ kph}}{1} \times \dfrac{0.62 \text{ mph}}{1 \text{ kph}} = 37 \text{ mph}$.
   You better slow down ;-)

7. 72.4 kph rounded to 72 kph or 37.3 mph rounded to 37 mph.

Bible and Discussion Questions

8. This will be unique to your home. "Go therefore and make disciples of all nations." (Matthew 28:19)

9. The more I understand how awesome God is, the more I appreciate and love Him.

10. We used to receive so many answered prayers at yard sales, that when we were praying for our needs in our family devotions, our sons expected to right away go to a yard sale to find the answer :-)

21.1

Lesson Practice Questions

1. He was in danger of diabetes, was tired, and had little energy.

2. 282 lbs $\times$ 15% = 42.3 pounds

3. The heat energy required to increase the temperature of one kilogram of water by one degree Celsius

4. Cola 136, cookie 59, quarter pounder 530, large fries 510 = 1,235. Salad bowl 1,200. They are close.

5. I think the chicken salad bowl may be healthier.

6. He and his friends wanted to eat veggies instead of the king's food. They asked and proposed a ten day test.

7. At the end of ten days they looked better.

Bible and Discussion Questions

8. When God redeems us and changes our heart our treasure is also affected, for "where your treasure is, there will your heart be also." (Luke 12:34)

9. He generally reads scripture and listens to Christian music.

10. Your thoughts!

21.2

Lesson Practice Questions

1. Protein, vegetables, fruit

2. Refined sugars, refined grains, and dairy

3. 3,500

4. Cobb salad and nuggets = 430 + 140 = 570 calories, BK whopper, cola, and fries, 677 + 510 + 136 = 1,323 calories

5. The salad and the nuggets

6. 1/28 = 3.5%

7. Be fully convinced in your own mind and then give each other space and grace.

Bible and Discussion Questions

8. Giving when you have a little, like the widow at the treasury is more important than giving a lot when you have more money. Give now when you are young to develop the habit which will carry over when you are older.

9. He reached out to 32 friends and asked them to pray. He also asked God Himself if He still loved him.

10. Are they? Are you?

21.3

Lesson Practice Questions

1. Men 2,500 and women 2,000

2. If you eat 500 calories less per day for 7 days you will lose 3,500 calories which is one pound.

3. I think God made our body to survive and when it senses we are eating less it will adapt.

4. Corn syrup and high fructose corn syrup

5. One banana 105, one cup of oatmeal 147, a slice of toast with butter 168, orange juice 56, 476 total calories.

6. Mmmm. I am a breakfast guy.

7. At least 20 years old.

Bible and Discussion Questions

8. December. Make giving a part of your budget and give throughout the year.

9. He asked God if it were biblical and then the Spirit reminded him of scriptures which affirmed the illumination.

10. This will be interesting. Read carefully.

21.4

Lesson Practice Questions

1. Body Mass Index. It is the ratio of your weight to your height. Your weight in kilograms is divided by your height in meters squared.

2. Metabolism is the process by which your body transforms and converts food into energy. It is also how quickly you burn fat.

3. Fellowship. We each need other people to help us make new habits.

4. When you eat the complete apple, you ingest a large amount of fructose, but I think you are also chewing, while consuming water, fiber, minerals, antioxidants, and vitamins. The amount of time needed to digest this delicious fruit keeps it from being dumped too quickly into the liver. Plus I feel full after eating a large apple. When drinking a soda the sugar is dumped in large quantities in your system and overloads the liver.

5. Spaghetti-221; spaghetti sauce-92; double-parmesan cheese-44: 1/2 cup corn: 90, 1/2 cup green beans-20:, with cake and frosting: -243, adds up to 710. Without the cake the total is 467.

6. What you eat and regular exercise

7. It will probably have fruit in it :-)

Bible and Discussion Questions

8. The Evangelical Council for Financial Accountability and the Charity Navigator.

9. Baggage is our wounds, scars, and stuff from our past. It hinders our ability to grasp and comprehend how much our Father loves us.

10. This will be different for everyone.

21.5

Lesson Practice Questions

1. This kind of metabolism burns a lot of energy.

2. Pepperoni pizza: $298 \times 2 = 596$, a bag of chips: 155, a cola: 136, and a chocolate chip cookie: 59. $596 + 155 + 136 + 59 = 946$ calories.

3. 3. $9/28 = 0.32$ or 32%

4. Have fun.

5. Are you getting hungry yet?

6. He slept better, felt better, and was able to begin exercising at the local gym.

7. The ingredient that has the largest amount. In ketchup it is tomatoes and in Cheerios it is oats.

Bible and Discussion Questions

8. Pray.

9. I hope it was helpful.

10. This will be interesting and valuable.

22.1

1. $150 \div 2 = 75$ oz $\div 16 = 4.7$ rounded to 5 full bottles

2. Most foods are primarily water, but fruits are particularly high in water

3. Measure your pulse of 30 seconds and double the answer.

4. Any exercise! Pick 3: lowering blood pressure, strengthening the heart, increasing the metabolism which contributes to weight loss, slowing the development of type 2 diabetes, lowering stress, burning unhealthy fat, making us happier, improving muscles and bones, increasing energy levels, improving brain activity, and deeper sleep.

5. 20 minutes × 6 calories burned per minute is 120 calories.

6. If you eat better you will only lose limited weight because your body will adapt. Exercise burns more calories and improves our metabolism, as well as the 11 reasons stated above.

7. $140 \times 36\% = 50.4$ lbs

Bible and Discussion Questions

8. The grace to give

9. Abandonment as a result of having a father who was absent the first five years

10. You probably know.

22.2

Lesson Practice Questions

1. $125 \div 2 = 62.5$ oz $\div 16 = 3.9$ rounded to 4 full bottles

2. 5 oz × 80% or 0.8 = 4 oz

3. 220 minus your age

4. Yes. It makes you feel fuller and you will most likely eat less for that meal.

5. $15 \times 15 = 225$ calories

6. This should be interesting.

7. 6 calories per day

Bible and Discussion Questions

8. Your thoughts may differ slightly, but if you give generously you will reap an abundant crop.

9. "I will never leave you nor forsake you." (Hebrews 13:5)
"I am with you always, even unto the end of the world." (Matthew 28:20)
"He is actually not far from each one of us, 'In Him we live and move and have our being.'" (Acts 17:27–28)

10. Only you will know.

22.3

Lesson Practice Questions

1. $184 \div 2 = 92$ oz $\div 16 = 5.75$ rounded to 6 full bottles.

2. 12 oz × 0.92 = 11.04 or 11 oz.

3. $220 - 40 = 180$
$180 \times 70\% = 126$ bpm and $180 \times 85\% = 153$ bpm
Between 126 and 153 bpm

4. $220 - 40 = 180$
$180 \times 85\% = 153$ bpm and $180 \times 95\% = 171$ bpm.
Between 153 and 171 bpm

5. $25 \times 10 = 250$ calories

6. 25 minutes times 23 calories per minute is 575 calories.

7. He likes the camaraderie. He enjoys the diversity of the activities. The time goes by quickly.

Bible and Discussion Questions

8. Since the Philippians had given so faithfully before, God would meet their needs now. Because they had given to others, God would give to them. "Give, and it will be given to you. Good measure, pressed down, shaken together, running over, will be put into your lap. For with the measure you use it will be measured back to you." (Luke 6:38)
"Whoever brings blessing will be enriched, and one who waters will himself be watered." (Proverbs 11:25)

9. "It is the LORD who goes before you. He will be with you; he will not leave you or forsake you. Do not fear or be dismayed.'" (Deuteronomy 31:8)

10. Since our body is a Temple of the Holy Spirit, taking care, or maintaining it, is temple maintenance.

22.4

Lesson Practice Questions

1. $110 \div 2 = 55$ oz $\div 16 = 3.44$ rounded to 4 full bottles.

2. Fruit makes me feel fuller.

3. When you first get up in the morning. (I drank two glasses this morning!)

4. $12 \times 16.7 = 200.4$ calories

5. Pick 3: lowering blood pressure, strengthening the heart, increasing the metabolism which contributes to weight loss, slowing the development of type 2 diabetes, lowering stress, burning unhealthy fat, making us happier, improving muscles and bones, increasing energy levels, improving brain activity, and improved sleep.

6. Rowing does not have as much impact on our joints as running.

7. Search your mind.

Bible and Discussion Questions

8. The Philippian church was a giving assembly. "You Philippians yourselves know that in the beginning of the gospel, when I left Macedonia, no church entered into partnership with me in giving and receiving, except you only." (Philippians 4:15)

9. God with us

10. Take a deep breath and think about exercising with them. Your folks may have exercised differently when they were your age.

22.5

Lesson Practice Questions

1. Small amounts throughout the day

2. If you drink ice-cold water it might take a little bit of energy to warm it up. According to one study, some adults who drank eight or more glasses of ice-cold water a day burned 8 more calories (in order to warm up the water) than those who only drank four glasses of ice water per day, which is roughly equivalent to 2 minutes of walking.

3. When you feel thirsty

4. Fast is 15 minutes $\times$ 23 = 345 and slow is 15 minutes $\times$ 18 = 270
   $270 + 345 = 615$ calories

5. 125 pound $\times$ 27% = 33.75 pounds

6. Water also aids in digesting the food we eat. Your body needs to be hydrated. If you do not drink enough to process the calories as they are being burned, your metabolism may slow down. When we feel the desire to eat we may be

thirsty. Water helps the kidneys flush out waste

7. National Institute of Diabetes and Digestive and Kidney Diseases. Because type 2 diabetes and kidney diseases can be prevented by eating a healthy diet and exercise.

Bible and Discussion Questions

8. Steve is convinced God will answer any prayer which is according to His will. Since God wants to be generous cheerful givers this is His will for each of us. "If we ask anything according to his will, he hears us: and if we know that he hears us whatsoever we ask, we know that we have the petitions which we have asked of him." (1 John 5:14–15)

9. Steve thinks they are all special, but he especially likes: "I will ask the Father, and he will give you another Helper, to be with you forever, even the Spirit of truth." (John 14:16–17)

10. I hope you found a few nuggets to improve and maintain your temple.

23.1

Lesson Practice Questions

1. After the Great London Fire in 1666.

2. Auto insurance, home insurance, renters insurance, life insurance, disability insurance, health insurance, pet insurance, dental insurance, vision insurance are several to choose from.

3. Flood, fire, tornado, hurricane, etc.

4. 1 out of 1,000 or 1 $\div$ 1,000 is 0.1%

5. Liability Insurance

6. Steve's first car was not worth enough to repair. It was a clunker :-)

7. While we live by faith and trust God completely, we live in a litigious culture and it is provident to carry some form of insurance to protect our chief assets, such as our car and home.

Bible and Discussion Questions

8. Describe God's blessing

9. Steve personalizes it by saying "thank You Jesus for leading me to the Father" or something similar.

10. This will be enlightening.

23.2

Lesson Practice Questions

1. 1736 aided by Benjamin Franklin

2. Auto, home, and some form of health insurance, possibly renters insurance, some form of life. It depends :-)

3. If the deductible is lower then you will be submitting more claims so you will need to pay higher premiums.

4. $50.00

5. Tier 250 is $200.00

6. The two components are for the death benefit and the savings account portion.

7. A term policy is for a specific timeframe or term. It is like renting a policy.

Bible and Discussion Questions

8. We need God. Even with our well-stocked grocery shelves, God is ultimately the provider of our needs.

9. Learn more about God by studying scripture and meditating on the character qualities of God.

10. Take lots of notes.

23.3

Lesson Practice Questions

1. Inspecting properties before selling them a policy, safety measures like not storing combustible materials in a wooden structure, developing a cash reserve for future claims, raising premiums of unsafe homes, and declining coverage to houses made of wood since they presented too great a risk.

2. Premium is the monthly, or annual amount of money, each member has to pay into the pool to cover the needs of their group.

3. $3.25 per month or $39.00 per year

4. $149.00 − $50.00 (deductible which Seth pays) = $99.00, which the group pays

5. $2,769.00 − $500.00 (deductible which the member pays) = $2,269.00, which the group pays

6. Whomever the holder of the policy designates

7. Term life is likened to renting a home, while permanent life is compared to owning a home. Term life is for a specific period of time. Whole life lasts for your whole life and is both an insurance policy with a benefit as well as an investment tool.

Bible and Discussion Questions

8. He fed them with manna and their clothes didn't wear out, and their feet didn't blister or swell.

9. Recognizing how much Jesus has done for me, makes me thankful and grateful.

10. This number will vary.

23.4

Lesson Practice Questions

1. Insurance is about being provident and prudent. Assurance is knowing that ultimately God has promised to care and provide for His children.

2. Deductible is the amount a member must pay before submitting their needs to the group. This is called out of pocket expense.

3. Generally a high deductible is preferred since there are so few home insurance needs which will be submitted as claims. I have lived in my current home for 12 years and have not submitted one claim. With a high deductible, I will pay lower premiums.

4. Have a way to find a lost smartphone and keep your phone in a case to protect the screen. If these measures are practiced they will have less screens to repair and less stolen phones to replace.

5. Matthew is an actuary. He studies data and statistics and figures out what a reasonable premium should be.

6. At the end of your term you have nothing to show for your investment. When you rent a home for a specific time frame, you have nothing left of what you have paid of all your monthly rental checks.

7. $4,750.00

Bible and Discussion Questions

8. When we live according to the principles of God's for and seek for His blessing, God will provide for our needs.

9. I hope you found some rich treasures in these passages.

10. This will be an interesting discussion.

23.5

Lesson Practice Questions

1. Pool is a verb meaning to gather together resources of a group. The amount which has been gathered is called a pool.

2. This is the money left over after the claims have all been paid and gives you a little nest egg for the next year.

3. First take it to a repair shop to get an estimate for the cost to fix it. Then if the amount is above $50.00 (her deductible) submit her claim to the Smartphone Owners.

4. Since $245.00 is less than $250.00 she will pay the whole amount and the owners will not pay anything.

5. $500,000.00

6. Common sense and data teach us that young students will live longer than an aged instructor.

7. Insurance is prudently protecting our assets, but he advocates never trusting in man, but in God alone.

Bible and Discussion Questions

8. Do not become proud at that time and forget the LORD your God and disobey His commandments.

9. Your observation. I hope you were edified.

10. This should be an informative conversation. Listen well.

24.1

Lesson Practice Questions

1. Preferred Provider Organizations. One half of health plans are PPOs. The policy holders receive substantial discounts by choosing from the health care providers who are partnered with their PPO.

2. Coinsurance, or cost sharing, is the percentage you pay after the deductible has been reached.

3. The insurance company pays 80%

and the policy holder pays 20%.

4. $88.88

5. A Christian sharing plan is made up of members who share a common faith in God and His word, and share each other's health care expenses.

6. Samaritan Ministries, Christian Healthcare Ministries, Liberty HealthShare, The Christian Care Ministry or Medi-Share, Altrua HealthShare

7. 106 million

Bible and Discussion Questions

8. This is a wonderful discipline to exercise your thanks muscles.

9. Jesus died on the cross to pay the penalty for our sins by dying in our place.

10. This will be specific to y'all :-)

24.2

Lesson Practice Questions

1. Health Maintenance Organization. Lower premiums. One fourth.

2. Primary Care Physician. They oversee your care and give referrals to specialists.

3. $4,524.00 each

4. Up to $11,115.56

5. Be a member of a church. Agree with the statement of faith. Agree with their lifestyle requirements.

6. For Samaritan Ministries, bills are received from the providers. Providers are encouraged to lower their costs since there is no insurance involved. The need is then sent in to headquarters where it is approved. Then they assign members to share this burden and send a check, with prayer, to the member to compensate for their bills.

7. Ultimately our hope is for God to heal us and provide for our needs.

Bible and Discussion Questions

8. I am always amazed the only one gave thanks. Then I am stirred to make sure that I am not one of the nine and commit myself to giving thanks regularly and intentionally to God.

9. I like "The message of the cross is foolish to those who are headed for destruction! But we who are being saved know it is the very power of God." (1 Corinthians 1:18 NLT)

10. This will be a helpful talk.

24.3

Lesson Practice Questions

1. Copay is a set fee for certain needs. Self-pay means the bills are all paid by the patient.

2. A network is a collection of providers who band together in an organization to provide services at a lower fee to its members.

3. $2,456.64

4. Up to $11,115.56

5. 3500 is the amount of the deductible.

6. The cost was divided up into nine portions and sent to nine members who wrote checks to Steve to cover the total expense.

7. An unexpected, serious, costly medical emergency. Cancer, a serious accident, or any numbers of possibilities. They are usually expensive and outside the normal health concerns.

Bible and Discussion Questions

8. From Above! From our Good God.

9. Jesus and Paul both instructed us to make personal sacrifices of self-denial daily.

10. Ask to find out.

24.4

Lesson Practice Questions

1. Deductible is a fixed amount the policy holder must pay during a given time period, usually a year, before his health insurance benefits cover the remaining costs. $2,000.00

2. If you choose health care providers and services outside of the network favored by your PPO you may pay more to them.

3. An adjustment is the amount the charges were lowered since they were self-pay.

4. He saved $8,658.92.

5. $8,658.92 of $11,115.56, or $8,658.92 divided by $11,115.56 is 0.779 or 78%.

6. $133.00 annually

7. They are making high mortgage and car payments and need the same level of income to maintain this lifestyle. When they are out of work and unable to make the payments they can go bankrupt.

Bible and Discussion Questions

8. Intentionally make lists of things you are grateful for. Focus on what you have and not what you want. You probably have some other good ideas that are better than this :-)

9. Steve's would be, "I have been crucified with Christ; and it is no longer I who live, but Christ lives in me." (Galatians 2:20)

10. This will vary from home to home.

24.5

Lesson Practice Questions

1. Insurance is a contract that moves the risk of financial loss from an individual or business to an insurance company.

2. An insurance policy is the document between you and the insurance provider specifying the arrangements you have agreed to. You agree to make your payments and they agree to pay their percentage of the claims.

3. 30% of $11,115.56 = $3,334.67

4. 70% of $11,115.56 = $7,780.89

5. Stress often contributes to dis-ease

6. Keep the Sabbath and rest one day per week. Let God bear your burdens and sleep well, knowing He will never slumber of sleep.

7. Begin saving money until you have enough to live on for several months in case you are unable to work.

Bible and Discussion Questions

8. This is a great activity. Be grateful and bless your folks.

9. We remember Jesus giving His body and blood

for us in the sacrament of Holy Communion. In baptism: "We have been buried with Him through baptism into death, in order that as Christ was raised from the dead through the glory of the Father, so we too might walk in newness of life." (Romans 6:4)

10. You might ask them about medicare if they are old enough to begin receiving these benefits.

25.1

Lesson Practice Questions

1. Before jumping into college, figure out how much it will cost you.

2. HACC has no residence dormitories so students need to commute to school.

3. Grants and scholarships are gifts and don't need to be repaid. A loan needs to be repaid, with interest.

4. $12,200 \div 10$ classes $= \$1,220$ per class

5. $26,000 \times 4 = \$104,000$

6. $3,341 \times 2 = \$6,682$
$26,000 \times 2 = \$52,000$
$52,000 + \$6,682 = \$58,682$
$104,000 - \$58,682 = \$45,318$

7. $4 \times \$1,220 = \$4,880$
If 4 CLEP tests cost $400, net savings would be $4,880 - \$400 = \$4,480$

Bible and Discussion Questions

8. Keeping the Sabbath holy is one of the ten commandments and God worked six days and then rested one day.

9. "Just-as-if-I-hadn't-sinned"

10. I hope you have good honest communication on this important subject. No one, except God, loves you more than your parents.

25.2

Lesson Practice Questions

1. Government issued fixed interest and private loans

2. To receive financial aid, the applicant should complete the FAFSA form which stands for Free Application for Federal Student Aid

3. 97%

4. $25,000 + \$8,750 = \$33,750$
$33,750 - \$15,000 - \$3,500 = \$15,250$ each year or $30,500 for both years

5. $75 \times 36 = \$2,700$
$8,750 - \$2,700 = \$6,050$ each year

6. $33,750 - \$15,000 - \$3,500 - \$6,050 = \$9,200$ each year or $18,400 for both years

7. $15,250 + \$15,250 + \$9,200 + \$9,200 = \$48,900$

Bible and Discussion Questions

8. Rest is an antidote to stress. As we are convinced that God commands us to rest, we can do so with a clear conscience, and not feel compelled to work every day.

9. Jesus is the pure spotless lamb who delivers God's people from death.

10. Listen, then brainstorm together. :-)

25.3

Lesson Practice Questions

1. A merit-based scholarship is given to a rewarding individual who excels at academics, sports, art, or some other endeavor.

2. Your parent's employer, your church, or Chick-fil-A.

3. Expected Family Contribution

4. $308.77

5. $9,552.43

6. $9,552.43 - \$8,165.81 = \$1,386.62$
One year and four months

7. $49,800 \times .79 = \$39,342$
$39,342 \div 12 = \$3,278.50$
$308.77 \div \$3,278.50 \approx 9.4\%$

Bible and Discussion Questions

8. "You shall take delight in the LORD, and I will make you ride on the heights of the earth; I will feed you with the heritage of Jacob your father, for the mouth of the LORD has spoken." (Isaiah 58:14)

9. "The blood of goats and bulls and the ashes of a young cow could cleanse people's bodies from ceremonial impurity. Just think how

293

much more the blood of Christ will purify our consciences from sinful deeds so that we can worship the living God." (Hebrews 9:13–14)

10. Each family will have their own ideas.

25.4

Lesson Practice Questions

1. CLEP stands for College-Level Examination Program

2. By sending less than $100 on an exam, you can save the cost of tuition for the same subject at a college or university.

3. As of 2018, 33 subjects

4. $310.49

5. $17,888.51

6. One year and seven months in time and $17,888.51 − $15,716.76 = $2,171.75

7. $56,500 × .78 = $44,070
   $46,410 ÷ 12 = $3,672.50
   $310.49 ÷ $3,672.50 = 8.5%

Bible and Discussion Questions

8. Be fully convinced in their own mind and give space to others to be fully convinced in their own mind.

9. "We can boldly enter heaven's Most Holy Place because of the blood of Jesus. By his death, Jesus opened a new and life-giving way through the curtain into the Most Holy Place." (Hebrews 10:19–20)

10. I enjoy networking and learning from others. I hope you do as well!

25.5

Lesson Practice Questions

1. A need based grant is based on your financial circumstances and/or the financial wherewithal of your family.

2. By taking CLEP exams, you save money, you save time in the classroom, you have more time to take classes that interest you. Some of the cons are not being in a class with others and the professor, and

the self-discipline needed to study on your own.

3. A good credit score for yourself, or your co-signer.

4. $4,000 ÷ 5 = $800
   3 × $800 = $2,400
   The CLEP tests are $100 each (3 × $100) so she saves $2,400 − (3 × $100) = $2,100

5. $50 × 36 weeks = $1,800
   $8,330 − $1,800 = $6,530

6.

Year	Tuition	Room and Board	Amount to Borrow
One	$8,000 − $2,100 = $5,900	$50 × 36 = $1,800	$7,700 − (2 × $1,000) − $3,500 = $2,200
Two	$8,000	$50 × 36 = $1,800	$9,800 − (2 × $1,000) − $3,500 = $4,300
Combined			$4,300 + $2,200 = $6,500

7. $6,500 − $5,000 = $1,500

Bible and Discussion Questions

8. Pause and reflect before answering.

9. We remember the price Jesus paid for our salvation from our sins. And "every time you eat this bread and drink this cup, you are announcing the Lord's death until he comes again." (1 Corinthians 11:26, NLT)

10. This could be enlightening. Enjoy.

26.1

Lesson Practice Questions

1. Bachelor of Arts in Business Administration

2. He sought to seek first the kingdom of God and enter some form of Christian Ministry.

3. In hindsight, Steve is attracted to the gap year concept to experience the different options while still acquiring a year's worth of college credit.

4. They attended a small Bible school and then attended a four-year Christian liberal arts school when they were in their twenties.

5. A student is more aware of who they are, what they want to learn, and more mature.

6. Your Heavenly Father!

7. Find wise counselors and listen to their input. After you have heard from men and women,

then listen to God, and make your decision.

Bible and Discussion Questions

8. He that hears God's Word and does it or obeys it, is a wise man. He who listens, but does not put into practice what he heard is a foolish man.

9. When we weep, He weeps. When we are afflicted, He is afflicted. He bears our burdens and is acquainted with our griefs and sorrows.

10. You may already know, but you might hear something new. :-)

26.2

Lesson Practice Questions

1. I found at least five and there may be more. Fellowship, making lifelong friends, visiting speakers, a faculty that cares about you, learning from a Biblical worldview.

2. Cynical attitude about spiritual things, and not working hard to maintain your own connection with God.

3. You will have plenty of opportunities to share your faith and be light in a dark place. You will grow stronger in your own walk with God as others look to you for guidance.

4. Besides a vibrant and intentional devotion time with God, every-single-day, fellowship with other believers, and being a part of a campus ministry.

5. What do you think?

6. 1. We share the Gospel with students and develop passionate disciples of Jesus Christ.
2. We serve together with the church and invite students into the lives of local congregations.
3. We give students a vision for serving Jesus Christ in their studies, jobs, communities, and families.

7. Rampant sin. Attacks from every side to your faith and Biblical lifestyle.

Bible and Discussion Questions

8. Conducting business with fear and just principles. Loving your neighbor as yourself is an extension of love God.

9. The whole chapter is rich with an inspired picture of the suffering Messiah. Here are

few nuggets: He was despised and rejected, a man of sorrows, acquainted with deepest grief. He was despised. He was pierced for our rebellion and crushed for our sins.

10. When you have children you will understand how on target a parent's recommendations can be. They have seen you grow into the person you are since the womb. Treasure their insights.

26.3

Lesson Practice Questions

1. The high cost of college and the emerging needs for construction workers and other non college occupations.

2. Construction, health care, and personal care

3. Seventy percent

4. A rookie who is willing to learn a trade from someone more experienced than they are.

5. The employer has a teachable, hard working employee at a reduced wage, and the apprentice learns skills which will benefit them for their future occupation.

6. This is your choice! Sometimes a short apprenticeship will show you that you don't want to pursue this career. That is still positive as now you have eliminated one future possibility.

7. It is a chance to experience an array of subjects and opportunities to learn more about your gifting while still receiving college credit.

Bible and Discussion Questions

8. Restitution is making amends or compensating for a loss. When Steve learned of this principle he thought about people he had wronged and stolen from, asked their forgiveness, and made monetary reparations for his errors.

9. "Whoever wants to be a leader among you must be your servant, and whoever wants to be first among you must become your slave." (Matthew 20:26–27)

10. This should be edifying.

26.4

Lesson Practice Questions

1. $22,900. This fee covers tuition, room and board, books, and travel expenses.

2. The student learns more about their gifts and talents, is involved with other students in learning a variety of subjects, and becoming more grounded in the Word of God.

3. Yes, 91% of OneLife receive some form of aid.

4. This assessment tool is professionally designed to help you identify how you have been designed and what occupations may fit with your personality and makeup.

5. Take the Career Direct Assessment to: get a full picture of your potential, explore your career opportunities, examine your results with a definition of your career type, and receive a personalized action plan with suggested job fits. The $80 option is the most preferred.

6. When you discover more about how God has wired you, you will have more information on possible careers. When you have narrowed down possible careers, you can then decide the most effective way to prepare for these opportunities.

7. Home School Legal Defense Association began as advocates for parents who wanted to teach and educate their children at home.

Bible and Discussion Questions

8. Isaac was an honest man and a mathematician. He was known and the people trusted his integrity of character for something as important as money.

9. On the night before He was crucified, He washed their feet. "If I then, your Lord and Teacher, have washed your feet, you also ought to wash one another's feet." (John 13:14)

10. Gap years are a relatively newcomer to traditional post high school options. Explore the many kinds of gap years.

26.5

Lesson Practice Questions

1. I hope you found it interesting.

2. Without leaving the comforts of home, you enroll in classes via the internet and earn your degree online, and at home.

3. With their help, you can take many required courses and save a lot of money by taking online classes, and clepping other courses.

4. You are also a part of an online community of students with similar goals and backgrounds. You have experienced coaches to help you navigate the online educational world.

5. You have learned how to think for yourself, read whole books, explore areas of interest without classroom or time constraints. You have probably traveled a good bit, and been on a lot of "field trips."

6. I wish I knew how many you have read :-)

7. Absolutely. Check out HSLDA for ideas along this line.

Bible and Discussion Questions

8. As soon as they have completed their work. "You must pay them their wages each day before sunset because they are poor and are counting on it. If you don't, they might cry out to the LORD against you, and it would be counted against you as sin." (Deuteronomy 24:15, NLT)

9. I hope you had several, but pick the best one.

10. "In an abundance of counselors there is safety." (Proverbs 11:14)

27.1

Lesson Practice Questions

1. A resume is a written record of what you have done to show to potential employers when you apply for a job. Resume comes from the French word *resumer*, meaning to sum up.

2. Hard skills are measurable. They are a record of your education and work experiences.

3. You and your parents know the answer to this one.

4. Reflect and think about what you do when you need some time for yourself.

5. Ruth from Moab

6. Daniel

7. Moses was a shepherd and his experiences prepared him to lead the children of Israel in the wilderness for forty years. David's experiences caring for and protecting sheep helped him lead the 600 families into the wilderness for many years. His experiences protecting sheep prepared him for slaying Goliath and being a warrior.

Bible and Discussion Questions

8. Benny is unable to secure a loan based on his lack of good credit and collateral. This is not wise for Steve.

9. The humble receive grace "God opposes the proud but gives grace to the humble." Humble yourselves, therefore, under the mighty hand of God so that at the proper time he may exalt you." (1 Peter 5:5–6)

10. They know you and have watched you grow up for decades. I hope their observations are encouraging to you.

27.2

Lesson Practice Questions

1. Pick four: Leadership, Teamwork, Written Communication, Problem Solving Ability, Strong Work Ethic, Verbal communication, Flexibility, Adaptability, Time Management, Conflict Resolution, Positive Attitude, Self-Confidence, Ability to Accept and Learn From Criticism, Willingness to Learn.

2. Hard skills are measurable and a record of what you have done. Soft skills are internal, difficult to measure, and provide a glimpse into who you are.

3. Did you find this interesting?

4. This may help clarify if your initial thoughts are spot on.

5. Bezalel and Oholiab

6. Jabal and Jubal were brothers. Jabal was the father of those who dwell in tents and have livestock, Jubal was the father of all those who play the lyre and pipe and their cousin Tubal-cain was a forger of instruments made of bronze and iron.

7. We don't know for sure, but probably a D or a lion!

Bible and Discussion Questions

8. When someone approaches you to co-sign, RUN!

9. Pride and we all have way too much of it.

10. I think you will find this interesting.

27.3

Lesson Practice Questions

1. This is good practice.

2. You live and learn with people of different ages, different abilities, different gender, and in the process develop lots of soft skills.

3. He is the ultimate amalgam of all the types and has a perfect blend. He is God. He is perfect.

4. A blend is a combination of one or more types.

5. Aquila and Priscilla

6. Joseph

7. This is your opinion.

Bible and Discussion Questions

8. If your parents or grandparents are trying to help you establish credit and understand all the risks.

9. Humility. May we share this with them as well.

10. This will be a history lesson as well as an occupation lesson :-)

27.4

Lesson Practice Questions

1. There are many advantages. I hope you can think of several.

2. A reference is from someone who knows your character. It could be a former employer or someone you have worked closely with. Think of a few that you may ask someday.

3. The high D, or lion.

4. The C personality, typified by the beaver

5. Mary, Joanna, and Susanna

6. Work to Bring Glory to God.
Work for the Lord
Work to Share With Others
Work to Provide for Your Family
Work to Preach the Gospel for Free
Work because God Designed Us to Work

7. This is your opinion.

Bible and Discussion Questions

8. Spell out all aspects of the agreement and put it in writing. Have all the parties involved sign it to ensure that they have read it and agree with the contents.

9. By humbling ourselves like a child and becoming servants.

10. We will all have tough jobs, thank God for redeeming and bringing good from them.

27.5

Lesson Practice Questions

1. Honestly

2. Besides being grateful and polite, you also set yourselves apart from those who don't.

3. The I type who is like an otter

4. Golden retriever

5. Jesus

6. As a lion, He cleansed the temple by himself. He was approachable and children were attracted to Him, like a golden retriever. He was likable and enjoyed being around people, as does every otter. Like a conscientious beaver, He fulfilled every jot and tittle of the law.

7. C, Beaver, carefully wrote the book of Luke and Acts

Bible and Discussion Questions

8. The borrower is the slave of the lender. When one person is the lender and the other is the borrower, this relationship subtly changes the way people relate to one another. My friend felt like a slave and not an equal.

9. God. "The LORD is near to the brokenhearted and saves the crushed in spirit." (Psalm 34:18)

10. God bless them for their labors in behalf of their family.

28.1

Lesson Practice Questions

1. A competitive advantage is something you possess that gives you an edge over your competition.

2. Think hard :-)

3. Entrepreneurs are willing to take risks, think outside the traditional box, and have creative ideas. They have a good amount of self-confidence and are often "D" types and first born children.

4. These people see opportunities and believe they can figure out and overcome obstacles. They like to be in charge.

5. The first part is unique to you. Steve thinks it is their attitude. One saw an obstacle and the other saw an opportunity, even though they both observed the same situation.

6. Have an enjoyable time dreaming.

7. The otter will make it fun and entertaining, but the beaver will help him have his facts right. Together they will create edutainment!

Bible and Discussion Questions

8. With Jesus in our yoke with us, we are moving in the same direction and He is helping to carry our share of the burden.

9. (Jesus was asked) "'Teacher, which is the great commandment in the Law?' And he said to him, 'You shall love the Lord your God with all your heart and with all your soul and with all your mind. This is the great and first commandment.'" (Matthew 22:36–38)

10. This should be insightful.

28.2

Lesson Practice Questions

1. He didn't mind climbing tall ladders. He was cheap. He had long arms. His dad sold paint.

2. I know you have something!

3. A staff. He was able, with God's help, to lead the children of Israel out of Egypt.

4. Cutting grass and shoveling snow for his family prepared Steve to help his neighbors.

5. Paint peels, weathers, and needs to be repainted and most people do not want to do the work themselves.

6. Make a list.

7. A lion is designed to be in charge. But the best answer might be to ask the lion if they would work with the golden retriever, to become a more thoughtful and gentle lion to the other members of the shipping department.

Bible and Discussion Questions

8. This passage clearly counsels believers to not enter into binding business arrangements with non-believers.

9. "You shall love your neighbor as yourself: I am the LORD." (Leviticus 19:18) The location surprised and blessed Steve.

10. I hope their advice and observations are helpful to you.

28.3

Lesson Practice Questions

1. If you make a profit, then you can eat, have a home, and wear warm clothes. :-)

2. He enjoyed the interaction with the customers, but it was a lot of work for a small sticky profit.

3. This is similar to what is in your hand, but I am hoping you have specific work experiences which will prepare you for an occupation some day.

4. Please pick two from the five listed. Take an inventory, pray, determine a need, identify your competitive advantage, and decide if it is profitable.

5. Remember, most people like to share their story.

6. There are nine listed, which of them appeal to you?

7. Probably an otter, although the lion is sure he can do it better :-)

Bible and Discussion Questions

8. There is no need to ask God or others what to do; if you are considering marrying a non-believer, please don't.

9. Love others, as Jesus has loved you. John 13:34–35 and John 15:12.

10. Now you can be young, and smart.

28.4

Lesson Practice Questions

1. He helped parents understand math, and then provided a tool and curriculum for them to be able to teach their children.

2. He had four. Operate the business by the golden rule, continue to improve, respond to the needs of the customer, and don't go into debt.

3. Outback Steakhouse and Southwest Airlines.

4. Necessity is the mother of invention.

5. A father was helping to create a plastic ball for his son and his friends that would curve.

6. We had health needs which were remedied by using natural herbs.

7. A golden retriever fits the bill. They are steady, sweet, sensitive and wired to be good with other people.

Bible and Discussion Questions

8. Be careful and make sure that everyone understands the parameters of this relationship. Put all expectations in writing.

9. Husbands are to love their wives, AS JESUS HAS LOVED THEM. They are not to love as they wished they were loved, but as they have been loved, by Jesus.

10. You are a good student for asking and listening.

28.5

Lesson Practice Questions

1. He was a teacher, a conference speaker, a sales rep for other educational products, and tutored home educated children.

2. Self-assessment is helpful when thinking about what you bring to the table and how you are wired to serve others.

3. Love of God, love of family, love of good literature

4. Customers had their house freshly painted, workers had a profitable income, Steve

made money for college expenses.

5. These will be unique to you.

6. Dream and think through an ideal scenario.

7. "Why Not" people are go getters. They jump in and do things without making excuses.

Bible and Discussion Questions

8. Be as specific and clear as possible. Use a written agreement which everyone can read and sign.

9. He loved us while we were messy sinners and not naturally attractive or lovable.

10. These kinds of questions will bless your grandparents and enrich you. Well done.

29.1

Lesson Practice Questions

1. Whether we have one employer or multiple customers, we all answer to someone.

2. His immediate family, his parents, his pastor

3. The servant hearted sales representatives

4. Show up on time, do the assigned task, and put in a full day's work

5. Find the work to be done, pay the employees, and interact with the customers

6. Work all day on the project, and in the evenings, visit prospective customers and give estimates.

7. Drive to Steve's house, wake him up, go to the job and do the assigned task for the day, drive home, and pick up a paycheck at the end of the week.

Bible and Discussion Questions

8. The stress on important relationships such as your spouse and children. If you spend money needlessly on the hopes of "striking it rich," your family may not receive their daily bread. If you do "win," the stress the large amount of money brings harm to most relationships.

9. Steve kept busy doing activities, because He didn't believe, deep in his heart, that God liked Him just the way he was.

10. I wish I could learn from them.

29.2

Lesson Practice Questions

1. If the job is estimated properly, you can receive a good profit. If the job is bid too low, you can lose money on a job.

2. We each have our own answers, but I like: potential for reward, do things your own way, ability to make changes quickly, and choose your work hours.

3. We each have our own perspective, but for me: long hours, when work is never over.

4. Each of us has a unique perspective. I like to leave work at work and receive benefits.

5. Feast when you have plenty of profitable work to do, famine when there is not enough good paying work to be done.

6. Have fun dreaming.

7. We all have tough lessons to learn, what are yours?

Bible and Discussion Questions

8. Be content with what you have and the money you have earned as a result of honorable work.

9. God never pushes His way into our lives. He seeks us, but stands at the door knocking. He is meek and gentle of heart.

10. They have a unique perspective.

29.3

Lesson Practice Questions

1. Employers often work all day and into the evening. Even when they are not actively working, they are thinking about work.

2. This is your opinion.

3. Also your own thoughts

4. You can be both, but if you had to choose, pick one.

5. Lions have difficulty working for Golden Retrievers. Golden Retrievers find it hard to lead others.

6. His experience as a shepherd, taught him how to defend the sheep and goats from bears and lions, and living in the wilderness prepared him to find water and food for the flock. He put both of these skills to work when

he shepherded hundreds of families in the wilderness and when he defended the children of Israel from the Philistines and Goliath.

7. Moses spent 40 years caring for his father-in-law's herds. He then spent another 40 years for the children of Israel in the same wilderness.

Bible and Discussion Questions

8. The "winners" receive money they did not work for and often spend it frivolously. The "losers" are wasting money on tickets that could be spent on food and other necessities for their family.

9. I hope so. If not, once a week, for two minutes is a great way to begin.

10. Who was your grandparents' favorite employer? Why?

29.4

Lesson Practice Questions

1. The boss leads by example and the employees will follow his lead.

2. How to speak on his feet, the importance of teaching concepts, the central role parents play in the education of their children, the superiority of tutoring over classroom teaching

3. A tutor has the ability to move at the student's pace, without discipline issues, or classroom distractions.

4. Your observations

5. While Steve was teaching a group of home educated students, he was asked to write materials for the children he was teaching.

6. Character qualities like diligence and teachability

7. The first man was teachable and diligent and the second did not take criticism well, thinking he knew more than he did.

Bible and Discussion Questions

8. Your opinion.

9. Search your heart.

10. They have watched your parents grow up and have years of experience themselves, plus they know and love you.

29.5

Lesson Practice Questions

1. Steve thinks so, how about you?

2. Six

3. He finds value and dignity in working. He senses he is a contributing part of a team.

4. Hopefully with respect and as you would like to be treated if you were he.

5. By only asking others to do tasks that we have done, and are willing to do, ourselves

6. Out identity is not a result of what we have accomplished, but of who we are in relationship with God. We are adopted children of God. We are loved for who we are and not based on what we do.

7. Even though we may have an earthly employer, ultimately, we serve and work for God alone.

Bible and Discussion Questions

8. This is up to you.

9. These verses are pretty clear already. "The Lord is good to those who wait for him, to the soul who seeks him. It is good that one should wait quietly for the salvation of the Lord."

10. May God bless your interactions with your parents.

30.1

Lesson Practice Questions

1. $500.00 \times 0.06 = 30.00. The original investment has grown to $530.00.

2. 6% ÷ 4 quarters = 1.5% per quarter and 1.5% converted to a decimal is 0.015.

Quarter	Interest	Total
First	$500.00 \times 0.015 = 7.50	$500.00 + $7.50 = 507.50
Second	$507.50 \times 0.015 = 7.61	$507.50 + $7.61 = 515.11
Third	$515.11 \times 0.015 = 7.73	$515.11 + $7.73 = 522.84
Fourth	$522.84 \times 0.015 = 7.84	$522.84 + $7.84 = 530.68

3. $500.00 at 6% annual interest compounded continuously for one year is $530.92.

4. $530.92 − $500.00 = $30.92

$W_p × \$500.00 = \$30.92$

$W_p = \$30.92/\$500.00$

$W_p = 0.06184$ rounded to 6.2%

We could divide both the principal and the earned interest by 5.

$W_p × \$500.00/5 = \$30.92/5$

$W_p × \$100.00 = \$6.184$

$W_p = 0.06184$ rounded to 6.2%

5. A $400.00 CD, a 6.5% interest rate compounded annually for two years

$$F_V = \$400\left(1 + \frac{0.065}{1}\right)^{2 \times 1}$$

$$F_V = \$400(1.065)^2$$

$$F_V = \$400(1.134) = \$453.69$$

A $400.00 CD, a 6% interest rate compounded quarterly for two years

$$F_V = \$400\left(1 + \frac{0.06}{4}\right)^{2 \times 4}$$

$$F_V = \$400(1.015)^8$$

$$F_V = \$400(1.1265) = \$450.60$$

The first CD with the 6.5% rate is better.

6. The CD with 6.5% annual interest compounded annually for two years yielded $453.60, while the CD with 6% annual interest compounded quarterly for two years yielded $450.60. The first CD has a higher yield.

7. Simple interest is the interest accrued or accumulated on only the principal each year. Compound interest is the interest accrued on the principle AND the interest for the preceding year. This interest accumulates and grows each time the interest is computed and added to the principal.

Bible and Discussion Questions

8. The Proverbs are rich with sage and timely advice that is always practical.

9. Steve reads Psalm 139 frequently to remind himself that God created and designed him, that God knows him intimately, and loves Steve just as he is, at that moment.

10. This will be "interest"-ing :-)

30.2

Lesson Practice Questions

1. $800.00 × 0.12 = $96.00. The original investment has grown to $896.00.

2. 12% ÷ 4 quarters = 3% per quarter and 3.0% converted to a decimal is 0.03.

Quarter	Interest	Total
First	$800.00 × 0.03 = $24.00	$800.00 + $24.00 = $824.00
Second	$824.00 × 0.03 = $24.72	$824.00 + $24.72 = $848.72
Third	$848.72 × 0.03 = $25.46	$848.72 + $25.46 = $874.18
Fourth	$874.18 × 0.03 = $26.23	$874.18 + $26.23 = $900.41

3. $800.00 at 12% annual interest compounded continuously for one year is $902.00.

4. $902.00 − $800.00 = $102.00

$W_p × \$800.00 = \$102.00$

$W_p = \$102.00/\$800.00$

$W_p = 12.75\%$

We could also divide both the principal and the earned interest by 8.

$W_p × \$800.00/8 = \$102.00/8$

$W_p × \$100.00 = 12.75$, and WP = 12.75%

5. $$F_V = \$250\left(1 + \frac{0.04}{12}\right)^{3 \times 12}$$

$$F_V = \$250(1.0033)^{36}$$

$$F_V = \$250(1.1273) = \$281.82$$

6. When the interest is compounded annually, the interest is calculated at the end of each year. Furthermore, since it is compound interest, you earn interest on the principal plus the interest rather than just the original principal amount.

7. $487.50

Bible and Discussion Questions

8. The word of God is living and active and helps us discern our own heart.

9. This is a precious Psalm. My favorite verses are: "How precious are your thoughts about me, O God. They cannot be numbered! I can't even count them; they outnumber the grains of sand! And when I wake up, you are still with me!" (Psalm 139:17–18, NLT)

10. More "interest"-ing conversation.

30.3

Lesson Practice Questions

1. $10,000.00 × 0.05 = $500.00.

$500.00 × 3 years is $1,500.00.

The original investment has grown to $11,500.00.

2.

Year	Interest	Total
First	$10,000.00 × 0.05 = $500.00	$10,000.00 + $500.00 = $10,500.00
Second	$10,500.00 × 0.05 = $525.00	$10,500.00 + $525.00 = $11,025.00
Third	$11,025.00 × 0.05 = $551.25	$11,025.00 + $551.25 = $11,576.25

3. The original investment has grown to $11,614.72

4. $11,614.72 − $10,000.00 = $1,614.72

$1,614.72 divided by 3 for the three

years, $1,614.72 ÷ 3 = $538.24

$W_P × $10,000 = 538.24

$W_P = $538.24/$10,000 = 0.0538$

$W_P = 5.38\%$

We could also divide both the principal and the earned interest by 100.

$W_P × $10,000 = 538.24

$W_P × $10,000/100 = $538.24/100$

$W_P × $100.00 = 5.38, and $W_P = 5.38\%$

5. $1,000.00 CD, a $4\frac{1}{2}\%$ (4.5%) annual interest rate compounded annually for six years is $1,302.26. $1,000.00 CD, $3\frac{3}{4}\%$ (3.75%) annual interest rate compounded monthly for six years is $1,251.88.

6. The principal is the amount you are originally depositing or beginning with.

7. $850.00 CD, $4\frac{1}{4}\%$ (4.25%) annual interest rate compounded monthly for eight years is $1,193.49.

Bible and Discussion Questions

8. Steve learned to pray and diligently apply himself to the work which God provided.

9. I battle condemnation the most. What is yours?

10. Usually by credit card debt. But your family may be different.

30.4

Lesson Practice Questions

1. $2,500.00 × 0.08 = $200.00.

$200.00 × 4 years is $800.00.

The original investment has grown to $3,300.00.

2.

Year	Interest	Total
First	$2,500.00 × 0.08 = $200.00	$2,500.00 + $200.00 = $2,700.00
Second	$2,700.00 × 0.08 = $216.00	$2,700.00 + $216.00 = $2,916.00
Third	$2,916.00 × 0.08 = $233.28	$2,916.00 + $233.28 = $3,149.28
Fourth	$3,149.28 × 0.08 = $251.94	$3,149.28 + $251.94 = $3,401.22

3. $3,439.17

4. $3,439.17 − $2,500.00 = $939.17

$939.17 divided by 4 for the four

years, $939.17 ÷ 4 = $234.79

$W_P × $2,500 = 234.79

$W_P = $234.79/$2,500 = 0.0939$

$W_P = 9.39\%$

We could also divide both the principal and the interest rate by 250 with $100.00 the new principal.

$W_P × $2,500 = 234.79

$W_P × $2,500/250 = $234.79/250$

$W_P × $100 = 9.39, and $W_P = 9.39\%$

5. A $3,000.00 CD with a 3.5% interest rate compounded monthly for 48 months is $3,450.12. $3,450.12 minus the principal of $3,000.00 is $450.12 which is how much interest is generated.

6. Three

7. A $1,000.00 CD with an interest rate of 2.5% compounded quarterly for eight years is $1,830.96.

Bible and Discussion Questions

8. Character is who you are inside. It is your integrity, honesty, and other unseen qualities. These positive qualities will make you an excellent employer or employee for you will treat others well and work diligently.

9. I hope you find several which encourage you. Mine is "There is therefore now no condemnation for those who are in Christ Jesus." (Romans 8:1)

10. Avoid credit card debt and invest wisely?

30.5

Lesson Practice Questions

1. $8,000.00, compounded annually for 10 years at 9% is $18,938.91.

2. $8,000.00, compounded quarterly for 10 years at 9% is $19,481.51.

3. $8,000.00, compounded continuously
   for 10 years at 9% is $19,676.82.

4. $19,676.82 − $8,000.00 = $11,676.82
   $11,676.82 divided this by 10 for
   the ten years = $1,167.68
   $W_p \times \$8,000 = \$1,167.68$
   $W_p = \$1,167.68/\$8,000 = 0.1459 = 0.146$
   $W_p = 14.6\%$

   We could also divide both the principal and the
   interest rate by 80 with $100.00 the new principal.
   $W_p \times \$8,000 = \$1,167.68$
   $W_p \times \$8,000/80 = \$1,167.68/80$
   $W_p \times \$100 = \$14.59$, and $W_p = 14.6\%$

5. A $750.00 CD with a 2.5% interest rate
   compounded monthly for 5 years is $839.22.
   $839.22 minus the principal of $750.00 is $89.22
   which is how much interest is generated.

6. Compound interest computes the interest on
   the principal AND the accumulated interest.

7. A $500.00 CD with an interest rate
   of $7\frac{1}{2}\%$ compounded continuously
   for eleven years is $1,140.94.

Bible and Discussion Questions

8. He was hungry :-) He needed work to
   provide for his family's needs.

9. Chew over these truths before
   putting into your own words.

10. Avoid credit card debt and invest wisely?

31.1

Lesson Practice Questions

1. Surplus is what you have left over, or
   extra, after you have returned your
   tithe and paid your obligations.

2. When you speculate, you are hoping to make a large
   return on your investment, but you may lose all of it.

3. Careful, methodical, patient

4. Price inflation is when prices gradually rise
   and are higher. Or inflation may be defined as
   taking more money to buy the same item.

5. Contributions are $100 × 12

months × 30 years equals $36,000
Final value is $83,225.86

6. Contributions are $240 × 12
   months × 15 years equals $43,200.
   Final value is $64,149.35

7. Beginning at age 18, even though you contribute
   less principal, is more lucrative since the money has
   grown longer. $83,225.86 is greater than 64,149.35.

Bible and Discussion Questions

8. "So that you may walk properly before outsiders and
   be dependent on no one." (1 Thessalonians 4:12)
   "So that he may have something to share
   with anyone in need." (Ephesians 4:28)

9. Believe.

10. This should an interesting conversation.

31.2

Lesson Practice Questions

1. Hopefully you learned that if your money is
   not growing at the rate of inflation then it is
   decreasing in value or purchasing power.

2. About 2%

3. I hope you are realistic, but also
   committed to saving some amount.

4. The exercise you do and the investment you begin.

5. Contributions are $75 × 12 months × 33
   years equals $29,700.
   Final value is $93,106.48

6. Contributions are $150 × 12
   months × 25 years equals $45,000.
   Final value is $103,949.09.

7. Number 6 invested much more money than
   number 5, $45,000 to $29,700. The return for #5
   is $93,106.48 - $29,700 = $63406.48 whereas
   the return for #6 is $103,949.09 - $45,000 =
   $58,949.09. This means you can invest less but
   still earn a greater return for the scenario in #5,
   simply by investing for a longer period of time.

Bible and Discussion Questions

8. He was able to supply his own needs
   and those who were with him.

9. Faith to me, is being utterly convinced that what God says is true, even if I can't see it with my eyes.

10. I am sure your parents have good advice on this subject.

31.3

Lesson Practice Questions

1. Annual Percentage Rate is similar to simple interest.

2. Annual Percentage Yield is similar to compound interest.

3. Annual Percentage Yield is the sum of one plus the interest rate divided by the number of times it is compounded, all raised to the power of the number of times it is compounded, minus 1.

4. For an investment to double in value, the rate times the years should equal 72.
$72 \div 9 = 8$.
$600 growing at 9% for 8 years will double to about $1,200.

5. $1,500.00 at 12%, compounded annually for two years is $1,881.60.
$1,881.60 − $1,500.00 = $381.60 interest

6. $1,500.00 at 12%, compounded quarterly for two years is $1,900.16.
$1,900.16 − $1,500.00 = $400.16 interest

7. $1,500.00 at 12%, compounded monthly for two years is $1,904.60.
$1,904.60 − $1,500.00 = $404.60 interest

Bible and Discussion Questions

8. Steve was able to identify with blue collar members of the congregation and he learned a skill which was put to good use helping others.

9. "Even when there was no reason for hope, Abraham kept hoping—believing that he would become the father of many nations. For God had said to him, 'That's how many descendants you will have!' And Abraham's faith did not weaken, even though, at about 100 years of age, he figured his body was as good as dead—and so was Sarah's womb. Abraham never wavered in believing God's promise." (Romans 4:18–20, NLT)

10. May their investments prosper and may they receive lots of free money.

31.4

Lesson Practice Questions

1. 2% of the outstanding balance, and 1% of the balance plus the monthly interest on the balance. In addition to these charges there is the transaction or late fee each month as well.

2. A portfolio is all of your different and varied investments from IRAs to baseball cards.

3. Many companies offer to match what the employee contributes, up to a certain amount. Since this money is not related to any work the employee has done, it is free.

4. For an investment to double in value, the rate times the years should equal 72.
$72 \div 12 = 6$
$1,350 growing at 12% for 6 years will double to about $2,700.

5. $250.00 in a 7.5% savings account compounded monthly for 30 years is $2,355.38.

6. $250.00 in a 7.5% savings account compounded continuously for 30 years is $2,371.93. This grew a little more by being compounded continuously.

7. $25.00 per month for 30 years at 6.25% compounded monthly grows to $26,348.00

Bible and Discussion Questions

8. "She seeks wool and flax, and works with willing hands. .... She brings her food from afar. She rises while it is yet night and provides food for her household and portions for her maidens." (Proverbs 31:13–15)
"She opens her hand to the poor and reaches out her hands to the needy. She looks well to the ways of her household, and eats not the bread of idleness." (Proverbs 31:20, 27)

9. By reading God's word. "Faith comes from hearing, and hearing through the word of Christ." (Romans 10:17)

10. This should be very interesting.

31.5

Lesson Practice Questions

1. Diversification is not putting all our eggs in one basket, but diversifying our investments. The rest of the question is up to you!

2. The difference between these two kinds of IRAs is when you pay taxes on them. The standard one defers taxes until you withdraw it when you are older. The Roth IRA is contributed and invested after you have already paid taxes on it. When you withdraw from these funds later, you will not have to pay taxes on these funds.

3. Probably a Roth IRA since you are making less money now than you will in the future so your taxes are less now then they will be.

4. For an investment to double in value, the rate times the years should equal 72.
$72 \times 3 = 24$
$250 growing at 3% for 24 years will double to about $500.

5. Woodchuck—$400.00 times 12 months times 15 years is $72,000 in principal. $400.00 per month, at 5.75%, compounded monthly for 15 years has a final value of $113,881.14.

6. Tortoise—$200.00 times 12 months times 30 years is also $72,000 in principal. $200.00 per month, at 5.75%, compounded monthly for 30 years has a final value of $191,559.52.

7. Be a lifelong learner and continue to learn from men like Dave Ramsey and Howard Dayton.

Bible and Discussion Questions

8. God Himself.

9. This is up to you. I like many of them, which is why they are listed here :-)

10. They have a lifetime of experience. Listen well.

32.1

Lesson Practice Questions

1. Praying-Giving-Going

2. In the kingdom of God every enterprise must begin with prayer. Then God can lead and bless any work of giving or going, after you have prayed.

3. He hoped to be able to live on 10% of his income and give away 90%.

4. God is the great first cause and the great initiator. Every good and perfect gift comes from Him. God gave us His Son. God gives us life.

5. 90%

6. "Freely ye have received, freely give." (Matthew 10:8 KJV)

7. When Steve volunteered to go to a poor county in Kentucky and serve and work side by side with the poor.

Bible and Discussion Questions

8. I do. I know several widows like my aunt Gloria.

9. Even though there are many people who upset me by their actions, ultimately God teaches us that our real enemy is a combination of principalities, powers, and the devil.

10. Hope so :-)

32.2

Lesson Practice Questions

1. When Steve was in his twenties, he traveled to South India to help a children's home ministry.

2. Do your research well before giving and going. All charities seem okay on the outside, but look deeper before committing to help them.

3. Our treasure and heart are connected. When our heart is moved to serve, then our time, energy, and treasure will follow closely. For Steve this is the importance of family, life, and spreading the gospel to the ends of the earth.

4. Love your neighbor as yourself.

5. *The Poor Will be Glad* by Peter Greer and *Toxic Charity* by Robert Lupton.

6. Lack of money, lack of food, lack of shelter, lack of clothing, lack of medical supplies, lack of drinkable water

7. Yes. There are many statistical studies that document these lacks.

Bible and Discussion Questions

8. "Whoever is generous to the poor lends to the LORD, and he will repay him for his deed." (Proverbs 19:17)

9. The devil is a thief who "comes only to steal and kill and destroy." (John 10:10) Jesus "came that they may have life and have it abundantly." (John 10:10)

10. You may have to ask your pastor as well.

32.3

Lesson Practice Questions

1. humiliation, shame, cripples

2. We are afraid of everything. We depend on everyone. No one needs us. We are like garbage. I feel ashamed. It's terrible. The lack of contact leaves one depressed and creates a constant feeling of unhappiness, and a sense of low esteem. I feel inferior. There is no progress.

3. Poverty of things we lack are outside our person. They are about what we have or do not have. Poverty of being, is about who we are and how we feel about ourself and perceive ourself.

4. Pride

5. Mine is "the more we have it ourselves, the more we dislike it in others."

6. Charity done thusly "affirms the superiority of the giver, who thus gains a point on the recipient, binds him, demands gratitude, humiliates him, and reduces him to a lower state than he had before" states Jacques Ellul.

7. He possesses food, clothing, shelter, water, family, a job, and has never missed a meal or lacked any material necessity. He has many churches nearby and owns several Bibles. He is prosperous physically, emotionally, and spiritually.

Bible and Discussion Questions

8. "Religion that is pure and undefiled before God the Father is this: to visit orphans and widows in their affliction." (James 1:27)

9. Yad Vashem was a visual demonstration of the meanness and total evil of the devil.

10. We all view our situation similarly and yet differently.

32.4

Lesson Practice Questions

1. We have a blind spot, thinking that we are self-sufficient and don't need help. We look upon the needy as less fortunate than ourselves and give out of a sense of obligation.

2. The antidote of pride and superiority is genuine humility.

3. As a humble baby.

4. By embracing the humble mindset of a servant, like Jesus, who came not to be served, but to serve, and to give His life of us.

5. Your answer may be different, but it means looking at others as people who are created in the image of God and have immense value and dignity.

6. I would have felt smug and pleased at the sacrifice I made coming to the poor city and giving up Christmas Eve in my middle-class home.

7. I would have been happy for the fancy gifts from the suburbs. I may have also felt a little funny, because my dad is not here, and mom is acting a little stiff.

Bible and Discussion Questions

8. We don't have to fly to another country to practice a life of service.

9. In Jesus' name he resists the devil.

10. Steve has.

32.5

Lesson Practice Questions

1. Grateful on one hand, but helpless and inferior on the other hand.

2. Because having someone else have the responsibility to provide for his children instead of him being the one to give the gifts made him feel like a failure.

3. She was trying to be grateful to the Millers, and happy for her children, but grieving

with her husband at the same time.

4. I think it showed wisdom and was a great start to rebuilding Mr. Kingston's self esteem.

5. I hope you can, my imagination is not working today.

6. I don't like acknowledging it, but yes I have.

7. For me, it is recognizing how traditional poverty encourages our despicable pride and wounds those we are trying to help.

Bible and Discussion Questions

8. This is your chance to reflect.

9. The name of Jesus is above every name. Jesus taught us to ask the Father in His name.

10. They probably have some good stories and wise insights.

33.1

Lesson Practice Questions

1. God, by His Spirit, working in our hearts.

2. When we are loved, we love God more, and we want to love our neighbor.

3. To love as we want to be loved, we need to do the work of putting ourselves in their shoes and recognizing how our best efforts are perceived.

4. A lack of water, food, sanitation, clothes, shelter, and medicine are physical needs.

5. Poverty of being includes, but is not limited to: dignity, self-worth, hopelessness, shame, and sense of inferiority.

6. This is your preference, but I am surprised by the lack of water.

7. W_p of 7.7 billion is 2.5 billion?
$W_p \times 7.7$ billion = 2.5 billion

$W_p = \dfrac{2.5 \text{ billion}}{7.7 \text{ billion}}$

$W_p = 0.\overline{324675}$ or 32%

Bible and Discussion Questions

8. Bribes blind us and affect our ability to make clear decisions.

9. This will be unique to you. I lean

towards sinful nature.

10. You may have to define your terms as they are not frequently used today.

33.2

Lesson Practice Questions

1. W_p of 7.7 billion is 1.2 billion?
$W_p \times 7.7$ billion = 1.2 billion

$W_p = \dfrac{1.2 \text{ billion}}{7.7 \text{ billion}}$

$W_p = 0.\overline{155844}$ or 16%

2. Bob Pierce asked God to "Let my heart be broken by the things that break the heart of God." He founded two international charity organizations: World Vision International in 1950 and Samaritan's Purse in 1970.

3. A tornado, hurricane, or natural disaster

4. His response was generous and appropriate. It was a short-term solution to an immediate need.

5. Anticipation, Expectation, Entitlement.

6. Our long term strategy is to teach people to fish and grow and mature. If we keep them in a state of dependency they will always be needy children.

7. Absolutely

Bible and Discussion Questions

8. Men who fear God, are trustworthy, and hate a bribe

9. This is up to you and where you are in your journey. I lean towards: "Let the Holy Spirit guide your lives. Then you won't be doing what your sinful nature craves." (Galatians 5:16. NLT)

10. This should be interesting and informative.

33.3

Lesson Practice Questions

1. Dependency fosters idleness instead of diligence, encourages the receiver to make a habit of soliciting aid instead of working, and it humiliates the receiver as they are made to feel like a beggar and inferior.

2. When children become adults, they unwittingly

model the behavior of their parent(s). They will remain "children" and not learn to grow up and stand on their own two feet.

3. Traditional charitable giving seems the right thing to do, but the end result is harmful.

4. Choose from: shame, inferiority, powerlessness, humiliation, fear, hopelessness, depression, social isolation, and voicelessness.

5. I like them both :-)

6. I do (that is why it is in the book). Productive work builds a person's sense of well-being while providing for their physical needs.

7. Paul chose to demonstrate and model a diligent work ethic for the church.

Bible and Discussion Questions

8. The leading priests decided to give the soldiers a large bribe and lie about what happened at the tomb to the body of Jesus.

9. Sexual immorality, impurity, sensuality, idolatry, sorcery, enmity, strife, jealousy, fits of anger, rivalries, dissensions, divisions, envy, drunkenness, and orgies. Not pretty, but this potential is present in each person.

10. I hope this discussion will prove informative and edifying.

33.4

Lesson Practice Questions

1. President Lincoln knew that a short-term solution wouldn't work now, and had not worked in the past. He then embarked on this long-term strategy to help develop John Johnston's character.

2. Ask some friends to keep an eye on his homestead, get a job, stick to it, and earn what is needed. Mr. Lincoln also offered to encourage him by matching his work with a contribution of his own, dollar for dollar.

3. Perhaps the fleshly nature would have rebelled, but hopefully the spirit nature would have seen the wisdom and been grateful for the advice and matching fund.

4. It is always easier to write a check.

5. John Johnston would have been making similar appeals in the future with no change of character or work ethic.

6. Sad but not unexpected.

7. We need to have a willing compassionate heart with a teachable inquiring mind. We also need to be humble enough to ask questions and truly listen to the weak and needy.

Bible and Discussion Questions

8. "The LORD your God is God of gods and Lord of lords, the great, the mighty, and the awesome God, Who is not partial and takes no bribe." (Deuteronomy 10:17)

9. This will be your perspective. For Steve, self-control is the main thought along with not needing to force our way in life, and affection for others.

10. This should lead to some interesting discussion.

33.5

Lesson Practice Questions

1. Bringing food, clothing, and meeting their immediate physical needs was appropriate and necessary at the beginning of the tragic result of genocide.

2. I have admiration for Jean's work ethic and his ability to respond to a need and build a business. I am saddened to see his work squashed by well-meaning efforts from my home country.

3. No eggs. More expensive eggs from a neighboring village. One of their own citizens out of a job.

4. If the church had shifted gears, humbly come alongside the people in Rwanda, and asked how they could serve and be a help, they would've been so much more effective.

5. Sadly, yes. We mean well in the U.S. but we have too much pride and inability to learn from other nations.

6. The first model is much easier to do for the western church because it is in keeping with our sense of superiority and it will be easy to raise funds from our congregations because it sounds dramatic and impactful. Watch out

for U.S. believers with Superman capes.

7. The church worked with an organization who knew how to work with and support the local village without supplanting them. The villagers were educated and empowered, performed the necessary work, and took ownership of this valuable asset. The value was not only in the water, but in the sense of well-being and satisfaction experienced by the villages.

Bible and Discussion Questions

8. Free gifts tend to create a sense of obligation to purchase something or respond in kind.

9. Steve likes all of them. He had heard about the fruits of the Spirit using these one word descriptions for so long they had lost much of their meaning him. The Message brought them back to life for Steve.

10. This will be interesting to compare with you parents' responses.

34.1

Lesson Practice Questions

1. A hand-up enables someone to stand and become independent. It is ennobling and empowering. A handout creates dependence. It is demeaning.

2. Small loans given to finance and encourage a small business or enterprise.

3. Both of these concepts are a significant improvement on traditional charity. Christian micro-finance not only improves the person and their financial situation, it also works to transform the heart of the person in the name of Jesus.

4. Well-meaning believers ventured to Ukraine after Eastern Europe opened up. They sought to not only provide spiritual help they also wanted to assist in the physical needs of the people coming out from under the oppression of communism.

5. In their efforts to help, they discovered through a brave pastor that their charity and aid was not helpful. Instead of abandoning their commitment, they strove to learn a better way to serve and learned about micro-enterprise.

6. By extending small business loans judiciously, small enterprises can prosper and grow.

7. Help the Needy (HTN) is an amicable attempt to match up individuals in a needy country with more affluent families who can sponsor a family and provide their basic physical necessities.

Bible and Discussion Questions

8. Steve was convicted by these words and followed through on his promise to change the structure of their family business, even though he did not want to make this change.

9. Within each of us are two wolves. One is good and one is evil. The one which survives and grows is the one which is fed.

10. It is a relatively new concept and they may not have heard of it.

34.2

Lesson Practice Questions

1. Building Families of Faith is a Christian micro-finance model which provides training, fellowship, and micro loans to empower and encourage families and their small businesses.

2. HTN is similar to a traditional charity and BFF is a Christian micro-finance model.

3. This is your opinion. They stuck to their plan for five years while Steve would probably have given all the funds to BFF after year two. Just saying.

4. At first it would be attractive to receive the handout for not doing anything, but after a year or so, I think I would be more attracted to what was happening in the Sams family.

5. Unfortunately, Christian micro-finance is not easily understood. Making an appeal to help a needy family by effortlessly wiring a check and receiving letters of appreciation and pictures makes Americans feel good about themselves and that they are making a difference.

6. At each meeting, they greet one another, pray and worship, study God's Word, report on their group savings, manage their loans, and wrap up with prayer.

7. This is your opinion, but Steve believes people need to be part of a body of like minded believers to grow and flourish.

Bible and Discussion Questions

8. God watches over His Word to perform it. (Jeremiah 1:12)

9. The good, faithful, powerful, wise, and loving Spirit of God

10. They have heard many pitches and appeals to give. They have plenty of experience.

34.3

Lesson Practice Questions

1. Return On Investment

2. CMF is all positive; from meeting the physical needs of the people, to building up their invisible needs for value and dignity, to impacting the community, the church, and the next generation of family members. TC is an admirable short-term solution which provides for physical lacks and needs, but which damages the soul of a family in the long run.

3. Overhead expenses pay for the infrastructure of an organization. These are generally 20% of a donation.

4. The results of year one are similar except HTN is able to fund two families with their donation while BFF is only able to offer a loan to one family.

5. The funds covered all of their physical needs for one year.

6. Half of the $200 loan paid for their physical expenses for one year, and the other half was invested in their dairy farm.

7. $200 comes from the U.S. and $108 is from the Sams paying back half of their loan. The $8 is interest on the loan and helps support the onsite loan officer.

Bible and Discussion Questions

8. We can emulate God by telling the truth, even when it hurts.

9. Each answer will be different, but Steve reads the Word of God daily, attends church regularly, prays throughout the day, and communes with the Spirit, particularly on his prayer walks.

10. Listen well.

34.4

Lesson Practice Questions

1. Mr. Turner was discouraged because he did not like to receive gifts. He wanted to be able to provide for his family and having someone else do so was discouraging. Each check that came in the mail communicated a message that he was a failure.

2. Life is harder in the home without a dad. Teachers have to provide special assistance to the children. People in the town also have to sacrifice to help this single parent.

3. He had two loans being paid back by the Sams and Peters, $100 remixing from year one, and another donation of $200 from the U.S.

4. Two more families were able to join the savings group and begin small enterprises with $100 being rolled over to the next year.

5. On the surface, they have been able to pay school tuition and have clothes, food, and medical care, but they lack the internal sense of hope and dignity that comes from having a thriving profitable enterprise.

6. Life is challenging, and good. They have a sense of purpose and look with expectancy towards the future. Parents are encouraged and making plans for growing their business and being helped to help others.

7. They may do a little grumbling for their responsibilities, but they are becoming hard working children who are learning a solid work ethic.

Bible and Discussion Questions

8. Is this a trick question? Honest and rich :-). Since there is a choice to be made, "Better is a poor man who walks in his integrity than a rich man who is crooked in his ways." (Proverbs 28:6)

9. Steve consciously and intentionally asks God to clothe him with these virtues and then imagine putting them on like a jacket or coat.

10. Ask for specific examples.

34.5

Lesson Practice Questions

1. The local congregation is benefiting from the spiritual growth of their members. Giving has increased, which has provided new impetus for outreach to their community.

2. Mr. Sams was elected to be a member of the town council and Mrs. Peters is on the school board. The savings group is making plans to pool their resources and dig a well so they do not have to walk for water. A committee has begun to study what needs to be done to make this dream come to fruition. They hope to sell the surplus water to the neighboring villages.

3. Happy to see Mr. Turner reconnected with his family and a new baby added to their home.

4. 98%

5. These contributions by the Raines family are investments and as they are extended first as loans, and then repaid, these funds are available to continue helping other Rwandans.

6. They seem fair and a good approximation.

7. If you do, send them to Steve :-)

Bible and Discussion Questions

8. We can lie. God can't lie. He is the Truth and He never changes. Ever.

9. Faith is work. Believing God's word when his own carnal wolf is still active takes faith. Focusing on the scripture by reading it and meditating on it helps to curb the desires of the sinful nature and encourage the fruit of the spiritual nature.

10. You may have covered this in your other questions, but ask one more time to see if they have any additional thoughts.

35.1

Lesson Practice Questions

1. To Steve, it is make disciples of all nations and teach them all things that Jesus commanded.

2. Each of the other gospels, Mark 16:15, Luke 24:46–47, and John 20:21, and Acts 1:8.

3. The whole church

4. A people group is the largest group within which the Gospel can spread as a church planting movement without encountering barriers of understanding or acceptance.

5. 17,014

6. 7,063

7. 41.5%

Bible and Discussion Questions

8. Unequivocally not. "No one can serve two masters, for either he will hate the one and love the other, or he will be devoted to the one and despise the other. You cannot serve God and money." (Matthew 6:24)

9. God does not exempt us from suffering, but transforms us in it. Steve understood that suffering was a normal part of the Christian life.

10. This is unique to them.

35.2

Lesson Practice Questions

1. Most missiologists thought every country had been penetrated with the gospel, but they discovered there were still over 40% that were unreached.

2. Judea, Samaria, and the uttermost parts of the earth

3. The main population, the Amish, and immigrants from around the world

4. People blindness is blindness to the existence of separate peoples within countries.

5. Matthew 28:18–20

6. Paul the apostle

7. This is the account of five young couples who moved to Ecuador, South America, in an attempt to reach the Auca tribe (Waorani) with the gospel of Jesus. In January, 1956, the five husbands were killed.

Bible and Discussion Questions

8. The scene on Mt. Carmel was to determine who was the true God, Yahweh or Baal. Elijah represented Yahweh and he was opposed by several hundred prophets of Baal.

9. Even when we walk through the darkest valley, we do not need to be afraid, for God is close beside us.

10. This may be a new way of describing nations in the Great Commission.

35.3

Lesson Practice Questions

1. Indigenous means natural.

2. They should train the local believers to lead their own church and fulfill the great commission to reach their neighbors with the gospel.

3. Deuteronomy 6:7. The first part of the verse to "Teach your children diligently" implied intentional Bible study. The second half of the verse indicated parents were to be with their children "when you sit in your house, walk by the way, lie down, and rise up."

4. Parents. They are designed and created to pass their faith on to their children.

5. They instinctively know they need to help their children become independent so they can grow up and train their children to be independent.

6. By teaching and modeling their faith to their children they are seeking to train them to live forever.

7. Missionaries and ministries should make disciples who can learn to grow and feed themselves as well as reach out to others. Those who have been reached should be taught to fish and not simply be given fish.

Bible and Discussion Questions

8. Your answer is your own, but Steve loves Joshua's set of soul. Even if everyone else forsakes God, he and his family will be faithful.

9. Jesus is a man of sorrows. He is acquainted with grief.

10. This may be enlightening.

35.4

Lesson Practice Questions

1. This is what the data suggest. Short term mission trips make Americans feel like they have made a difference and done some good, while experiencing life in a different culture.

2. Teaching English as a second language

3. The time taken from the on-site missionary and his work and work taken from local businesses.

4. He thought about the impact on himself. He would have a new experience. He would feel good about helping others and have fun interacting with his peers on the trip.

5. Steve Saint is the son of the pilot who flew the men into the jungle in January, 1956. He was four years old at the time.

6. Steve Saint's parents were cross-cultural missionaries. He lived with his mother and aunt as missionaries on the field. After being educated in the U.S. he went back and lived with the Waorani with his family as an adult. He has seen all sides of reaching an unreached people group.

7. The traditional approach to reaching an unreached people group uses western methods, western resources, and western manpower, but it does not utilize the indigenous church. I think his observations are valid.

Bible and Discussion Questions

8. It seems like zero to Elijah, but God knew that it was 7,000.

9. Sanctify means to be made holy, like God, who is holy.

10. The death of these five men was on the cover of major magazines of the time.

35.5

Lesson Practice Questions

1. These believers know the language and the culture. They live side by side with their neighbors for whom Christ also died. They do not need to raise large amounts of support in order to go to a foreign land. They do not need to invest years

at a language school learning a new language.

2. Western missionaries sometimes have more training, resources, and financial support at home.

3. Training and encouragement

4. Indigenous People's Education and Training Center

5. I-DENT, I-SEE, I-MED, are tools and training which ITEC has developed to meet the needs of people in their community and surrounding communities.

6. If we want people to listen to our message of God's love and forgiveness we need to first be like Jesus when he came to the earth as a humble dependent baby. He came to serve and not be served. Like Jesus, we need to come alongside the local people and proceed humbly with an attitude of a teachable servant.

7. An attitude of humility.

Bible and Discussion Questions

8. Steve has read the book and now he knows the end of the story. God wins, as well as those who are with Him.

9. When we keep our eyes on Jesus we will become more like Him.

10. Every generation has different perspectives. I have learned to value the wisdom of those who are older.

36.1

Lesson Practice Questions

1. A person's disability describes a condition they have, but it does not define who they are.

2. The first few days he was aware of the physical signs, but then he began to know their true person.

3. It takes effort and intentionality but we attempt to put ourselves in their shoes and treat them like we would want to be treated.

4. Absolutely not. Some were born with their condition, others were in an accident, a few were the result of medical mistakes, but no one Steve knows ever chose to have a disability.

5. 15% of 543,000 is 81,450 which is a lot for one county.

6. 20% of 81,450 is 16,290.

7. I wanted to do what I can to pray and look for opportunities to reach them for Christ.

Bible and Discussion Questions

8. Soon after God created the world in 6 days, He rested 1 day, then created woman. He made Adam and Eve one flesh, then instructed them to be fruitful and multiply and fill the earth.

9. Steve and the Spirit have become forever friends.

10. I hope so, if not it has been a pleasure introducing her to your family.

36.2

Lesson Practice Questions

1. Steve gives the modern church an A for setting up meal trains and coming alongside with practical solutions for several weeks.

2. People do not outgrow their chromosome count. Disability support requires long term strategies.

3. This solution was doable and meaningful. Many hands make light work!

4. John knows he is contributing to the life of the church. He is valued and respected for his efforts. He belongs to the usher team.

5. This team of men treated John with respect, they did not patronize him, or look at him like the church mascot.

6. When a family comes to church, a special buddy is assigned to the child. This blesses the young person and frees up the parent(s) to worship and enjoy fellowship uninterrupted with other adults.

7. Come alongside a family in your church or community. Invest time to get to know them, and they you. Ask how you can serve. Consider volunteering at a JAF Family Retreat as an STM. Pray and ask God to help you think of other ways.

Bible and Discussion Questions

8. Noah, 2,300 years before Christ, took his family into the ark during the worldwide flood, thus preserving their lives.

9. Conviction of sin, being able to say Jesus is

Lord, pointing us to Jesus in the Word

10. I hope so. The disability community has had a meaningful impact on our family.

36.3

Lesson Practice Questions

1. They listen attentively when he is trying to communicate. They include him in family and church functions. They value him and treat him with respect.

2. He belongs to the shipping team. He is active. He is growing and learning new skills. He feels productive.

3. When he is not respected they step up and make sure that he is, like during a munchly, which is the term for the monthly company luncheon.

4. Demme Learning has hard working employees. The whole company is much more cognizant of the special need and hearing-impaired community. The people with impairments are a part of our culture. They are valued and respected. They are productive and earn a fair wage for their job.

5. Lighthouse Vocational Services and Ephrata Area Rehabilitation Services.

6. YES!!!

7. Joni speaks, exhorts, encourages, inspires, and represents the special needs community. David is an interpreter at his workplace. He is devoted to his friend. John is a light to all who meet him. He loves unconditionally and is kind and thoughtful.

Bible and Discussion Questions

8. To tell the next generation about the glorious deeds of the LORD, about his power and his mighty wonders, so they in turn might pass these truths on to their children. So each generation would not forget God but remember His works and obey His commands.

9. "God's love has been poured into our hearts through the Holy Spirit." (Romans 5:5)

10. This will be unique to your fellowship.

36.4

Lesson Practice Questions

1. Did I mention John is an extrovert? He likes people. He also experiences community at work. He is valued and productive.

2. We are seeking to deepen our relationship with our co-workers by learning how to communicate with them.

3. John has purpose. He receives a paycheck, which he then can use to be a man and pay his own way. When he is happy we are happy.

4. This is a no-brainer to Steve. He wants to work and earn his way.

5. Any job is better than no job. But to travel to a warehouse and work side by side with "normal" people and learn new skills and be treated as part of the team is very encouraging.

6. They have hopes, dreams, want to be valued, respected and included. These are invisible and unseen yet meaningful similarities.

7. Maybe a different chromosome count, or a genetic defect, or a physical limitation. All superficial stuff!

Bible and Discussion Questions

8. Just as Jesus taught His disciples to wait for the coming of the Spirit, Paul counsels men and women to: "Be filled with the Spirit."

9. The Holy Spirit. "No prophecy was ever produced by the will of man, but men spoke from God as they were carried along by the Holy Spirit." (2 Peter 1:21)

10. You'll have to ask to find out!

36.5

Lesson Practice Questions

1. I would want to be treated as someone who is created in the image of God with gifts and talents to be used to serve others. I would want a hand-up and not a hand-out. How about you?

2. This is up to you, but treating them with compassion and not pity is a huge first step.

3. Perhaps immigrants who have moved into your community? Perhaps the homeless.

Or victims of human trafficking?

4. NO!! "He does not deal with us according to our sins, nor repay us according to our iniquities." (Psalm 103:10)

5. God redeems and works all things for our good. He has taken Steve through valleys of grief which has led to a company which has been a help to customers and employees alike.

6. This will be unique to you.

7. Also applicable to you alone.

Bible and Discussion Questions

8. These husbands must be faithful to their wife, exercise self-control, live wisely, and have a good reputation. They must enjoy having guests in their home, and be able to teach. They must not be a heavy drinker or violent, but be gentle, not quarrelsome, and not love money. They must manage their own family well.

9. I hope many touched your heart, but pick some :-)

10. I wish I could hear their answer. If you want to tell me, I am at sdemme@demmelearning.com.

REVISION CODE: VERSION 1119

BUILDING FAITH
FAMILIES™

ABOUT THE AUTHOR

Steve Demme and his wife Sandra have been married since 1979. They have been blessed with four sons, three lovely daughters-in-law, and five special grandchildren.

Steve has served in full or part time pastoral ministry for many years after graduating from Gordon-Conwell Theological Seminary. He is the creator of Math-U-See and the founder of Building Faith Families.

Steve is a regular speaker at home education conventions, men's ministry events, special needs conferences, and church retreats. His desire is to teach, validate, and exhort parents and families in following the biblical model for the Christian home.

Scripture declares God created the sacred institution of the family. In His wisdom, He designed marriage to be between one man and one woman. Healthy God-fearing families are the principal building block for church and society.

BUILDING FAITH FAMILIES was created to encourage and strengthen families.
In addition to the Stewardship Curriculum, Steve has created the following resources for your family.

- The free **Monthly Newsletter**, which is an encouraging biblical exhortation.
  Sign up at BuildingFaithFamilies.org.

- A weekly **Podcast** available for free download on our website, iTunes, and other platforms, and is released weekly on our Facebook page.

- The **Building Faith Families website** has many other resources for your edification including video and audio messages. Listen or watch them at BuildingFaithFamilies.org

- Like us on **Facebook** to be notified of new Podcasts and receive the monthly newsletter.

BUILDING FAITH
FAMILIES™

CRISIS TO CHRIST, THE HARDEST AND BEST YEAR OF MY LIFE

This difficult timewas instrumental in changing my life and transforming my most important relationships. My pain led me to acknowledge my own needs, and get help from the body of Christ. I am now in the best place I have ever been with God and my family.

KNOWING GOD'S LOVE, BECOMING ROOTED AND GROUNDED IN GRACE

I have believed in my mind that God loves me for over forty years. And now I know that He likes me for who I am and not because of what I do. His care for me is not tied to my performance but to His unconditional grace.

LOVED TO LOVE, WE LOVE BECAUSE HE FIRST LOVED US

The new command does not consider how I want to be loved, but how I have been loved. The more I comprehend how Jesus loves me, the better equipped I am to love my wife and children as I have been loved.

SPEAKING THE TRUTH IN LOVE, LESSONS I'VE LEARNED ABOUT FAMILY COMMUNICATION

My relationship with my wife and children is built on safe communication that builds up and encourages each person without quenching or wounding their spirit. I am learning how to thoughtfully respond instead of emotionally reacting.

HYMNS FOR FAMILY WORSHIP

This time-honored collection of 100 classic hymns will be a rich addition to your family worship. In addition to the music for these sacred songs, the history of each hymn enhances the meaning of the lyrics, as do the four CDs with piano accompaniment for singing along.

FAMILY WORSHIP

In this readable book, Steve shares practical scripture-based tips for teaching tips for teaching the word of God to children of all ages. He also addresses common obstacles we all face in establishing the discipline of regular family worship. Be encouraged by Steve's experiences teaching his four sons and learn from other families as well.